THE
DOGLOPAEDIA

J. M. Evans & Kay White

HENSTON

First published, 1985

© Henston Ltd., 1985

ISBN 0-9510620-0-X

Henston Ltd., Russell House, 137-139 High Street, Guildford, Surrey, England

Typeset by Monarch Origination Ltd., Ipswich, Suffolk
Printed and bound by H. E. Warne Ltd., St. Austell, Cornwall

ACKNOWLEDGEMENTS

Writing the book is only half the story. *The Doglopaedia* would not be in your hands without the cooperation and skill of a lot of other people to whom we wish to extend our gratitude.

We would like to thank the artists who have contributed their talents to our book, and to acknowledge the expertise of the publishing team at Sutton-Siebert Publications Ltd. and Henston Ltd., and especially Sara Green who brought all the ends together and got the book to the printer on time.

Both of us realise how much we owe to all the dogs who have shared our lives; the things they taught us are reflected in the practical experience which has gone into making this book.

We are grateful to Anna (Evans), the well-mannered Dobermann, for being such an agreeable and willing model for the illustrations, and to the Boxers of the White household, who guarded the manuscript, checked over the wastepaper basket, and gave enthusiastic assistance at every stage.

Thank you all — it's your book as well as ours.

J.M. Evans & Kay White

CONTENTS

ILLUSTRATIONS

INTRODUCTION

We know that the friendly, uncritical companionship of a dog can be a valuable morale booster and relaxation inducer to help counter the stresses imposed by life today. We need dogs as never before, but we need dogs which are kept properly — healthy, well-behaved dogs, which are not permitted to annoy other people, dogs which are valued by their owners and kept until the end of their days as important members of their household.

Owning a dog is a privilege and one which many people have to deny themselves through limitations on housing, exercise areas, working hours, and even because of the frank anti-dog attitude taken by a small segment of our society.

The authors, both of whom have had a wide experience with a variety of dogs, and who value dogs as important parts of their lives, want to share with you some of the knowledge they have gained over the years, in order to make dog-ownership smoother and more rewarding for you.

We believe that the book we have written tells you the things the other books leave out. We hope that you, and your dog-owning friends, will refer to *The Doglopaedia* frequently and, with this in mind, you will find that many facts are cross-referenced for easy retrieval.

We begin with anatomy and physiology, to show you how your dog, small or large, is built, and how its body systems work. We show you how the dog thinks, and how it learns, and help you to teach your dog acceptable behaviour in the correct way — too many people are, unwittingly, teaching their dogs to do the things they *don't* want them to do! We believe that you can teach your dog to behave acceptably with just a little "magic" and no shouting or bullying.

The "What ifs" in Chapter 4 are unique, for we have looked at illnesses and injuries through the signs the owner will see, and advise on the action to be taken. Another exclusive feature to this book is the History Tip given for many of the illnesses, to help you give the most important information to the veterinary surgeon when you take your dog for consultation. We know only too well how it is easy to become tongue-tied and flustered, so we remind you of the things you wanted to ask the vet, and we also explain the difficult words that vets tend to use in reply.

We hope that if you follow the advice we have given, the veterinary surgeon will be able to use his skill to best effect to help your dog. Similarly, the section which deals with post-surgical nursing will save you anxiety and promote the dog's smooth recovery and, incidentally, win you the approbation of your veterinary surgeon, if you look after your dog in the professional way we have described.

Accidents and misdemeanours occur in the best of managed households and the most immaculate dogs; consult our "What ifs" around the house for those problems other books gloss over — like the best way to clean up vomit and how to introduce your dog to a new kitten. We believe in facing the practicalities too, and we hope this part of the book will prove to be particularly useful.

Choosing a dog is a very personal matter, and difficult to cover in a limited space, but we have outlined in concise tables the advantages and disadvantages of puppies and older dogs, mongrels and pedigree animals, rescued dogs and surplus kennel dogs. We trust that this information will make it easier for you to choose the dog that will suit your home and family best.

Because we want you to enjoy your dog, we have included a list of the activities you can undertake with your pet. Some of them may not have come to your attention before, and we have indicated where you may find "the way in" to many of these activities which, like the dog itself, may become a very vital part of your life.

Our intention is that *The Doglopaedia* shall fill the role of a knowledgeable dog-owning friend, forever at your elbow to answer the questions that don't get answered elsewhere and, most importantly, to help you, your family and your dog to enjoy a happy, lifelong relationship.

CHAPTER 1

PART I

ANATOMY AND PHYSIOLOGY

Introduction

In order that owners can properly look after their pets and get the most out of them, it is important to have at least a fundamental understanding of how dogs are "made" and how they "work". Furthermore, owners who know the names of the various parts and organs, and their functions, can more easily describe any signs and symptoms shown by their dogs to a veterinary surgeon or breeder when seeking advice and can better understand why a specific treatment or course of action has been advised. The information given in this chapter is intended to provide this necessary information in an easily understandable and interesting way. It makes sense for all owners, and especially new ones, to read this chapter in its entirety as one would do with a manual for a new car. Thereafter, it should be necessary only to "brush-up" on specific points. The information has been provided in such a way that details can be quickly retrieved when required.

Essentially the chapter is in two parts:

Part I Anatomy and Physiology — the structure of the various parts of the body and how they work. Notes are made where specific structures or functions have a relation to a disease condition.

Part II Motivation and Intelligence — how dogs think and how they react to their environment.

The Points of the Dog

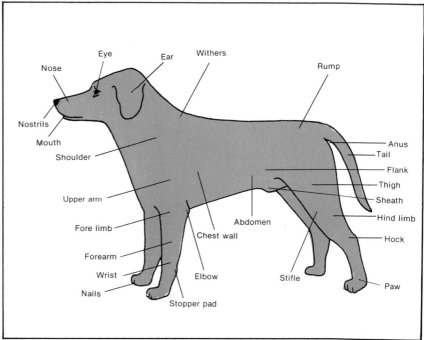

Fig. 1 **The points of the dog**

NOTE
- The flank refers to the side of the dog including the chest and the abdomen.
- The paw is from the stopper pad to the ground in the foreleg and from the hock to the ground in the hindleg. See Fig. 2.
- The ventral surface is the underneath side of any part of the dog.
- The dorsal surface is the upper side of any part of the dog.
- Recumbency is used to describe a dog that is lying down:
  Dorsal recumbency = lying on its back
  Sternal recumbency = lying on its chest
  Lateral recumbency = lying on its side.

The Paw

(a) Right fore paw from below

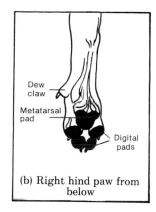

(b) Right hind paw from below

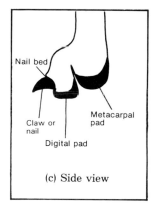

(c) Side view

Fig. 2 **The paw**

Lamoncoo is very frequently caused by problems in the paw e.g.
- Excessively cracked pads
- Thorns in the pad
- Cuts in the web
- Interdigital cysts
- Torn claws
- Cut pads

In cases of lameness it always makes sense to examine the paw of the affected leg first, especially if the leg is being carried.

The pads become very much harder, thicker and more cracked in some cases of Canine Distemper — so-called Hard Pad.

The spring clips of leads sometimes become caught in the web. Seek veterinary advice since removal can be very difficult and painful unless undertaken properly.

The Skeletal System

Essentially the skeletal system is made up of bones joined by ligaments, muscles and tendons. The function of the skeleton is to support and protect the body organs and, through the muscles which are connected to the bones by tendons, to make locomotion possible.

The major bones in the skeleton

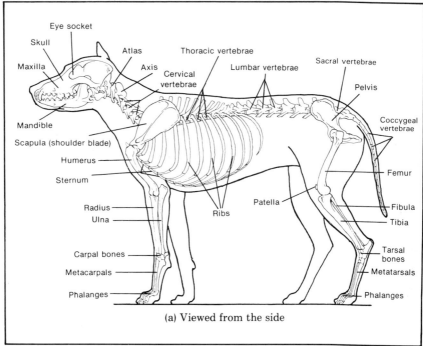

(a) Viewed from the side

Fig. 3 **The skeleton of the dog**   (Harold White 1984)

NOTE ● The long bones, e.g. the humerus, radius and ulna, the femur and the tibia, are most prone to fracture, particularly in road traffic accidents.

● In adult animals the bones usually break into two or more separate parts. In young animals the bone may bend and split, causing the so-called "green-stick" fracture.

● The fore limb is not joined to the remainder of the skeleton, it is held in place simply by muscles — there is no collar bone.

Skull
Eye socket
Maxilla
Mandible
Cervical vertebrae
Shoulder blade
Ribs
Humerus
Sternum
Radius
Ulna
Carpal bones
Metacarpals
Phalanges

Sacral vertebrae
Pelvis
Hip joint
Coccygeal vertebrae
Femur
Fibula
Tibia
Tarsal bones
Metatarsals
Phalanges

(b) Viewed from the front   (c) Viewed from behind

Fig. 3 **The skeleton of the dog**   (Harold White 1984)

The structure of long bones

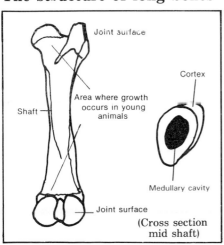

Joint surface
Cortex
Shaft
Area where growth
occurs in young
animals
Medullary cavity
Joint surface
(Cross section
mid shaft)

Fig. 4 **The structure of a long bone**

NOTE ●
Fractured bones can be repaired
by placing a pin in the medullary
cavity or by screwing a metal
plate to the cortex where
appropriate.

The structure of the vertebrae

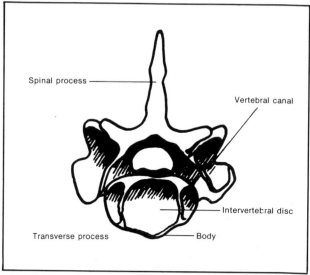

Spinal process

Vertebral canal

Intervertebral disc

Transverse process

Body

Fig. 5 **The structure of a vertebra**

There are a total of 29 vertebrae plus a variable number in the tail:
Seven cervical vertebrae make up the neck.
Thirteen thoracic vertebrae make up the spine over the chest and articulate with the ribs.
Six lumbar vertebrae and three sacral vertebrae form the lower back.
The number of coccygeal vertebrae depend on the length of the tail.

NOTE
- The spinal cord lies within the vertebral canal and is thus protected by bone.
- The vertebrae are separated by discs of cartilage which give protection against trauma and allows the spine to be more flexible. The centre of the disc may slip out of place and press on the spinal cord causing pain and paralysis.
- The vertebrae are joined together by ligaments and muscles which are anchored to the vertebral processes. Contraction of the muscles make the spine bend vertically and from side to side.

6

The structure of the skull

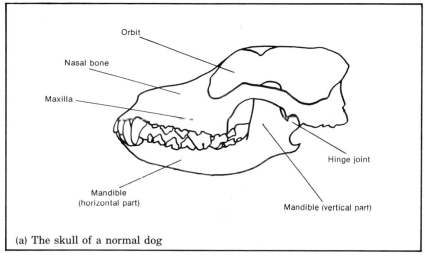

(a) The skull of a normal dog

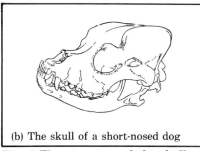

(b) The skull of a short-nosed dog

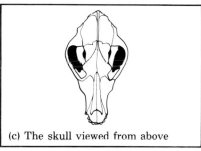

(c) The skull viewed from above

Fig. 6 **The structure of the skull**

The upper jaw is made up of the maxilla bone. The lower jaw is hinged to the skull and consists of the mandible which has both horizontal and vertical parts. These can become fractured quite easily in road traffic accidents. The jaw may become dislocated by trauma but that is comparatively rare. It is quite common however for the left and right horizontal parts of the mandible, where they are joined in the front of the mouth, to become separated in traumatic accidents. Sometimes the bones that make up the roof of the mouth do not fuse properly giving rise to a cleft palate. Puppies with severe cleft palates cannot suck because they cannot form a vacuum in the mouth and so often die. It is sensible to check all puppies as they are born for this congenital abnormality.

In short-nosed breeds, such as Boxers, the maxilla is much shorter than normal, while the lower jaw remains of normal length, giving the typical undershot mouth formation (see Fig. 6(b)).

The bony plates that make up the top of the skull are fused together in the middle of the forehead. In some small breeds with very domed heads (apple headed), such as Chihuahuas, this fusion fails to occur leaving a gap or "fontanelle", which is also called by breeders a "molero". Such animals are of course very vulnerable to brain injury.

7

The teeth

Adult dogs have a total of 42 teeth. These are made up as shown in the following table.

Tooth Type	Upper Jaw	Lower Jaw
Incisors	6	6
Canine	2	2
Premolars	8	8
Molars	4	6

Puppies begin to cut their milk teeth at about 14 days after birth. There are no molars in this set.

Milk teeth are shed and replaced by adult teeth at four to six months old. If any milk teeth persist which threaten to obstruct the correct growth of the permanent teeth, they can easily be removed by a veterinary surgeon.

Dogs' teeth are shaped for tearing and cutting rather than grinding, thus particles of food do not tend to become lodged in the teeth and dental decay is therefore relatively rare. Two of the molars provide exceptions to this rule.

Dogs' teeth frequently accumulate "tartar" (a hard deposit) on their surface, particularly if they only have access to soft food. This scale can be fairly easily removed by veterinary surgeons and should not be allowed to accumulate as it can lead to gingivitis (inflammation of the gums) associated with smelly breath and premature loss of teeth.

Fig. 7 **The teeth**

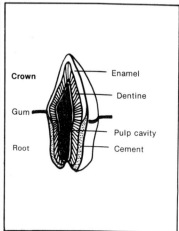

Fig. 8 **The structure of a tooth**

Two molars in the upper and lower jaws are much larger than the rest of the teeth. They are called the carnassial teeth. They have more than one root which can make them difficult to extract.

Tartar starts to accumulate at tooth/gum junction. Infection can also enter at this point. Both can lead to inflammation of the gum.

The joints

A joint is the region where two or more bones come together to form a "hinge". Simple joints allow movement in one plane only, whereas ball and socket joints, e.g. the hip, allow rotation to occur. The ends of the bones which form joints are covered with smooth cartilage to facilitate movement and the joint itself is lubricated with an oily liquid called synovial fluid. The bones are bound together with ligaments which may become damaged if the joint is "sprained" by being bent or straightened beyond its normal limits. If the ligaments break, or are so stretched that the bones become separated, a "dislocation" occurs. The stifle and hip joints are particularly prone to problems in dogs. Their structure is shown in the following figures.

- In arthritis the articular cartilage becomes inflamed and makes movement painful.

Fig. 9 **The structure of a simple joint**

(a) Front view   (b) Side view

Fig. 10 **The structure of the stifle joint**

- The upper part of the patella is joined by a tendon to the muscles which straighten the leg.
- The lower part of the patella is joined by a ligament to the tibia.
- The patella runs in a groove in the femur and moves up and down as the leg is straightened and bent.
- The patella may be dislocated to either side if the joint is subjected to trauma. This can occur quite easily if the animal is born with a groove which is abnormally shallow.
- Within the joint lie two cartilages which cushion the joint against trauma, and two ligaments — the cruciate ligaments. These structures may become ruptured so allowing excessive, sometimes painful, movement of the joint.

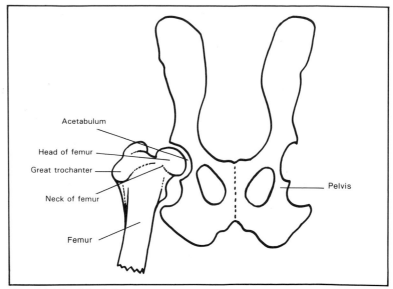

Fig. 11 **The hip joint**

- The hip joint is a typical ball and socket joint.
- In cases of hip dysplasia changes occur in the acetabulum (the socket) and/or to the head of the femur so that the joint cannot function properly. In severe cases the joint may be dislocated. This condition can be painful and cause affected animals to limp severely. Hip dysplasia often affects both hips since it is partly an inherited condition. It is commonly seen in the larger breeds of dogs, i.e. those weighing over 45lbs.

The Skeletal Muscles

Muscles are made up of fibres which contract when stimulated by a nerve impulse. Some muscles, for example those making up the stomach wall, are flat and relatively thin, others are cylindrical and when contracted are quite fat (e.g. the biceps muscle which flexes the elbow and the quadriceps muscle which lies in front of the femur and straightens the hind leg). Since the ends of the muscles are attached to bone by tendons, contraction and relaxation causes movement in the joints, making them bend (flex), extend, move inwards (adduction), move outwards (abduction) or rotate. In principle each muscle is opposed by another which exerts the opposite effect, thus the animal can adjust the position of any joint very precisely.

Apart from their obvious actions in causing locomotion, the muscles also serve to generate body heat by shivering. The muscles over the chest contract and relax to bring about respiratory movements. The abdominal muscles come into play when a dog passes motions or gives birth, as well as helping to flex the spine when the dog is galloping. The shoulder muscles hold the fore leg to the dog's trunk.

Over-extension of muscles can cause damage and this is called a muscle strain. Myositis is the word used to describe inflammation of muscles, often accompanied by acute pain.

The Skin

The overall purpose of the skin is to cover the body and protect the underlying tissues and organs, but it is also responsible for carrying information about objects that come in contact with the animal, and the environmental temperature. The skin is also, of course, sensitive to pain and will warn the animal of danger from sharp objects etc. The skin consists of two main layers — *the epidermis* and *the dermis.*

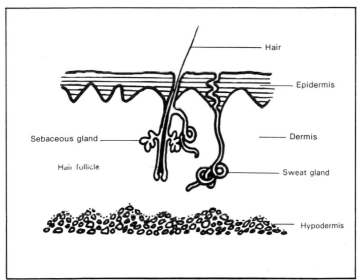

Fig. 12 **The structure of the skin**

The epidermis

This layer is made up of hardened plate-like cells which are formed continuously from the bottom layer and are shed or worn away from the top. The layer contains no blood vessels. The epidermis may become thickened and cause callouses on the hocks and elbows of heavy dogs through pressure on contact points when lying down (see also "What if" No. 18, Chapter 4 Part I).

In places, the epidermis extends down into the underlying layer to form a hair follicle which produces a single hair by growth from the bottom. When this growth stops that hair is shed and usually another begins to grow in its place. In dogs a number of hairs group together to emerge through a common opening. One hair in such a group is often thicker and longer than the others and is called a "guard hair". The rest of the coat is formed by the smaller, softer hairs in the bunch. The size of these hair bunches will vary according to the coat type. Sebaceous glands feed into the hair follicle producing a thick fluid that lubricates the skin and keeps it pliable.

Sweat glands also open up to the surface through the epidermis. In man, the evaporation of fluid produced by these glands is a major cooling mechanism. However, dogs lose heat principally by panting over their tongues.

11

The dermis

This layer contains blood vessels, that nourish the lower layer of the epidermis, and connective tissue, which supports the hair follicles and sweat glands. It also contains nerve ends which are sensitive to pain and touch. Small muscle fibres in the dermis, which can lengthen and contract, alter the shape of the skin and erect or lower the hairs. This effect is noticeable particularly in the centre back area and neck when the dog is mentally aroused, aggressive or fearful.

Modified skin structures

- **The mammary glands** are skin glands that have become specially modified to produce milk.
- **The anal sacs** (or so-called scent glands) are inversions of the skin where it joins the end of the digestive tract. The cavity formed is, in most dogs, big enough to take a broad bean. There are two sacs which lie on either side of the anus, producing a sickly smelling fluid of varying consistency. Occasionally the opening of these cavities becomes blocked and, unless expressed, the fluid may become infected and a painful anal abscess will form and possibly burst to the outside. (See also "What if" No. 22, Chapter 4 Part I.)
- **The claws** originate from the coronary border, the circular junction between the base of the claw and the skin. The claw grows down over the dermis that lies over the underlying phalanx. The dermis contains a lot of blood vessels and will bleed profusely if cut.

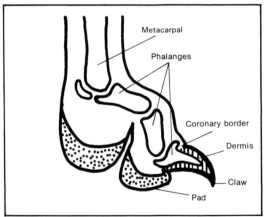

Fig. 13 **The claws**

NOTE: In *subcutaneous injections* the needle passes through the epidermis and dermis and the medicament is deposited in the hypodermis. *Intramuscular injections* are given into the muscles (usually in the hind leg) underlying the skin, *Intravenous injections* are given straight into the bloodstream (usually the vein running down the front of one of the forelegs is used). *Intraperitoneal injections* are given into the cavity between the abdominal wall and the abdominal organs.

The Ear

The ear consists of four parts:
1. The ear flap
2. The external ear canal
3. The middle ear
4. The internal ear

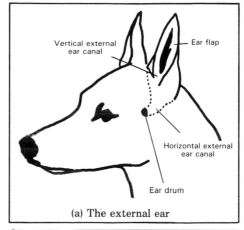

(a) The external ear

1. The ear flap is made up of a sheet of cartilage covered with skin. It varies in size between breeds and may be held erect, as in Terriers, or folded over as in Spaniels and Basset Hounds.

2. The external ear canal is composed of tubular cartilage and is lined with a specially developed skin called the integument, which produces a waxy material. In some breeds the canal is hairy. The canal has a sharp bend at its lower end where the vertical part joins the horizontal part. The end of the horizontal part of the canal is sealed by the ear drum.

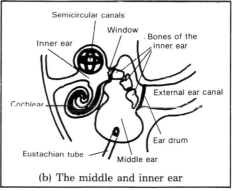

(b) The middle and inner ear

Fig. 14 **The ear**

It is important that the external ear canal be kept clear of excessive amounts of wax and debris, otherwise infection may occur resulting in *otitis externa* (ear canker). It may be necessary to pluck or remove some of the hair in dogs with very hairy ears, such as Poodles, to allow proper ventilation and prevent the accumulation of wax. This should be done, however, with great care. (See also "What if" No. 14, Chapter 4 Part I.) In chronic cases of *otitis externa* the lining of the ear becomes very thickened so that the canal is occluded and the ridges often rub together to form ulcers. By the time that has happened the only sure cure is to open the canal to the outside by carrying out an operation called an aural resection.

3. The middle ear is housed in a cavity in one of the bones which makes up the skull. It consists of a chamber that contains three small bones which connect the ear drum to a window at the opposite side. These bones transmit sound vibrations to the inner ear. Pressure differences between the middle and external ear are equalised by means of the eustachian tube, which leads to the back of the mouth and which is also situated in a cavity in a bone of the skull.

4. The inner ear consists of a number of sealed tubes which contain fluid. The cochlea picks up vibrations from the middle ear and is concerned with hearing. The semi-circular canals contain nerve ends which sense the fluid movement in the tubes that are set at right angles to each other. By monitoring the fluid movement the animal is able to keep its balance and orientate itself in space.

While disease of the external ear is common, middle and inner ear disease is rare, but is usually very serious when it does occur.

If external ear disease is not treated promptly and properly, it can lead to a serious problem that may need a surgical operation to correct. (See also "What if" No. 14, Chapter 4 Part I.)

The Eye

Essentially the eye is a fluid-filled globe that is "housed" in the orbit in the skull. Attached to the outside of the globe are a number of muscles which are able to move the eye upwards, downwards and from side to side.

The lens, pupil and the ciliary body divide the eye into two parts:

(i) the anterior chamber which is filled with fluid called the aqueous humour;

(ii) the posterior chamber which is filled with a thick fluid called the vitreous humour.

The correct pressure within the eye is maintained by fluid being continually produced and drained away. If this mechanism goes wrong the pressure in the eye will rise, resulting in the eye increasing in size and the cornea becoming opaque — this is called glaucoma. (See also "What if" No. 13, Chapter 4 Part I.)

The outermost layer of the eye is tough and thick and is called the sclera. Over the front of the eye this layer takes the form of a transparent window called the cornea.

The lens is attached by a ligament to the ciliary body which is muscular. Contraction of this muscle alters the shape of the lens so that the animal can focus on objects at different distances.

The back of the eye is lined with the retina. Nerves which have light-sensitive endings in this layer transmit messages through the optic nerve to the brain, where they are "decoded" into a "picture" of what is being seen. The back of the eye of dogs and cats also contains a separate area called the tapetum which reflects light. The glowing effect of dogs' and cats' eyes at night is produced when a beam of light falls on to the tapetum in surrounding darkness and is reflected.

The front of the eye is protected by the upper and lower eyelids which when closed completely cover the eye in most dogs. The place where the eyelids join is known as "the corner of the eye". Dogs have a third eyelid which lies close to the surface of the eye in the inner corner of the eyelids. When the eye recedes into the skull, as can occur when the dog is out of condition and the fat behind the eye decreases in amount, or when the eye is pushed backwards into the head, the third eyelid will come across to protect the eye from possible damage. A gland which produces lubricating fluid (the Harderian gland) lies under the third eyelid. It may occasionally become enlarged and protrude from behind the third eyelid and cause a problem.

The skin on the outside of the eyelid is continued on the inside of the eyelid and over the cornea as a thin layer called the conjunctiva. Because the lids protrude over the eye the conjunctiva is bent back on itself to form a sac as it continues over the eye. The surface of the eye is lubricated by fluid (tears) produced by the lachrymal glands that have their outlet into the conjunctival sac. Any excess tears are carried away in small ducts that are situated in the inner corner of the eye and which lead to the nose. If more tears than normal are produced, or if this duct becomes blocked, fluid will run down the side of the animal's face and may cause staining or inflammation of the skin. The upper and lower eyelashes protrude from the point where the skin on the outer side of the eyelids and the conjunctiva join. Sometimes there is an extra layer of lashes, distichiasis, which rub on the surface of the eye and cause a problem. In other cases the eyelids may turn inwards, again making the lashes rub on the surface of the eye causing inflammation — this is called entropion. The reverse of this situation, when the eyelids turn outwards exposing the conjunctiva as occurs quite commonly in breeds such as Bloodhounds where it is known as "the haw", is called ectropion. Both these conditions require veterinary attention and in some situations surgery may be needed. (See also "What if" No. 11, Chapter 4 Part I.)

(a) External appearance

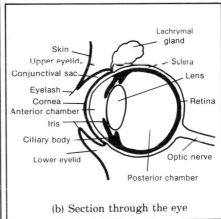

(b) Section through the eye

Fig. 15 **The eye**

- If the cornea is damaged or the pressure in the eye increases it will become opaque.
- In young animals the lens is elastic. This elasticity decreases as animals age so focusing becomes more difficult.
- Sometimes the lens will become detached from its ligaments and fall either forward or backward. This is a lens luxation (dislocation) and can lead to glaucoma.
- Opacity of the lens is known as a cataract which may be partial or complete.
- Hereditary defects in the retina can affect vision viz. *Collie Eye Anomaly* (CEA) and *Progressive Retinal Atrophy* (PRA). (See "What if" Nos. 12 and 13, Chapter 4 Part I.)
- Bacterial infection of the conjunctival sac leads to inflammation — conjunctivitis.

The Internal Organs

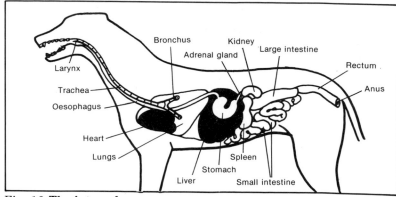

Fig. 16 **The internal organs**

The inside of the body is divided into two parts by the diaphragm:
1.   The Thoracic cavity — the chest (thorax)
2.   The Abdominal cavity — the abdomen

1. The Circulatory System

All the organs which make up the body need oxygen in order to function normally. This essential requirement is brought by the red cells in the blood, which in turn are carried around the body in a continuous tube called the circulatory system. The blood is propelled round the system by the action of the heart, which is in fact a muscular pump fitted with valves to ensure that the blood travels in the right direction. Problems can occur if the heart valves leak (incompetence) or do not open properly (stenosis). Sometimes drugs need to be given to strengthen the beat of the heart if the muscle becomes weakened by age or inactivity.

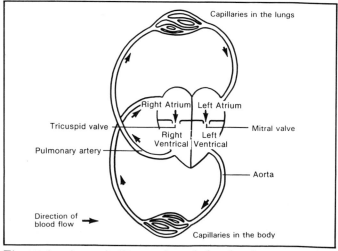

Fig. 17 **A schematic illustration of the circulatory system**

Essentially, blood which has circulated round the body and become exhausted of oxygen returns to the right atrium. It is pumped through the tricuspid valve into the right ventricle which pumps it through the pulmonary artery to the lungs. As the blood passes through the small tubes in the lungs (the capillaries) it picks up oxygen. Oxygen-enriched blood returns from the lungs to the left atrium, is pumped through to the left ventricle and then via the aorta to be distributed to the capillaries throughout the body. A small amount of the fluid from the blood and some cells leak out into the tissues to be gathered up in another series of channels called the lymphatic system, which in turn drains back into the blood system. This lymphatic system has a number of "glands" or "nodes" situated throughout its length. These glands, which sometimes become swollen in the case of infection in a tissue, act as filters to remove bacteria and other debris from the blood and they are also responsible for the production of some types of white blood cells and antibodies that protect the body against infection.

The spleen — lies near the stomach in the abdomen. It is responsible for producing some of the elements that make up blood and also for removing old worn out red blood cells. It also acts as a storage area for blood and thus varies considerably in size according to the amount of blood required in the circulatory system at any particular time.
The bone marrow — the cavity of the long bones is filled with marrow which produces red blood cells and some types of white blood cells.

Blood contains:
- Red blood cells — which carry oxygen
- White blood cells — which can engulf bacteria and other foreign matter within the body
- Blood platelets — cell fragments

These components are carried in a fluid called plasma.

Clotting — if blood leaks from the system, fibrin filaments formed from one of the constituents in the plasma link together to form a web or net which traps the cells in the blood to form a clot. The clear fluid that remains is called serum.

Blood Tests — veterinary surgeons will sometimes take a blood sample to test for:
- The number of cells of each type in a standard volume of blood.
- The packed cell volume (PCV) — the amount of space taken up by the cells, when they are are allowed to sediment, in comparison with the plasma.
- The erythrocyte sedimentation rate (ESR) — the speed with which the red blood cells sediment out when the blood is left to stand.
- The levels of various enzymes and other constituents normally found in blood.
- The levels of protective antibodies to various diseases for diagnostic purposes to identify the best time for vaccination or to check that vaccination has been effective.

Such tests help in the diagnosis of diseases and can also give a guide to the prognosis of a case.

2. The Digestive System

In order to work, the body needs food to provide a source of energy to allow organs to grow and to replace worn out tissues. Food needs to be "processed" by the digestive system in order to provide materials in a form that can be utilised. Essentially, the digestive system is a muscular tube, or tract, with openings at one end where food goes in and at the other end where waste material (excreta) comes out. A number of glands associated with the digestive system discharge the fluid they produce into the tube to facilitate the breakdown of food into essential elements. The procedure is as follows.

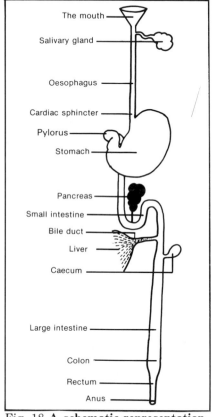

The mouth
Salivary gland
Oesophagus
Cardiac sphincter
Pylorus
Stomach
Pancreas
Small intestine
Bile duct
Liver
Caecum
Large intestine
Colon
Rectum
Anus

Fig. 18 **A schematic representation of the digestive tract**

The digestive process

1. If the food is presented in chunks it is torn into small pieces and crushed by the teeth in the mouth, otherwise it is swallowed whole.
2. Saliva, produced by the salivary gland, helps to lubricate the food as it passes through the oesophagus into the stomach. The salivary juices also begin the digestive process.
3. The oesophagus is a simple tube which passes down the neck and enters the chest, passes over the heart and through the diaphragm into the stomach. Inadvertently swallowed large objects may become stuck in the oesophagus at the entrance to the chest, over the heart and where the oesophagus goes through the diaphragm, and may require surgical removal.
4. The entrance and exit to the stomach are guarded by a ring of muscle, the cardiac sphincter and the pyloric sphincter. The pyloric sphincter is responsible for regulating the passage of food from the stomach. The stomach wall produces juices which help to process the food, particularly proteins. Inflammation of the stomach is called gastritis.
5. Digestion continues in the small intestine aided by the bile and pancreatic juice. The useful products are absorbed through its wall into the blood stream.
6. The digestive process, aided by bacteria, and absorption of useful material, particularly fluids, continues in the large intestine.
7. The caecum is equivalent to the appendix in man. It seldom causes a problem in dogs.
8. The faeces (the motions or stools) are made up of waste material and are "stored" in the rectum to be passed, usually twice a day.

3. The Pancreas

The pancreas produces juices which help digestion, but it also manufactures the hormone insulin which circulates in the blood and is responsible for regulating the amount of available glucose in the body.

4. The Liver

Besides producing bile, which helps digestion, the liver is also responsible for regulating the storage and usage of carbohydrate, the mobilisation of body fat, the detoxification and excretion of toxic substances, the synthesis of proteins that occur in the blood and to help stabilise the body temperature.

NOTE:
- The collective word viscera is used to describe all the abdominal organs together.
- Sometimes the rectum will protrude through the anus — this is called a rectal prolapse. It is nearly always a sequel to a severe and protracted attack of diarrhoea and requires veterinary attention and possibly surgical correction.

The Urinary System

The urinary system is responsible for removing much of the excess water and many waste products that accumulate in the body. The kidneys, which lie one on each side of the body near the spine, high up in the abdomen, filter these materials from their blood supply. Fluid leaves the kidney by the ureter which leads to the bladder. The urethra leads from the bladder, either through the vulva in the female or the penis in the male. In the female the urethra is short, whereas in the male it is long and arches over the pelvis.

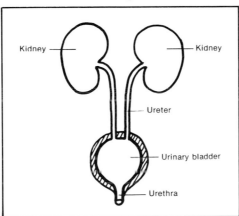

Fig. 19 **The urinary system**

- Stones made up of various waste materials may accumulate in the bladder and need surgical removal.
- In male animals, small stones may become stuck in the urethra as it passes over the pelvis or in the penis itself behind the bone that is present in the penis of the dog.
- Nephritis is the word used to describe inflammation of the kidneys.

The Respiratory System

It has already been said that in order to function the body needs oxygen. The main function of the respiratory system is to bring about effective oxygenation of the blood but it also plays a role in heat regulation and the loss of excess water. Expansion of the chest, brought about by the movement of muscles in the chest wall and a downward movement of the diaphragm, creates a negative pressure in the thorax which inflates the lungs and causes air to be drawn in through the nose and, during exercise, through the mouth. Air passes through the pharynx, which is common to the respiratory and the digestive tracts, into the larynx and reaches the lungs via the trachea. Within the lungs, the trachea divides into two bronchi and these divide again like the branches of a tree to form bronchioles which end in air sacs, the alveoli. Blood circulating in the wall of the air sacs picks up oxygen as it passes through. The lungs are made up of a mass of grape-like air sacs supported in connective tissue.

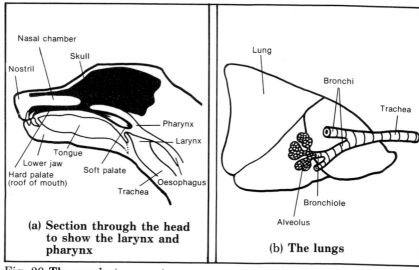

(a) **Section through the head to show the larynx and pharynx**

(b) **The lungs**

Fig. 20 **The respiratory system**

- **The nasal chamber** is lined by scrolls of delicate bone covered with a sensitive lining. Its main function is to warm and filter air and to aid the sense of smell. The chamber is linked to sinuses which are cavities in the bones that make up the skull.
- **The pharynx** is common to the respiratory and digestive tracts. When the dog is eating, the trachea is closed by the epiglottis and the nasal cavity is sealed by the soft palate.
- **The larynx** consists of a tube made up of cartilage. Its function is to prevent food entering the trachea and to produce sound (vocalisation) by vibration of the vocal chords it contains.
- **The trachea** is a straight tube held permanently open by ringed cartilages.
- The respiratory rate in a normal resting dog is ten to 30 breaths per minute.

The Genital System

The male

Like all male animals, dogs have two testicles in a pouch (the scrotum) between the hind legs. The testicles produce spermatozoa which pass down tubules to a duct called the epididymis where they are stored. During mating the spermatozoa pass from the epididymis to another duct which joins the urethra (see also under The Urinary System). On the way the spermatozoa are mixed with fluid from the prostate and other glands to form the semen which is ejaculated from the erect penis through the urethra during coitus.

The testicles also produce the male sex hormone, testosterone, which is responsible for producing the secondary male characteristics. The testicles descend into the scrotum from the abdomen during puppyhood in normal dogs. In some animals, one or both testicles are permanently retained in the abdomen. A dog with only one testicle descended is known as a unilateral cryptorchid (monorchid) and where neither is descended, a cryptorchid. Retained testicles are a hereditary problem, and although a monorchid dog is fertile, it should never be used for breeding as the fault may be transmitted to its offspring. Monorchidism is regarded as a major fault in the show ring.

A castrated dog is one in which the testicles have been completely removed surgically, usually to curb excessive inter-male aggression and objectionable sexual behaviour. Such dogs, are of course, infertile, although they may continue to be interested in bitches and may even mount bitches that are in season. The castrated male tends to put on weight and the diet should be adjusted accordingly.

The female

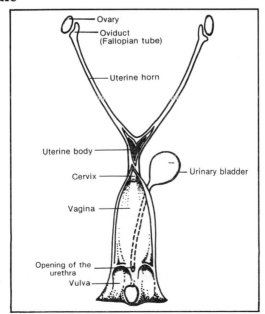

Fig. 21 **The genital organs of the bitch**

Bitches have two ovaries which are situated in the abdomen near the kidneys. When the bitch is in season the ovaries produce eggs which are caught by the fimbriae and pass down the oviducts into the uterus where they develop into foetuses, if the bitch has been successfully mated. The bitch's uterus is made up of two long horns and the uterine body. It opens into the vagina by the cervix which is kept shut, except during oestrus and when giving birth. The female genital tract opens to the exterior through two lips which which make up the vulva.

Between heats the uterine horns are no thicker than a piece of string, but when the bitch is in season they increase in size to become rather thicker than a pencil. The pregnant uterus has a diameter of two to four inches according to the breed and may contain, in the case of the large breeds, as many as 12 or 14 puppies.

Besides producing eggs, the ovaries manufacture the female sex hormones, oestrogen and progesterone. These are responsible for bringing about the secondary female sex characteristics and the development of the mammary glands (see also The Hormonal System page 24).

● During coitus, spermatozoa ejaculated from the male penis are deposited around the cervix. They pass through into the uterus and up the fallopian tubes where the eggs are fertilized.

● Spaying (ovarohysterectomy) involves the complete removal of the uterus and the ovaries of the bitch. This is of course done under general anaesthesia and is a major operation.

● Very occasionally the lining of the vagina will protrude through the vulva after whelping, this is called a vaginal prolapse and requires veterinary attention.

● Vaginal hyperplasia is the term used to describe a swelling and protuberance of the lining of the vagina that occurs during heat, particularly in Boxers and Bulldogs.

The Nervous System

The function of the nervous system is to receive messages from outside the body and, after analysing them, to cause the animal to respond in an appropriate way.

The nervous system is essentially divided into two parts:

1. The central nervous system
This consists of the brain and spinal cord, both of which are protected by bone — the skull in the case of the brain and the bony canal through the vertebrae in the case of the spinal cord.

2. The peripheral nervous system
This consists of nerves which connect the central nervous system to the rest of the body.

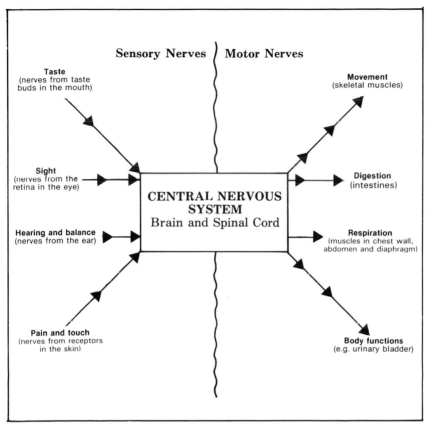

Fig. 22 **A diagrammatic illustration of how
the central nervous system works**

If a ball is thrown for a dog to catch, messages are sent through the sensory nerves from the light sensitive nerve endings in the eye to the brain. This in turn sends messages via the motor nerves to the muscles which move the dog into the right place and open its mouth at the correct time. All this, of course, takes place in a split second of time.

Some nerve impulses are sent automatically from an organ when it is full, and the central nervous system responds, also automatically, to send a nerve impulse to the muscles in the organ to make them contract and empty it. In some such cases, e.g. the urinary bladder, the brain can override the automatic response, as occurs in house-trained animals. In other cases, for example the filling and emptying of the stomach, the nervous impulses which cause contraction of the muscles and dilation of the sphincters are purely automatic and cannot be overridden consciously.

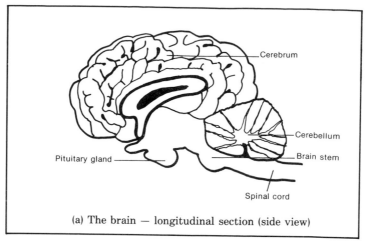

(a) The brain — longitudinal section (side view)

(b) The brain from above

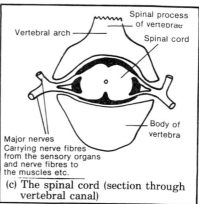

(c) The spinal cord (section through vertebral canal)

Fig. 23 **The central nervous system**

The Hormonal System

A number of glands called "endocrine glands", situated in various parts of the body, produce hormones which are spread by the circulatory system throughout the body. They instruct the organ or body system they control to perform a specific function. Many organs which are under hormonal control receive messages from one hormone which makes them work more quickly and from another which makes them work more slowly or stop. Thus the hormones act rather like the accelerator and brakes on a car and control very precisely the body's activity.

Besides their effect on specific parts of the body, the hormones work together rather like the players in an orchestra, the whole being conducted by the hormones produced by the pituitary gland which is situated at the base of the brain. The amount of hormones present in the blood is being continually monitored by the body and adjusted to meet the animal's need at any particular time.

THE ENDOCRINE GLANDS AND THE HORMONES THEY PRODUCE

Gland	Situation	Hormone/s produced	Action
Thyroid.	The gland lies alongside the trachea at the end nearest the mouth.	Thyroid hormone.	Controls the activity of the body tissues. Deficiency (hypothyroidism) results in poor growth in young animals. Older animals, lacking in the hormone, become sluggish, overweight, and have poor hair growth. Excess amounts of the hormone cause hyper-activity.
Parathyroid.	The two parathyroids are small glands situated alongside the thyroid.	Parathyroid hormone.	Controls the calcium stores in the body and is there-fore important in the development of the skeleton.
Adrenal.	The two adrenal glands are small glands which lie near the kidneys.	Adrenaline — produced by the centre of the gland (the medulla). Corticosteroids — produced by the outer layer of the gland (the cortex).	Prepares the animal for action and is excreted in quantity if the animal is frightened, needs to fight or run away. One group of these hormones controls the salt and water content of the body. The other hormones produced by the adrenal cortex enhance the animal's resistance to stress and infection. Excessive production of corticosteroids causes Cushing's syndrome. Addison's disease is caused when too little hormone is produced.
Pancreas.	Lies in a loop in the small intestine.	Insulin.	Controls the amount of glucose in the blood. Animals with sugar diabetes are lacking in the hormone.
Testes.	The two testes are situated in the scrotal sac.	Testosterone.	Responsible for the male characteristics of dogs, particularly aggression.
Ovaries.	Contained in the abdomen near the kidneys.	Oestrogens. Progesterone.	Responsible for the female characteristics of bitches. Stimulates the genital tract and causes bleeding when the bitch is "on heat". Also brings about development of the mammary glands. Progesterone is responsible for preparing the uterus so that it can support the foetuses. It maintains pregnancy. It causes the mammary glands to develop so that they can eventually produce milk.

25

THE ENDOCRINE GLANDS AND THE HORMONES THEY PRODUCE (continued)

Gland	Situation	Hormone/s produced	Action

Pituitary.	Situated at the base of the brain. The gland is divided into two parts, the anterior part which produces the first four hormones listed in the next column and the posterior part which produces the remaining two.	1. Thyrotropic hormone.
		2. Corticotropic hormone.
		3. Growth hormone.
		
		4. Gonadotropins —
		   Follicle-stimulating hormone.
		   Luteinizing hormone.
		   Prolactin.
		
		5. Anti-diuretic hormone.
		
		6. Oxytocin.
			1. Controls the action of the thyroid.
			2. Controls action of the adrenal cortex.
			3. Controls the animals growth particularly up to puberty.
			4. Promotes the ripening of eggs in the ovaries.
			   Causes ovulation.
			   Stimulates the mammary glands so that they are ready to produce milk.
			5. Acts on the kidney to prevent excessive excretion of water.
			6. Makes the pregnant uterus contract at whelping and stimulates the release of milk from the mammary glands.

CHAPTER 1
PART II

MOTIVATION AND INTELLIGENCE

The family pack

The senses

Behaviour patterns

Body language

By understanding the nature and motivation of their pet owners will ensure that training and living with a dog is an easy, fulfilling and pleasurable experience.

In the 20th Century we have a situation where dogs bred for working and sporting activities are commonly being chosen as pets. Such dogs need to adapt to a role of relative idleness, thus there is a need to find ways to compromise between the life the dog is equipped to live and the one in which the domestic pet finds itself. Some small dogs have been deliberately bred for a "toy" or pet role, but it is still necessary for owners to remember that they nevertheless retain the basic instincts common to the canine species as a whole and to act accordingly.

The Family Pack

Dogs are not solitary animals. By nature they prefer to live within a family or pack structure. The pack provides moral and physical support, and also protection for its members. For dogs below the rank of pack leader, the pack also supplies leadership and direction, and takes decisions for its members. Dogs respond very well to being provided with a framework of guidelines within which they must live. The dog which is allowed to do just as it likes is not a happy dog.

When a dog lives within a canine pack it will dominate some of the pack members but will defer to others which are above it in the pack hierarchy. Ambitious dogs and bitches will make intermittent bids to improve their ranking, even challenging the pack leader, with the hope of usurping the position themselves.

Domestication has not altered the dog's desire either to be in charge or to accept being dominated by a person it respects. **The pack of the pet or companion dog is its owner and the immediate family of people and animals with which it lives.**

In a wholly canine pack, leadership is somewhat flexible, in that a slightly lower-ranking dog than the pack leader may assume leadership in some particular situations. In the domestic pet we see a typical example of this in the dog which is dutifully obedient within the home but which pulls continually on the lead and so dominates a walk when out of doors. The dog is taking decisions and imposing its will upon the handler—this dog is pack leader in taking a walk. **It is important that the dog's owner shall be the pack leader in all situations** and be aware that dogs of all sizes and characters may make periodic bids for supremacy, especially during adolescence. The concept of pack behaviour and submission to the pack leader is inherited by puppies at birth, and is reinforced by their mothers. While the litter is in the nest, the mother is the only pack leader and all the puppies defer to her. But in adult life in the full canine pack, and in a canine/human pack family situation, there will be several individuals who are above the dog in ranking and yet who also defer to the pack leader. **It is important that in the canine/human pack, the dog should not be allowed to consider itself superior to any of the human members of the pack.** If other animals are kept, the dog may assume dominant or submissive ranking with them, but it must not be dominant to any human.

The bitch is able to use sharp and immediate physical punishment, often preceded by warning growls, at her puppies. An adult pack leader subdues and disciplines the pack most frequently by eye contact and body language, with some vocalisation (growling) and there is rarely need for physical conflict except where an individual makes constant bids to assume power.

From observation of the way a canine or wolf pack is disciplined we can discover how to build a rewarding and agreeable relationship with the family pet (see also Chapter 3).

The Senses

Puppies are born relatively immature compared to a human baby. In the first four weeks of life they develop eyesight, hearing, mobility and adult vocalisation, as well as their first set of teeth. Some important features in respect of the senses are given in the following table.

The Senses and Body Language

Sense	Puppies	Adults	Training Aid
SIGHT	Puppies are born quite blind with only an indication where the eye will be. Eyes are fully developed and open by ten to 14 days after birth.	Dogs see better than humans in twilight and darkness. They are long-sighted, seeing moving objects best. They have difficulty seeing stationary figures at a distance and in focusing on small objects at close range. Dogs can see some colours; bright red and bright green are the easiest to see.	Use hand signals and move slightly when calling a dog from a long distance.
HEARING	The ears are not functional at birth but hearing is fully developed at three to four weeks of age. Congenital deafness does sometimes occur, often associated with white coat colouring.	Dogs can hear a wider range of sounds over longer distances than man. Hearing is most acute in dogs with open, funnel-shaped ears and in breeds that can "prick" and swivel their ear flaps. Very loud noise and some high-pitched sounds from some household appliances may cause discomfort and even pain to dogs.	There should never be any need to shout at dogs.
VOCALISATION	Puppies cry in a variety of tones from the moment of birth. Contented puppies make a soft murmur while feeding. The first bark is usually heard at about four to six weeks.	Barking is used in different tones and cadences, to communicate with humans, to warn off intruders etc., and as a challenge to other dogs. The howl carries over long distances and is used as a means of communication with other dogs. Some dogs will talk to their owner when content by using a low grumbling growl of varying pitch.	Dogs can be trained to bark and to stop barking on command.
TOUCH	For the first two weeks of their lives puppies can only maintain their body temperature by huddling close to each other and to their mother's mammary glands. Their very lives depend on being close to another animal or source of heat.	Most dogs enjoy being stroked on the head, down the spine, and the chest between the front legs, but some are reluctant to be touched on their feet and tail.	Body sensitivity varies. Some dogs will need strong handling while others will respond to the lightest touch on the lead. The force used in punishment needs to be suited to the particular dog's sensitivity to touch.

29

The Senses and Body Language (continued)

Sense	Puppies	Adults	Training Aid
TASTE	From weaning time onwards puppies are introduced to a variety of tastes, and they will also investigate plants, earth, and many other substances (some of which may be harmful) in order to identify edible things.	Dogs can enjoy as rewards and titbits a very wide range of sweet, salt, or sharp flavours. Foods which lack a strong smell or taste are liable to be rejected.	Cherished food rewards, given **immediately** a command has been obeyed are a valuable training aid.
BODY LANGUAGE	Puppies do not begin to use canine body language until they are about eight weeks old.	Dogs display a variety of facial expressions, using mouth, eyes and ears, sometimes with vocalisation, to express dominant or submissive intentions. Body posture, type of walk and the angle at which the tail is held are also important indicators of a dog's feelings — *also p.32.*	The observant owner will have warning of a dog's intentions by intelligent interpretation of facial expression and body posture, and so can often prevent an unhappy confrontation with an aggressive or fearful dog.

Behaviour Patterns

1. General habits

Although dogs have been domesticated for thousands of years, they are still in many ways close to the primitive animal. Many of the actions and behaviour patterns which are natural behaviour to the dog can be unpleasing to us and to the community when we keep dogs as pets. Although dogs can be trained to modify some of these unwelcome behaviour patterns it may well be cruel to go too far in trying to eradicate them altogether. It is, however, anti-social to allow some "natural" behaviours to go unchecked. Dogs, like people, must learn to control certain natural behaviours if they are to integrate properly into society.

It is a natural behaviour for a dog...

- to investigate any unfamiliar object, animal or person by vigorous sniffing and possibly by urine marking. Information about other dogs is obtained by sniffing at their genitals and/or faeces and urine.
- to re-mark with a stream of urine key points and objects if another dog has been on the territory.
- to help itself to any edible object left within its reach—this is *not* stealing.
- to dig, either for vermin or to bury bones and trophies.
- to appropriate any object bearing the fresh scent of the owner or close members of the family.
- to be possessive about food and toys unless trained from an early age to give up possessions to those above it in the pack hierarchy.
- to flush out game birds and rabbits and to give chase if not restrained.
- to feel lonely and to bark as a means of gaining attention and company.
- to feel jealous of newcomers to the family, especially if more notice is taken of a new puppy or a new baby than is given to the resident dog.

- to lick the muzzles of dogs, and to attempt to lick the faces and hands of humans. This is a sign of submission and affection. Puppies lick the dam's muzzle to induce her to regurgitate food for them.
- to jump up to greet familiar humans, in an effort to get as near the face as possible.
- to need to chew hard objects, especially at four to eight months old, while teething. Chewing on bones or hard objects also alleviates boredom.
- to eat the faeces of other species, especially cow manure, horse droppings, cat faeces and rabbit pellets.
- to roll in obnoxious, highly odorous substances, such as the carcasses of carrion.

2. Bitches

Bitches come into season for the first time at between six and 18 months old, and heat occurs at six to ten month intervals for the rest of the bitch's life, unless the reproductive cycle is controlled by chemical means (your veterinary surgeon will advise) or unless the bitch's ovaries and uterus are removed (spaying). See also Chapter 2.

Where bitches are kept together it is likely that they will stimulate each other to come into oestrus. Bitches often engage in mock-mating play with each other. This is harmless provided it does not provoke irritability and fighting.

It is *normal* for bitches to vary in temperament at different stages of their cycle. This must be borne in mind when training bitches and when looking for signs of disease.

It is a natural behaviour for a bitch to seek to escape and to invite a dog to mate her when she is at the fertile peak of her heat period. This behaviour pattern must be prevented for social reasons (she may cause a road traffic or some other accident and of course give birth to unwanted puppies). The options are:

1. Keep the bitch under the strongest supervision. This means ensuring that doors and gates are shut all the time, which can be difficult especially when there are young children in the home.
2. Having the bitch's uterus and ovaries removed.
3. Averting the season by chemical means. Preferably see your veterinary surgeon well ahead of the time she is expected in season.

3. Males

Male dogs are usually capable of siring a litter from between six to ten months old and until late middle age.

A dog at the height of his fertility will mate several bitches every week, if the opportunity is available, but eagerness to perform the mating act is no guide to the dog's fertility. A veterinary surgeon can perform a sperm count on stud dogs as a positive check on fertility if it is needed.

It is a natural behaviour for a male dog with a high libido to escape to track down a bitch on heat, sometimes over quite a long distance from his home. This behaviour is accentuated if the dog has had an occasional mating experience, so it is better not to allow a pet dog to be used at stud in order to oblige a friend. Owners of dogs which have started wandering in search of bitches should seek veterinary help without delay since early treatment with hormones or possibly castration may be indicated. See also Chapter 2.

4. Elimination behaviour

Adult dogs pass faeces two to three times a day depending on what is fed. Puppies defaecate on average four to five times a day, again depending on what is fed and how often. In general terms, foods high in protein are likely to be low residue producers, while some of the cereal based complete diets produce a large volume of faeces.

Some foods, for example carrots, nuts, dried fruit, some beans and flaked maize, are not digested by the dog and will be seen unchanged in faeces. The colour of the faeces is related to the type of food eaten. The dog's food is normally digested and faeces eliminated within 12 to 24 hours of feeding, but when a small indigestible object has been swallowed, it may take two to three weeks or even longer for it to appear in the faeces.

Young puppies urinate very frequently, as many as ten times a day. Adult dogs urinate about three times daily, excluding territory marking behaviour and the message-leaving urination of a bitch coming on heat.

Both dogs and bitches should have full control of urine and faeces by the age of six months, except possibly during illness. Very old dogs may become incontinent. If a puppy continues to dribble urine after the age of six months and when house-training is understood, veterinary advice should be sought, as a malformation of the urinary system is not uncommon and may need to be corrected by surgery.

The urine of most bitches will burn patches on the lawn, and the stream of urine from an adult dog will kill plants and shrubs. The only remedy is to pour quantities of cold water on the place as soon as possible after the urine has been passed. See also Chapter 7.

Adult bitches are often very particular about the surface on which they will urinate. Some will only use their own garden. Many more will only use the surface (grass, concrete, gravel etc.) to which they are accustomed. When away from home a bitch may resist passing urine for as long as 48 hours, although drinking normally. The only remedy is to give her every opportunity to empty her bladder in conditions as near as possible to those with which she is familiar at home, and eventually she will have to give in. It can be very useful for their owners to train dogs and bitches to urinate to the sound of an undulating whistle, as horse owners often used to do in the past.

Very submissive puppies may have an involuntary emission of urine at moments of great fear or great pleasure, for instance when being punished or when greeting their owner. Some bitches will continue this behaviour past puppyhood, and this may be a sign that the bitch has become too low in the pack structure, or that more orders are being given her than she is capable of comprehending. Such a bitch should have her ego built up by brisk praise and encouragement of good behaviour rather than sympathy or scolding when she dribbles urine.

Body Language

A dog's emotions and intentions can be judged by observing the way it stands, how it holds its ears and tail and by other tell-tale signs. Good dog owners will observe their pet carefully and continually so that they can interpret what dogs are "saying". The details given below and illustrated on page 34 will serve as a guide and hopefully help observation of the individual pet.

The head

(i) *The ears* are pricked or erect when alert or listening intently, but held back to the head as an indication of submission or pleasure, and also when the dog is ready to attack. Other body signs help to distinguish the dog's intentions.

(ii) *The eyes* are narrowed and half-closed in pleasure or submission, but wide open, full and glowing when the dog feels aggressive.

The leader of a dog or wolf pack often exerts control by means of eye contact alone. The superior dog will give a lower ranking animal, which is perhaps contemplating some forbidden behaviour, a long, hard stare. The submissive dog will lower its head and turn away, to avoid meeting the pack leader's eyes. The dog which means to challenge the pack leader will return the stare, often for several minutes, until one or the other mounts a physical attack.

Lower ranking dogs also recognise and appreciate a soft-eyed glance of approval from the pack leader. Direct eye contact from human to dog should be avoided where a dog is known to have aggressive tendencies. Frequent, gentle eye contact between dog and owner signifies acceptance of the current behaviour pattern and is very beneficial to the relationship.

(iii) *The mouth* in some breeds, particularly Labradors, is opened to show the teeth in an almost human one sided "grin" of friendly greeting. Both lips are drawn further back and more of the teeth are exposed in the snarl of aggression.

Body posture

Body posture is used to convey mood by all dogs. When expressing aggression, a dog seeks to make itself look as large and as frightening as possible. It stands on its toes, the chest thrust forward, and some of the hair is held erect, often the ruff around the neck and a wide band of hair right down the spine. The tail is held stiffly in line with the back and may wave gently, but *is not wagged.* It is a mistake to assume that because the tail is moving, the dog is ambivilent about its attitude or is, after all, friendly. The head is usually lowered, and barking stops when an attack is imminent. The dog which assumes an aggressive stance while barking with mouth wide open is probably fearful and will back away when challenged.

A submissive dog will adopt a posture the opposite of that described above.

Vocalisation

(i) *Growling* is used to communicate with other animals and people. The dog owner should be aware of the difference between the low throat murmur of pleasure and "conversation" made by some dogs when being petted, and the true rumbling growl used as a warning that an attack will be made if the offending behaviour of human or dog is continued. *Never challenge or tease a growling dog.*

(ii) *Roaring* with mouth wide open, and mock biting without clenching the jaws, is a play sequence between dogs, and dog and human. This mode of play should not however be encouraged with children or by older people with fragile skin, and extremely cautiously, if at all, with the guard dog breeds.

(iii) *Howling,* always done from a standing position, produces a sound that carries a long way. It is used as a distress call and for dog/dog communication, never in connection with aggression.

The tail

Tail wagging and the angle at which the tail is carried are prime methods of communication used by dogs. The angle at which the tail is held is usually determined by conformation and breed habit, but in general the tail held at 45 degrees or higher to the spine expresses alertness and interest. The tail clamped low over the anus expresses a fear posture, while extreme nervousness brings the tail right down between the legs with the hind-quarters at the crouch. N.B. Whippets and Italian Greyhounds naturally carry their tails in the "fear" position. Dogs wag their tails to signify pleasure—puppies as young as four weeks old will wag their tails while eating. Dogs whose tails are docked very short will express pleasure by gyrating their whole hindquarters.

Summary

By observing closely the dog's signals the informed owner will be able to identify dogs that are fearful and submissive from those that are aggressive.

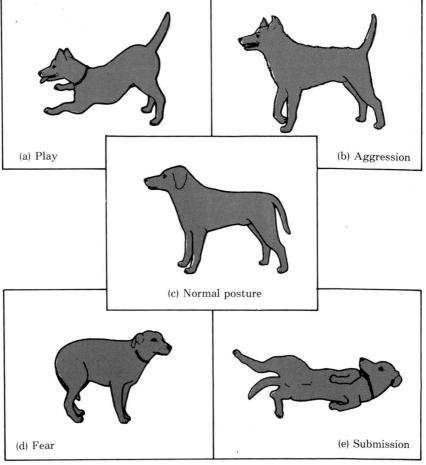

(a) Play

(b) Aggression

(c) Normal posture

(d) Fear

(e) Submission

Fig. 24 **Body language**

34

In summary:

Submission

Submissive dogs approach from the side, never head on. The tail is held low, the body crouching with the rear end held high. The animal will try to lick the face or hands of the dominant dog or person and may roll on its back to expose its groin. In many dogs there is a one-sided grin and most dogs will wag their tails in friendly greeting with the tail held parallel to the ground.

Fear

Fear is expressed by shaking, shivering, a look of apprehension, hiding beneath furniture and keeping the head low. Some dogs may urinate involuntarily. Extreme pleasure may also produce a body tremor but is accompanied by tail wagging.

Aggression

Beware of dogs that are standing tall, waving their tails slowly, having both lips drawn back and are uttering a low, threatening growl. Such animals are best ignored and eye contact avoided. Dogs have a very well-developed fight or flight mechanism, which coupled with extremely acute hearing and quick reaction time, enables them to get out of a danger zone very quickly, and also to mount an attack with hardly any warning if the opportunity presents itself. Veterinary surgeons and breeders learn to read the premonitory tell-tale signs early and so are prepared.

Getting it right

(i) *Move carefully*

Their very quickness of reaction may sometimes lead a dog to misinterpret the intentions of children or adult strangers. An arm raised in greeting may appear as a threat to a dog, a child's high-pitched screams may offend or over-excite the dog.

(ii) *Don't stare and run away*

Since a dog's natural instinct is to chase, an animal or person running away is a target to be caught and brought to the ground. It is helpful to teach children to move slowly when in contact with animals and to walk away deliberately without looking at the dog rather than running away if they think that a dog is threatening them. This tip may prevent a disaster.

(iii) *Stand up naturally*

Dogs expect humans to be upright or sitting down. A person who falls to the ground is vulnerable to attack, especially where several dogs are working as a pack.

(iv) *Speak to dogs*

Because a dog's sight is poor in certain lights, a dog may fail to recognise a friend until they speak or come within scenting distance. Always warn a dog of your presence, by speaking gently, especially if the dog is sleeping. If you know the dog's name, use it.

The well-informed dog owner will help his pet "get it right" by communicating through voice, movement and, where appropriate, touch. With a little thought and by talking to dogs as one would a child, situations of conflict can be easily averted.

(v) *Familiarise your dog with possible frightening situations*

Dogs are wary of loud noises, sudden currents of air (sometimes even high winds), people with unusual or distorted voices, people with unusual body outline (e.g. carrying a sack), people with hesitant or lame walk, or an object or place associated with an unpleasant happening. They will also react strongly to a fear scent left by other dogs, e.g. at a veterinary surgery, and also to unfamiliar body scent of people from other races. It is most important when bringing up a puppy to familiarise it with all these situations and praise it for correct behaviour. Some dogs will run away from fear situations but others will attack if they feel threatened.

Leave dogs to sort themselves out — by and large

An active domination sequence between members of a dog pack is shown by the superior dog putting its muzzle alongside that of its opponent, and then leaning its body against the other's so that the aggressor dog is closer than a shadow wherever the rival dog moves. Eventually the weaker dog will be driven into a corner and attacked about the head.

This behaviour pattern is often used to keep lower ranking dogs away from food, or some trophy, or even from approaching the owner.

A further step in aggressive behaviour is made by the aggressor leaping on to another animal and gripping the back of its neck. If the victim is submissive it will assume a crouching position with head low and eyes closed, making the back of the neck prominent for the aggressor to bite. Once complete domination is expressed in this way the aggressor makes no further attack.

Even greater submission is expressed by the dog which rolls over on to its back exposing its abdomen and genitals to be bitten. The aggressor normally accepts this surrender and takes the attack no further.

The balance of such a situation can easily be upset by inopportune interference by owners. See also Chapter 7, "What if" Nos. 35 and 43.

Be dominant but fair

All normal dogs understand the act of submission to a superior animal or human. Training a pet dog for acceptable behaviour as a lower member of the family pack is aided by using some of the methods a canine pack leader would use to maintain discipline. Once the habit of submission to a human or dog pack leader is established, any sign of rebellion can usually be quelled by a look or a gesture from the dominant individual, but in order to do this effectively, the human pack leader must be watching for signs of rebellion as the dog pack leader would do. Once an actual bid for dominance has taken place, it is usually necessary to apply more physical means to subdue the offender. (See Chapter 3.)

It should be noted that physical strength is not always necessary for a canine pack leader and **never** necessary in a human pack leader after the dog is six months old. Physical and mental dominance of the dog should be established very early in the dog's life. There may be subsequent attempts by the dog to assume leadership, but the owner's always superior brain power can be employed to re-establish the correct relationship.

Dominance exercises — how to reinforce your dominance

(a) Method 1   (b) Method 2

Fig. 25 **Dominance exercises**

1. Stand over the dog and lift its front legs off the ground, as illustrated in Fig.25(a). Keep the dog's feet off the ground for at least 30 seconds. Reward the dog verbally if it remains quiet — rebuke struggling.
2. Put the dog in a submissive position on its side, as illustrated in Fig.25(b), and hold it there, with one hand over its mouth and the other on its chest, for at least 30 seconds. Praise or rebuke as appropriate.
3. Go through a set period, lasting for about five minutes, of obedience exercises, making the dog sit, stay, heel etc. Reward good behaviour with titbits and lavish praise.

The exercises noted above should normally be practised once weekly or so, but will need to be carried out once or even twice daily for dogs that have a tendency to be very dominant. As such dogs become more submissive the frequency can be reduced gradually.

Sometimes dogs and bitches, especially those with signs of false pregnancy, will become *over-submissive*. In such cases the pet can be "built up" by giving plenty of praise for good behaviour and ignoring the dog when submissive postures are adopted. In some cases the dog can be allowed to stand on its hind legs and place its forelegs on your lap or shoulders briefly, whilst you adopt a squatting position — but be careful to handle this exercise carefully and not to overdo it.

CHAPTER 2

DOG MANAGEMENT

Choosing a Dog

There is an infinite variety of size, shape, coat texture and inherited ability in the pedigree breeds which have been developed by knowledgeable dog breeders over the years.

In the past, breeds were developed to encourage an ability for certain types of work, such as herding, tracking game, retrieving, guarding, or as warning watch-dogs. The characteristics which made the dogs suitable for these jobs are still present today, although the majority of dogs are kept in idleness and boredom.

Although your selection of a companion dog may be based on the fact that you admire its looks, do not forget that its behaviour patterns as a domestic pet will be strongly influenced by the work it once did. For instance, the hound may be difficult to halt or recall when it is following scent; the untrained gundog will flush and pursue game, perhaps to your cost and embarrassment, and the dog specifically designed to dig and to work underground will exercise its talents in your flower beds.

The dog whose looks you admire may be completely unsuitable for the place in which you live and for your lifestyle. An example would be the Beagle living in a house which has more ground than can be effectively fenced. Although this breed has appealing looks, is a convenient size and has an easy-care coat, its ancestors were pack hounds and were bred to follow scent all day if necessary. Your pet Beagle will do the same unless it is very securely fenced in.

The result could be that you are labelled as anti-social, a careless owner, whose dog is a nuisance, even though your pet is perfectly charming when at home.

The decision to buy a dog is an important one, because it implies a commitment to look after a dependent relative for at least the next ten years. The dog's needs and comfort must be considered in relation to all the activities the family likes to undertake. The house and garden may never be as immaculate as before the dog came into them. The dog which sheds hair constantly may make a great deal of housework and so become an intolerable nuisance through no fault of its own.

It is far better to be realistic about the amount of commitment you are prepared to make than to be in the unhappy situation of having bought the wrong type of dog.

The right dog for you

There is help at hand to select the kind of dog which will suit your family. Pedigree Chum have set up the "Selectadog" system which will suggest several different breeds for you according to the specification you supply, and the cost is only £1.

You will be sent a form on which you enter the amount of time and money you are prepared to spend on a dog among other things, together with your preferences for coat and size. You will then receive a shortlist of breeds to consider, some of which may not have occurred to you before. To obtain a form write to "Selectadog", P.O. Box 6, Burton Latimer, Kettering, Northants. (Do not send any money at this stage.)

Alternatively, your public library will be able to obtain a variety of books which describe the breeds of dog and their origins.

A Dog of Your Own, by Joan Palmer, (Salamander) describes the breeds in size order and gives helpful hints about them.

Choose and Bring Up Your Puppy, by Kay White, (Elliot Paperfront Books) is an inexpensive guide to popular breeds.

The important matters to consider are size, coat type, dog or bitch, adult or puppy, pedigree or mongrel, what you require it for — just as a pet or as a guard-dog — and where to obtain it from. The following notes and the table at the end of this chapter give pointers to the things you should consider when making your choice.

Size

Giant Breeds:	Magnificent animals, often gentle in temperament and very quiet and restful in the house, making themselves quite small in their own corner. However, they do need a lot of room in a car.
	Giant breeds tend to be shortlived.
Large Breeds:	May be boisterous in play, and aggressive with other dogs if not properly controlled.
	Large breeds which have full swishing tails can do a lot of damage to articles on low tables.

Medium Sized Dogs: Suit many families, their homes and their cars. There is plenty of choice within this group.

Small Dogs: This category tends to be noisy.
Small terriers bred to be vermin exterminators have quick snapping jaws which may make them unsuitable as pets for small children.

Very small toy dogs: Dogs under 10lbs in weight are not really suitable for the rough and tumble of family life.
Toy dogs tend to become devoted to one or two adults who handle them carefully.

Coat type

Once more there is an infinite variety in coat type in dogs, from the absolutely hairless, naked-skinned Chinese Crested, through to smooth-coated dogs like Bull Terriers; thick, double weatherproof coats like Labradors'; Spaniel type silky coats; harsh bristly Terrier coats; curly, non-shedding Poodles; rough, wiry Wolfhounds; right up to the dogs with very deep, corded coats like the Komondor and the Puli.

All dog hair tangles and matts more quickly than human hair. Smooth-coated dogs require minimal grooming and they dry mud more quickly if they have been swimming or wallowing. All other coat types will require some attention. Dogs like the Old English Sheepdog, and the Afghan, will need to be brushed and combed daily in order to keep the skin healthy and the coat clean. Long-coated dogs tend to smell when they are wet or damp.

Poodles and Bedlingtons will require clipping and bathing, every six to eight weeks. Unless you are a budding hairdresser you will need to make regular appointments with a poodle parlour if your dog is to look its best. Many terriers will need handstripping twice a year.

In a companion dog it is possible to have the long coat of some breeds clipped right down, and this "new look" can be very attractive, especially on the Old English Sheepdog.

A long-coated dog is a big commitment in time and requires somewhere convenient to do the grooming. A bench of suitable height, and conveniently placed hooks to tether the dog while you work, make things easier, but the main problem is hair flying about. You will not want to groom the dog in your living room or kitchen.

Dog or bitch

This is one of the major decisions when you are considering acquiring a dog, and it is better to come to a majority agreement within the family **before** you start looking for an adult dog or puppy. If you take a dog, or a bitch, just because there was only one sex available at the time, you may find that the animal you bought does not fulfil your need.

In the smaller breeds, character and size do not differ very much between the sexes, but you may find that the males in small terrier breeds are the ones which tend to be hyper-sexed, and so too are some mongrels.

In the larger, guarding breeds, males tend to be significantly larger in size, more dominant in temperament, and require firm handling. Bitches in general are more biddable, more sympathetic and kindly with children, and often intuitively quicker to define their owners' wishes. On the other hand, bitches can experience mood swings and variable temperament during the oestrous cycle. If you want a dog as a permanent companion to be available for anything the family wants to do, then the male is perhaps more suitable, unless there are definite plans to control oestrus in the bitch.

In the bleeding phase of heat, the bitch must be confined to an easily cleaned room, which usually means leaving her in a "punishment situation" in the kitchen during the evenings — unless the whole household is willing to go into punishment and sit with her. Entire bitches are not very suitable for obedience competition, gun dog work, etc. as they have to be withdrawn during oestrus, and perhaps also during a false pregnancy.

In beauty competitions, the entry in dog classes is usually lower, so giving better odds on a prize, but the male which fails to win has really no future at all, whereas the bitch can be mated to a dog which excels where she fails in conformation, colouring etc. There is no absolute rule about showing bitches in season, but the practice is frowned upon. Spayed bitches can only be shown by special permission of the Kennel Club, and it is usually required that they have progeny which is registered at the Kennel Club.

The casting vote in the choice between dog and bitch often lies with the sex of the animals which are constant visitors to the house. It may not be a happy thing to have a male if mother-in-law often brings her bitch to stay, but if she happens to own a Rottweiler dog, you may be in for trouble in the future if you get yourself a "stallion" Boxer, as the two males will eventually dispute the territory and inevitably fight. Some consideration may also be given to the dogs belonging to neighbours — male rivalry, or bitch/male sexual attraction — can lead to human disputes.

Obtaining a Puppy

Consult a veterinary surgeon about any hereditary diseases in the breed of your choice, and what clearance certificates you should ask for.

Try to see as many dogs of the breed as possible, at dog shows, and in the homes of people that own them. You may find that the dog you admire outdoors is not the dog you would want in your own sitting-room.

Ask your veterinary surgeon if there are any reliable local breeders.

Buy as close to home as possible.

Be prepared to wait for the right puppy from the right breeder. The majority of buying mistakes are made because of the impulse for "instant puppy".

Buy from the breeder, *not* from a dealer. Places which advertise several breeds at the same time are likely to be dealers who buy in puppies from several different sources. The risk of infectious disease and stress-induced illnesses is high when puppies have made long journeys at an early age, and been mixed with other litters.

Do not take offence if the breeder cross-questions you about your lifestyle and the way the dog will be kept. It is done partly to protect you from making a mistake in buying a puppy which will not suit you.

Never buy a puppy because you feel sorry for it. If a puppy is sickly, the breeder is the best person to look after it, and to decide what its future is to be.

Never buy a puppy which is cheaply priced because it is deaf, lame or has some other disability or illness. It could prove to be very expensive in the end.

Be very cautious about buying a puppy with an umbilical or inguinal hernia. Get a veterinary surgeon's opinion on the puppy.

The puppy should come from clean premises, where there is not an overpowering smell of urine and faeces. It should be in a well-lit but shaded room, with enough space to move about.

It is best not to buy a puppy unless you have seen the mother of the litter and found her to be an agreeable dog in reasonable health after her litter. Furthermore, it is sensible to ask if you may make arrangements to go to see the sire of the litter.

Try to take your puppy as early as possible, ideally from six and a half weeks. The puppy will fit into your home and family best while it is still very young.

Expect to pay a deposit on the puppy of your choice — about 20 per cent of the purchase price. The balance is payable when you collect.

When you collect your puppy

Expect to receive:-
- A signed receipt for your payment.
- The puppy's signed pedigree.
- A diet sheet stating what foods, when and how much the puppy is fed.
- Hints on grooming and the tools to use.
- Some notes on the specific care of the breed.
- Some article, a piece of cloth will do, which has been in the nest with the bitch and puppies and will convey a comfort-smell to the puppy.

If the puppy is a pure bred pedigree the Kennel Club registration card and a signed transfer form are likely to follow some weeks later owing to delay with registrations.

Initial budgeted costs

There is a considerable initial expenditure on any puppy very soon after purchase.

Among the immediate expenses will be:-
- Kennel Club transfer of ownership for pedigree puppies.
- Full course of vaccinations.
- Collar and lead.
- Insurance premium for veterinary fees and Third Party insurance.
- Dog licence.
- And possibly a folding wire crate, preferably for an adult size dog.

While the puppy is very young, a bed can be made from a cardboard carton, and bowls can be appropriated from the household stock, but as a medium to large or giant breed grows on, it will be necessary to buy the dog's own equipment.

Continuing costs

Your continuing commitment to the dog will include feeding, boarding kennels during your holidays, the amount of the exclusion on veterinary fee insurance (about the cost of an initial consultation), booster vaccinations, contraceptive measures for a bitch, renewal of collars, leads, bowls etc, and of course an annual Licence.

Remember:
- Some of these expenses will vary according to the size of the dog you choose, so be prepared.
- Weight for weight, the running costs of a mongrel are the same as those of a pedigree dog. Only the initial purchase differs.

Rail Travel: A child's fare is paid for all dogs, except those which can be carried in a travelling case as hand luggage.

Very large dogs may have to travel in the guard's van and be equipped with muzzles.

All these costs must be considered before you purchase a puppy. Be sure you can cope before you buy.

Equipment

Collars

A very young puppy should wear a soft collar for short periods every day. Always remove the collar when the puppy is unsupervised as it could easily get hung by the collar on a cupboard handle, for instance, or get a paw caught in the collar.

Neck size enlarges rapidly as the puppy grows. Care should be taken that the collar is neither too loose nor too tight. Slip collars which slacken round the neck when the lead is not held taut are unsuitable for use in urban situations.

Choke or check chains have been found to cause extensive bruising on dogs' necks, and they should only be used under expert instruction, if at all. It is wise not to leave a loose neck chain on a dog which is running free outdoors or in the house, as the slack may catch on a projecting object and throttle the dog.

Many breeds look best in their own specific type of collar. Ask the breeder to show you the kind of collar traditionally worn by your breed.

Every dog must by law have some means of identification attached to the collar when outside the home. Check frequently to make certain that engraved discs are still readable and bear the correct address. It is convenient to use a cylinder containing a slip of paper to bear the address if you are travelling with your dog on holiday.

Leather collars become hard and uncomfortable if they are allowed to get wet. Test the collar and the D ring often to make sure it is still adequately strong.

Anti-flea collars contain a small amount of highly poisonous chemical. Do not risk compounding the chemical action by spraying the dog with anti-flea spray as well, or by hanging anti-fly strips above its bed or spraying the room with an insect killer.

Anti-flea collars should be taken from the packet and aired for a day or two before being put on the dog. Children should not be allowed to handle these collars, either on or off the dog, and the collar must not be allowed to become wet.

If the dog's skin shows any sign of allergic reaction in the area of the collar, remove it at once and consult a veterinary surgeon.

Anti-flea collars do not have a strong enough fastening to be used with a lead.

The Halti head collar

The newest idea in dog control aids, especially useful for dogs which tend to lunge out at passers-by, is the Halti head collar, made in strong nylon tape and designed by an animal behaviourist on the principle of the hackenmore used on unbroken foals.

The control point is under the dog's chin rather than around the neck. The Halti is well tolerated by most dogs and offers the owner greater security when leading a strong animal.

Leads

The most important part of a lead is the hook which attaches it to the collar. Check frequently the hooks and the D rings which attach them to the lead.

Check also the stitching on the loop handle. A saddler will re-stitch it for you if it is becoming frayed. Many accidents happen because the collar or the lead broke at the critical moment.

A helpful modern invention is the Flexi-lead, over 30 feet of lead contained in a box-like handle. The length of the lead the dog is allowed is controlled by the handler, so allowing it a lot of freedom or bringing it up close to heel. This can be a most useful aid in controlling dogs which will not come when called because their attention is held by something which interests them.

Beds

Every dog should have a bed, in a quiet warm corner of one room in the house. The dog can then be told to go to its bed to prevent it being a nuisance. A collapsible wire crate can serve a useful purpose to contain dogs as it is easily erected wherever it is needed, even in the garden and around the swimming pool.

A puppy's first bed should be a cardboard carton, placed inside the wire crate.

A suitable bed for the next stage is the oval or round rigid polystyrene bed. Made only in brown, this is an economical choice as it is easily cleaned, light to move and almost indestructible.

In general, woven wicker baskets are not really suitable as they are most inviting to chew, and can be difficult to clean and disinfect properly. However many owners find them very convenient especially for dogs of the smaller breeds. If such baskets are used they should be thoroughly scrubbed regularly and put out in the sunshine to dry and air. For older dogs a bean bag filled with polystyrene beads offers warmth, comfort and support, and this type of bed does not harbour parasites. Buy one with the strongest inner cover you can find, which allows for topping up with extra beads, and also has a washable top cover.

Blankets

The most hygienic and work-saving blankets for dogs are those made of porous polyester fur fabric which is warm, longlasting, very easily washed and quickly dried. Dogs will not chew this fabric as they do woollen rugs. The colour is white or pale beige, so you can easily see when the rug is soiled. As these rugs are easily transportable, you can train your dog to sit upon it wherever it may be laid. This can be very useful when travelling or visiting friends. Manufacturers advertise in the canine press, or the blankets can be obtained through pet shops.

Care of puppies

The following hints should ease those anxious but happy days when a new puppy first joins your household.

Before you bring a puppy home, make a small fenced off area in the kitchen in a warm draught-proofed corner, to contain the puppy's bed, and a paper covered area for toilet purposes. A den of this kind gives the puppy security, and also keeps it from getting underfoot when you are busy. Later the puppy's bed can be in the same corner and the fencing dispensed with. Panels intended for enclosing compost heaps make good indoor fencing and are useful in the garden later.

Although the puppy appears to be delighted with its new home, there is bound to be inner stress at the complete change of environment. Do not ask too many people to see the puppy and keep it quiet for a few days while it adjusts to the immediate family.

Eight week old puppies tend to play for half an hour and then sleep for an hour and a half at a time. Long periods of rest are essential for the development of a healthy body and good temperament. Do not disturb the puppy until it wakes naturally. If during play periods the puppy appears to be getting over-excited, remove it from stimulating circumstances, give it a hot water bottle (well wrapped), and a comforting toy to chew, and allow the puppy to be quiet. Over-stimulation in puppy days can produce a hyperactive, restless dog which is no pleasure to own.

Feed the puppy at regular times with small amounts of food, perhaps four or five times daily with the first meal being early in the morning and the last at bedtime. Keep to the foods advised by the breeder for at least the first two weeks in your home. See also Chapter 5.

Observe the puppy closely, and regard any deviation from normal as quite serious in the very young puppy. Ask for veterinary advice quickly, as young puppies can deteriorate very rapidly. As the puppy grows older, veterinary attention for illness should still be a matter of urgency, remembering that the first six to twelve months of a puppy's life are the most traumatic for illness and accidents.

Take veterinary advice on the vaccination programme to be followed, and present the puppy at the surgery at the correct time. Take precautions to avoid picking up infection from other dogs until two weeks after the final vaccination. See also Chapter 4 Parts II and VII.

Follow the worming programme advised by the veterinary surgeon faithfully.

Do not be in too much hurry to take your puppy out on a lead. Walking on the lead should be carefully and properly taught by a responsible adult, so that the puppy realises that pulling is never allowed. Do not permit children to drag the puppy around the roads on a lead in the guise of training it — bad habits may be instilled, and the puppy's neck may be irrevocably harmed by tugging on the collar.

House-training

Everyone wants their puppy to be reliably house-trained as soon as possible, but it is unkind, and brings disappointment, to expect too much too soon.

Eight week old puppies have very little bladder control — achieving elimination outside means that someone responsible must be watching the puppy all the time.

Getting the puppy to eliminate in the garden means going out with the puppy, and staying out, encouraging it, until success is achieved. Putting the puppy out on its own is quite useless.

It may be better to allow the puppy to use newspaper indoors (which good breeders will have trained it to do) for a week or so, if the weather is bad when you bring the puppy home. You may then make quicker progress when you are able to take the puppy out every time it needs to go, when the weather is kinder to both of you. It is in any case unrealistic to hope for 100 per cent day and night house cleanliness before the age of six months, and if that seems a long time, remember that children take much longer.

Bitches

Although bitch owning can involve some additional problems and responsibilities, many owners consider that these are far outweighed by the benefits. In comparison with dogs, bitches are generally:
● More companionable
● More biddable
● Less likely to roam
● Less aggressive, particularly to other dogs

The attentive bitch owner should have at least a fundamental knowledge of the matters described in this chapter, so that correct action can be taken should any problems occur, or if any differences from the normal are observed. The informed owner will know when to seek advice from a veterinary surgeon or breeder, how to describe the problem, and understand the advice given so to implement it effectively.

Heat in bitches

Signs and Frequency

Most bitches reach puberty when they are between six and seven months of age, but possibly as early as four months or as late as two years. At this time the bitch's vulva will become enlarged and a varying amount of blood stained fluid is passed — the bitch is said to have "come on heat" or, to "be in season".

Some bitches may show signs of abdominal discomfort, increased excitability, and be less inclined to eat for a few days before heat commences. Bitches become attractive to dogs, usually from the first day of heat, but mostly they are not interested in their admirers until seven to ten days have passed. At this stage the bitch is equally anxious to escape to meet the male.

Conception is more likely to occur if mating takes place ten to twelve days after the first obvious signs of heat are noticed, but can sometimes occur at earlier or later matings. Most bitches will subsequently come "on heat" at intervals of six to nine months throughout the rest of their lives — there is no equivalent to the menopause.

The Oestrous Cycle

Stage of cycle	Duration	Comment
Pro-oestrus	Average 9 days	This stage is the beginning of heat. The vulva is swollen and there is a blood stained discharge. Although the bitch is attractive to dogs she will not allow them to mate her.
Oestrus	Average 9 days	This stage is defined as the period when the bitch will accept the male. The vulva is much enlarged and turgid. The discharge is straw coloured rather than blood stained. Ovulation occurs about 2 days after the start of oestrus.
Met-oestrus	Average 90 days	This stage occurs in the unmated bitch and hormone changes equivalent to those seen in pregnancy occur. At the end of this stage the bitch may show signs of false pregnancy. The beginning of this stage and its end are not marked by any obvious external signs.
Anoestrus	Variable — but on average 2½ months	The duration of anoestrus largely determines how frequently the bitch will come in season. This is the period of sexual inactivity between cycles.

False pregnancy

This term is used to describe the condition in which bitches show the signs of pregnancy, nursing and lactation, and yet have no puppies, either because they have not been mated or have failed to conceive. The signs occur late in met-oestrus, i.e. one to two months after the bitch has been on heat, and vary in type and severity from one bitch to another. Characteristically, however, most bitches will produce milk and display obvious maternal behaviour. Many of them show nervous signs including panting and breathlessness. A lot of bitches will carry shoes and other toys around the house and collect them in their bed. In severe cases, some bitches will actually strain as if they are producing a litter. Once a bitch has had false pregnancy she will probably have it again after each heat with the signs becoming progressively more severe on each occasion.

With regard to treatment, it is worth noting that the condition is really a normal occurrence in that something like 60 per cent of bitches have false pregnancy to a degree. Indeed, in the wild state or in a breeding kennel false pregnant bitches will be capable of nursing a litter from a bitch that has died, so the condition serves a useful purpose. Thus if the signs are mild it is probably better not to give treatment. The nervous signs will disappear more quickly if the bitch is denied sympathy and if toys and brooding objects are removed. Less milk will be produced if the carbohydrate content of the diet is reduced, if the bitch's water intake is reduced somewhat (she must not of course be denied access to water entirely for long periods) and if the amount of exercise is increased.

If the signs are severe and the above action does not lead to an improvement, veterinary assistance should be sought. A course of hormone tablets or a hormone injection may help and in some cases it may be considered necessary to bathe the mammary glands to help the milk to be reabsorbed. Sedatives may be required to control the nervous signs, especially if the bitch is very disturbed and cannot rest. Veterinary surgeons often advise that bitches that have severe false pregnancy be spayed, since bitches that do not come on heat do not have false pregnancy. The chemical control of heat by giving regular hormone injections helps to reduce the incidence of false pregnancy and may be advocated in some cases.

Pyometra

Definition: Accumulation of large amounts of fluid in the uterus usually occurring one to two months after a bitch has been on heat.

Cause: Not entirely clear, but probably brought about by hormone imbalance.

Signs: Drinking excessively, frequent urination, depression often with a raised temperature. Abdominal tension. In open cases there is a thick red-brown evil smelling discharge from the vulva. The condition is usually seen in older bitches that have not had puppies, but exceptions do occur.

Treatment: If a bitch owner suspects that his pet is suffering from the condition, it is most important to seek veterinary advice without delay, since an emergency operation involving surgical removal of the uterus and ovaries may be needed to save the animal. Some open cases, that is those with vaginal discharge, can respond to medical treatment.

Mating

Readers are strongly advised to seek advice from their veterinary surgeon and/or an experienced dog breeder and to read specialist books that are available on this subject before they have their bitch mated. It is important that the bitch is mated at the right time if she is to conceive, and in maiden bitches an experienced dog should be used. Mating with a suitably selected and screened sire is necessary if congenital abnormalities, such as umbilical hernias, poorly formed joints etc., are to be avoided. It is also important to establish wherever possible that there is every chance that homes will be able to be found for the puppies. Where this is not the case it is very often kinder to reduce the size of the litter by putting down some of the puppies at birth. Owners wishing to breed from their bitch should also be fully prepared to look after her throughout pregnancy, which lasts for about nine weeks (57—69 days), and to cope with the whelping, and be prepared to help the bitch nurse her puppies and to feed, clean and handle them at least four times a day after weaning until they are ready for permanent homes. Puppy rearing is a full time job that carries a great number of responsibilities, thus in general it is better left to experts. There is no truth in the old wives' tale that having a litter of puppies is good for a bitch.

NOTE: The muscles in the vagina contract at the end of coitus preventing the male penis from being withdrawn. This constitutes the "tie" that is a desirable feature of mating that mostly, but not always, occurs. The dog will step over the bitch, or be turned by handlers into this position so that the animals are tied back to back. There is no point in trying to separate animals that are locked in this way, since the dog will be released in good time. Buckets of cold water thrown over the animals simply wet them and do little to speed up the process of separation.

Mismating

What if my bitch is mismated?

It is very important to act immediately, as an injection to avert pregnancy can only be given within 48 hours of the mating. Visit your veterinary surgeon at once.

The effect of the injection will be to reverse the dominating hormones of the bitch's oestrous cycle, so that she will begin her heat all over again. Even more vigilant control will be needed, as the bitch may be even more willing to be mated on a second occasion.

More positive control methods must be used in future, as it is dangerous to the bitch's health to rely on averting the pregnancy after mismating.

Unexpected pregnancy

What if my bitch is found to be pregnant unexpectedly?

Your veterinary surgeon will advise you if it is possible and wise to spay the bitch, removing the uterus and foetuses.

If this is not a practical proposition, or if the bitch is wanted for breeding in future, the only option is to allow the pregnancy to proceed, and whelping to take place naturally, but resolving to cull the litter down to a maximum of two puppies which should be left to assuage the bitch's maternal instinct and to utilise the milk supply.

It may be difficult to persuade a veterinary surgeon to cull the litter, as their training is orientated entirely to preserving life, but if the litter cannot be reared conveniently, and there is no assured market for the puppies, it is kinder to have them destroyed soon after birth, rather than allow them to swell the thousands of unwanted dogs already hoping that someone will give them the right kind of home.

Rearing a large litter properly is also an expensive exercise, and there can be no hope of recouping the cost of a litter of crossbreds and mongrels.

Mammary tumours

A high percentage of bitches will develop mammary tumours (growths in the mammary glands) as they get older, although as mentioned later, heat control does help reduce the incidence. It makes sense therefore to inspect the mammary glands of bitches at least four times a year. This is preferably done when the bitch is on heat and about one month later. If lumps are felt, their size should be recorded and monitored carefully under veterinary supervision and advice taken about their removal before the tumour has a chance to spread to other parts of the body. Fortunately many of the growths are benign and are relatively easily removed, provided they have not been allowed to grow too large and action is taken before the skin over them has become thin and ulcerated.

Heat control

There are many reasons why bitch owners should control heat in their pets. However, the most important are:

1. To gain a health advantage — the chance of the bitch developing uterine problems, mammary tumours and false pregnancy will be reduced.
2. To prevent unwanted pregnancy.
3. To make the pet more consistently companionable — during heat and other stages of the cycle (especially if the animal suffers from False Pregnancy) a bitch's temperament will be changed.
4. To make owning a bitch more convenient — to avoid problems of messy bleeding, unsightly vulval swelling, attractiveness to dogs and the need to keep the bitch confined twice a year.

Remember, in most bitches heat lasts for three weeks and occurs twice a year — it may last longer and occcur more frequently in some. Thus bitches are not 100 per cent fit and are less enjoyable companions for about three months in every year.

Sprays and lotions which claim to disguise the odour of a bitch in heat are largely ineffective, and even seem to be recognised as a heat indicator by keen and experienced male dogs.

Chlorophyll and other specially prepared tablets are also a waste of money and in addition to not deterring males, will certainly not prevent the bitch herself from trying to meet the opposite sex.

Various contrivances based on knickers and sanitary pads are obtainable and are considered useful by some bitch owners to prevent the bitch staining furniture and carpets.

Heat control can be achieved by spaying or by chemical methods using an artificial hormone similar to that contained in the human Pill. Each has advantages and disadvantages and thus the matter should be discussed with a veterinary surgeon so that the most appropriate action can be chosen to suit the particular animal and circumstances.

It is important to realise that the choice will be different for different breeds of dogs and will vary according to the owner's needs. By and large, however, small Terrier type bitches do not have too many problems associated with spaying, but in bitches of the large breeds, and especially Old English Sheepdogs, difficulties like incontinence occur quite commonly after the operation.

Coat changes can occur in Spaniels and in bitches with short hair. Unfortunately no operative procedure can be guaranteed to be completely safe and problem free, but thanks to modern anaesthetics and techniques few difficulties arise when young healthy bitches are spayed.

Whelping

Pregnancy usually lasts about 63 days from the day of mating, but may be as short as 57 or as long as 69 days.

If you are aware of the pregnancy during its late stages, the bitch will appreciate being fed about one-third more food than normal, and also being given her daily intake in several small meals during the day. Her appetite may be variable and she may vomit in the mornings. It is normal for a bitch to refuse food entirely for 24 hours when whelping is imminent.

Provide a cardboard box of appropriate size in a secluded, darkened and warm place in which the bitch can whelp. Plenty of clean newspaper should be available to line the box, and it is normal behaviour for the bitch to shred up this paper during the early stages of whelping.

Stage I of labour may last from two to 24 hours. During this stage the bitch will be restless and may pant compulsively.

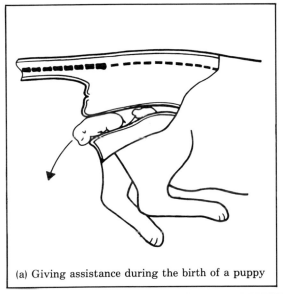

Hold the puppy's head, or hind legs if it is coming backwards, in a clean, dry face-flannel. Pull gently downwards and backwards away from the spine. Don't use force and try to pull at the same time as the bitch strains.

(a) Giving assistance during the birth of a puppy

Break the cord with your fingers, or cut with clean scissors, 1½" to 2" from the pup, without pulling on the puppy's stomach wall. Use clean hands and wash them afterwards.

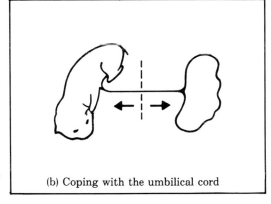

Fig. 26 Whelping — if a bitch needs a little help!

(b) Coping with the umbilical cord

Stage II begins with the first big expelling contraction or straining movement and it is as well to make a note of when this occurs.

If the first puppy has not appeared after an hour, the veterinary surgeon should be contacted by telephone for advice.

Normally a dark coloured sac of fluid will appear at the vulva ahead of the first puppy, which will be wrapped in another fluid-filled membrane. The puppy should be born very soon after this stage is reached. If not, gentle assistance may be given as indicated in Fig. 26(a). The bitch should tear open this sac at once, to release the puppy and will proceed to lick it clean and dry. If the bitch cannot do this, it must be done for her, and the puppy should be held upside down to allow any fluids to drain from the lungs.

A further expelling movement should bring the placenta, or afterbirth — a piece of liver-like tissue. The bitch will instinctively eat the placenta and make an attempt to clear up the fluids which will have escaped during the birth of the puppy. Green and brown staining from these fluids is normal. If the puppy remains attached to the placenta and the cord is not severed by the bitch this can be done as indicated in Fig. 26(b).

It is wise to keep a note of the number of placentas passed, there should be one for each puppy. A retained placenta can be dangerous — contact your veterinary surgeon if you think all have not been expelled soon after whelping is finished. A delay of more than one hour in births, when there are obviously more puppies to come, should be reported to the veterinary surgeon for advice.

It is always wise to ask a veterinary surgeon to call at the house during the 24 hours after whelping to check the bitch and to put down any puppies which, perhaps because they have some congenital abnormality, need to be culled.

Some veterinary surgeons feel that they have more assistance at their disposal, more convenient equipment to hand, and can make the best use of their time, if all their patients are brought to them at the surgery. Parking problems in large towns also add to problems with housecalls.

If you are required to take a litter, or a sick dog, to the surgery, make up a bed which will protect the car and keep the dog warm. In the case of a dog which may have an infectious illness, or where puppies are unvaccinated, do not take the animals into the waiting room, but ask the receptionist where the vet would prefer to see the dogs.

It may be possible to give puppies their first vaccinations in the car to avoid their meeting other dogs which may be carrying infections.

Docking puppies

Veterinary surgeons are in general very much against mutilations made in the name of fashion, and it will not be unusual for them to refuse to dock tails. Several breeds have now declared that docking is optional in their standard at the Kennel Club. Ask advice from the breeder of your bitch if in doubt.

If docking and dewclaw removal is to be done, it must be at between one to five days old, otherwise a full anaesthetic will be needed.

Further reading — *Dog Breeding*, by Kay White, (Bartholomews)

Male Dogs

Entirety

It is essential when choosing a male puppy to ensure that it is **entire**, i.e. that it has two testicles descended into the scrotum.

The testicles may retract temporarily in a young puppy and the seller may be optimistic that the puppy will become entire in time, but a veterinary surgeon can give you an informed opinion when the puppy is about eight weeks old.

Dogs which are monorchids, (more correctly, unilateral cryptorchids, with only one testicle descended into the scrotum) can sire puppies, but as the condition is hereditary such a puppy is an unwise buy, since it has greater than normal chance of not being entire.

Cryptorchidism is important to the buyer even if there is no intention of using the dog at stud. A testicle retained within the abdomen is particularly susceptible to growths (tumours) which can affect the whole hormonal system, and may be life-threatening if they spread to other parts of the body.

House-training

Male dogs are often slower to house-train than bitches. Dogs squat to urinate until they are adolescent, when the customary leg-raising posture is adopted to facilitate territory marking.

Male Adolescence

In late puppyhood, during the adolescent phase, a young male may experience an upsurge of hormones making him indulge in excessive sexual behaviour. If the dog is suitably discouraged (see Chapter 3) this behaviour will often prove only transient.

Wandering

Male dogs are more motivated to wander from home than females. Security of gates and fencing of a height to enclose the dog is essential. For dogs with the inclination to dig or burrow, fencing must be buried in the ground.

Use at stud

It is unwise to allow a dog to be used at stud to oblige a casual request. Unless a dog is a show winner there is not likely to be a regular demand for his services and, in this case, it is better for the dog **never** to have had stud experience.

It is unfair to keep a male dog, which is not to be used at stud, with entire bitches which are undergoing regular oestrous cycles.

The owner of a pet male will be wise to "screen" bitches which may accompany visitors to the house, and request that they be left at home if they are coming into oestrus. An encounter with such a bitch on his own territory can be upsetting to the male and will almost inevitably lead to territory marking, even indoors, which may get the male into undeserved trouble.

Contraceptive measures for male dogs

Hormones

Consult your veterinary surgeon about a hormonal preparation which may be given by injection to male dogs to mimic the effects of castration in respect of behaviour. However, such injections may not affect fertility.

Vasectomy

In this operation the tubes that transport sperm from the testicles are cut, so rendering the dog unable to sire puppies, but still able and willing to perform a mating act. Such a dog is sometimes used as a "teaser" in breeding kennels. Since this operation does not affect the dog's behaviour, it will still be interested in mating bitches and may still roam, so it is not of relevance in the domestic situation.

Castration

Castration involves removal of the testes from the scrotum, leaving the dog with an empty scrotal sac which is not unsightly. Although the operation is carried out under general anaesthesia it does not require abdominal surgery and healing is usually rapid. The operation is performed:

(a) To render a dog sterile when his services as a stud are unwanted.

(b) To help overcome hyper-sexual behaviour which has persisted beyond adolescence, particularly inter-dog aggression and the tendency to roam to seek out bitches.

It is as well to remember that the traits mentioned above may have become a learned behaviour which may persist even after castration. In some cases it may be as long as four to six months before the effect of castration becomes apparent.

Guarding ability, intelligence, playfulness and owner-affection are not usually significantly altered in the castrated male.

Elderly Dogs

We have to thank the high nutritional standards of commercially prepared dog foods, the modern effective vaccines, and the tremendous advances in veterinary knowledge for the welcome news that dogs are living longer, giving an average two to four year increase on the expected life-span of 20 years ago.

The life expectancy of dogs differs widely, ranging from seven to ten years in Bulldogs and the giant breeds, to well into the late teens in some Spaniels and small Terriers. Longevity is to some extent a hereditary factor, as well as depending on good care by the owner and freedom from congenital factors which may shorten life.

Greying of the muzzle and eyebrows is seen in some dogs as early as five years old, but this does not signify that the dog is to be regarded as old at that stage. In extreme old age the whole coat may become dusted with white hairs, or even white all over.

Old dogs have a capacity for deep and prolonged sleep; take care not to startle an elderly pet as it may respond with a growl or snap which was not really intended. Their years should be respected and they should not be teased by puppies, cats or children.

There are many ways in which the quality of life of an old dog can be increased, often just by a little forethought and consideration on the part of the owner. The following hints may be of help . . .

● Avoid turning an old dog out on winter mornings and evenings. The shock of very cold air can precipitate "drop attacks" and "strokes".

● Avoid boarding an elderly dog in kennels. Stress can trigger a latent illness.

● Keep distemper/parvovirus/hepatitis/leptospirosis boosters up to date. An elderly dog can lack immunity to these diseases.

● Have anal sacs checked regularly. Blocked sacs are uncomfortable for the dog as well as unpleasant for the owner.

● If the dog is unable to take much exercise, keep the food intake down, but offer small amounts more often, so that the dog does not feel its pleasures are taken away. An overweight dog is more prone to heart disease. Your veterinary surgeon may advise you to feed one of the special diets that are available for old or obese dogs. The use of such foods can help prevent some of the problems that beset older dogs.

● Bearing in mind that old dogs are not as mobile as before, take care that they do not sit on cold damp concrete, or in full sun, for too long. Put rugs and beds in favourite sitting-places, so that they are convenient to go to.

● Take care that an old dog does not sit or lie on rough surfaces, as elbow and hock callouses can become painful and even chronically ulcerated.

● Do not allow an old dog to get too far away on walks. They can easily become lost through being disorientated when sense of smell, sight and hearing is deteriorating.

CARE OF THE ELDERLY DOG

Aspects of Care.	Signs	Action	Comment
Deterioration of general health	Loss of energy, poor coat, dullness, body odour, weakness.	Veterinary consultation possibly complete blood profile to monitor function of body organs.	Laboratory screening of a small blood sample may reveal the need for dietary adjustment and mineral/vitamin supplementation.
Senility	Increased demand for owner's company. Disorientation, restlessness.	Veterinary check. Medication may be necessary.	The old dog will have good days and worse days. Sympathy and tolerance by owners can create a happy life for an old dog.
Loss of hearing	Increased barking, altered voice, failure to respond to call.	Veterinary check to eliminate ear disease.	Once the owner is aware of the disability, special care should be taken to keep the dog close on walks, and to protect it from possible danger. "Fetch" rather than call the dog.
Deteriorating sight	Bluish film over the eyeball, and/or scars on the eye surface. Blundering into furniture. Reluctance to go out at night, and/or in bright sunlight.	Veterinary check to see if treatment will improve the condition.	A dog which is partially or even completely blind can live a contented life in familiar surroundings provided care is taken not to move furniture etc. and to protect the dog from danger. A dog should not be destroyed solely because it is blind, unless there are particular risks in its environment or to people likely to be in contact with the dog.
Incontinence	Wet beds, puddles where dog sits down.	Veterinary consultation to check for disease; medication may be necessary, but "leaks" may be due to reluctance to rise from bed.	Cover cushions with plastic bags, and lay porous polyester fur rug on top so that dog is not lying in a puddle.
Reduced bladder capacity	Dog asking to go out several times during the night or puddles in the room where the dog sleeps — often on the door mat.	Veterinary surgeon may prescribe a medicine which will help regulate urination pattern but often little can be done.	Lapses of house-training must be excused in the very old.
Constipation	Irregular passage of faeces, difficulty in passing faeces, difficulty in adopting normal excretory posture.	Increase fibre in diet, via bran biscuits, or grated vegetables and apples. Medicinal paraffin, (up to 1 tablespoonful) may be given as a lubricant.	Faeces should be passed ideally twice a day and at least once daily.
Changed coat character	Even smooth-coated dogs tend to an over-growth of coat in old age. Nails grow at an accelerated rate.	"Strip" thickened areas of coat regularly. Give more frequent baths and face washes. Regular clipping of nails by veterinary surgeon makes walking more comfortable.	Sunflower oil, 1 teaspoon to 1 tablespoon according to size helps to prevent dryness of coat.

CARE OF THE ELDERLY DOG (continued)

Aspect of Care	Signs	Action	Comment
Tooth decay	Painful eating, refusal of hard biscuit, unpleasant mouth odour.	Veterinary consultation.	Extraction of decayed teeth can make a great improvement in total health.
Digestive problems	Vomiting of food or saliva and bile. Diarrhoea — constipation	Revert to puppy feeding regime of 3-4 small meals daily. Seek veterinary advice on diet — less protein may be needed. Special diets are available through veterinary surgeons.	Cooked eggs are the most easily digested form of protein. Pedigree Petfoods' Convalescent Diet (from the vet) is a useful, easily digested food for elderly dogs.
Inappetence	Total food refusal.	Seek veterinary advice if no food taken for 48 hours.	Complan, Brands Essence, and sponge cake are useful invalid foods.
Reduced mobility	Difficulty in rising from bed, tottering gait, unable to use hind legs.	Veterinary consultation, since it is possible to effect an improvement by medication.	Supplying warmth (via heated pad) a comfortable bed (polystyrene bean bag beds are good), a coat to be worn even indoors and hand massage of the limbs will all help to increase mobility. Make sure to protect such dogs from dangerous falls; put a barrier across the stairs to prevent dog climbing and falling down. Gentle exercise should be given whenever the dog feels able to go for a walk.

Special Care for the Older Dog

● WATER Monitor the amount of water being drunk daily.
Consult veterinary surgeon if there is an increase without apparent cause.
If necessary, offer the dog water, as it might be too lethargic to help itself.

● FOOD Provide food at consistency and temperature which dog prefers. Slightly warmed food can be more appetising.
Trial and error will show which type of bowl is most convenient for the dog to eat from — mouth dexterity is not as good as in the young. Raising the bowl on a step or platform can help as bending the neck may be painful.

● Observing and caring for your elderly dog can be interesting and rewarding in terms of the dog's visible gratitude for the arrangements you make for its comfort, and for the many ways you will be able to devise for continuing to enjoy the companionship which you have valued for so many years.
● Remember dogs live for now rather than for yesterday or tomorrow. This makes being old and caring for the old so much easier in the dog than in the human.
Some specific aspects relating to the care of elderly dogs are noted in the previous table.

The Fundamental Rules of Dog Ownership

"Buster", the character on the left, has been created to illustrate the "Golden Rules of Dog Ownership" in a way that children can readily understand.

The children of all dog owners should be encouraged to follow these principles so that they can enjoy "their Buster" to the full and so that he fits properly into society. "Buster" appears later in *The Doglopaedia* (see Chapter 7).

"BUSTER"

. . . likes his own warm basket or box where he can lie quietly out of the way.

. . . loves going for regular interesting walks whatever the weather.

. . . adores riding in the back of the car, but likes some fresh air and to be left in a shady spot.

. . . likes to jump onto beds and chairs but knows it is not allowed.

. . . much prefers his own drinking and eating bowl as he knows he shouldn't eat from people's plates.

. . . likes titbits as a reward when he has behaved especially well.

. . . enjoys visiting food shops but knows it is forbidden.

. . . likes showing off how obedient he is by sitting, staying and walking to heel.

. . . is proud of his Licence and vaccination certificates.
But most of all, he wants to be loved and to be part of the family.

. . . doesn't like having his ears and tail pulled.

. . . hates being left alone for long periods or being shouted at and kicked.

. . . is frightened of eating crunchy bones as he knows they could make him ill.

. . . is upset if he makes a mess on the pavement or in a playground by mistake.

. . . dislikes being dirty and having a tangled coat.

. . . is afraid of busy roads so prefers to be on the lead in traffic.

. . . hates not going away with the family but knows that sometimes he has to go to a good kennel where he will be well looked after.

. . . dislikes not having an identity disc on his collar in case he gets lost.

. . . is worried if he is let out on his own, in case he gets run over, upsets other people or can't find his way home.

OBTAINING A PEDIGREE DOG.

	Pedigree Puppy from 6½ weeks	Pedigree Adult direct from First Owners	Pedigree Adult from Breed Rescue Service	Pedigree Adult Kennel Surplus Animal
Purchase Price.	Average £80-£200. Rare breeds up to £1,000. Resale value drops sharply after 16 weeks except for major show winners.	Nominal price unless major show winner.	Donation requested. Home probably inspected before you are considered for ownership.	Nominal (negotiable).
Maintenance costs.	High in first year then levels out according to size and grooming needs.	Average for breed.	If medical history is unknown, there may be hidden costs. May need rehabilitation and careful feeding.	Average for breed.
Precautions on purchase.	Essential to see the dam. Visit the sire if possible, also see adolescents in the breed. Consult veterinary surgeon about possible inherited diseases, and suitability of the breed as a pet in your home and locality.	Ensure that the seller has the right to dispose of the dog, and that no breeding terms agreements are unfulfilled. Check health record with veterinary surgeon who has attended the dog, or ask your own vet to contact the first owner's vet.	Try to find out as much as possible of the dog's background. As there is a possibility that the previous owner may try to reclaim the dog, get a signed statement that the dog has been made over to you by the rescue organisation.	Consider deeply whether a dog which has always lived a kennel life will make a satisfactory pet. Do not expect the dog to be grateful to you for removing it from the environment it grew up in.
Pedigree, Kennel Club registration and transfer of ownership form.	Signed pedigree should be given at the time of purchase. Several weeks/months delay common for Kennel Club forms.	Pedigree should be supplied. Obtain a transfer of ownership form from the Kennel Club and request first owners to sign it. Transfer to your ownership at the Kennel Club as soon as possible.	Pedigrees are not given with rescued dogs even if the rescue society has them.	Pedigree may be withheld to prevent future breeding.
Vaccinations necessary.	Full course as recommended by veterinary surgeon.	Vaccination certificates should be available. Boosters if due.	Full booster vaccinations.	Up to date vaccination certificates should be available.
Insurance and veterinary fees.	Can be enrolled from the age of 8 weeks. Claims payable 2 weeks after enrolment.	Enrol at once if under 8 years old. Previous illnesses have to be declared and may be subject to exclusion.	Enrol at once if under 8 years old.	Enrol at once if under 8 years old. Previous conditions may be subject to exclusion.

OBTAINING A PEDIGREE DOG (continued)

	Pedigree Puppy from 6½ weeks	Pedigree Adult direct from First Owners	Pedigree Adult from Breed Rescue Service	Pedigree Adult Kennel Surplus Animal
Possibility of breeding.	Bitches: Possible under the guidance of original breeder. Males: No demand for services unless a major show winner. Stud use inadvisable in a companion dog.	Bitches: On veterinary advice only. Males: No demand. Inadvisable in a companion dog.	Not advisable. You and your home may be subjected to periodic inspection to see if the dog is happy.	Failure to breed easily is a probable reason for disposal. Not advisable.
Health status to be expected.	Should be in first class condition. Parents should have been screened for hereditary diseases and copies of current certificates given. There is the possibility of illness already being incubated and/or illness brought on by stress at change of home.	Life history of illness should be supplied. Veterinary check is advisable before dog is acquired. Ask when oestrous period is due and if contraceptive medication has been given.	Veterinary check advisable before dog is acquired. May need a lot of care/ veterinary attention if dog has been deprived or cruelly treated.	Should be in first class condition. Bitches: Ask for record of oestrous periods and/or contraceptive medication used.
Feeding.	As prescribed by breeder for first 2 weeks. Feed 4/5 times a day. Make feeding changes gradually.	Feed what the dog has been accustomed to for 2 weeks. Make changes gradually.	Rescue Kennel should advise what suits the dog.	Feed as the kennel did for 2 weeks if possible. Change gradually to domestic type feeding.
Temperament.	According to breed and inherited traits.	Make in-depth enquiries about phobias.	Rescue service should screen temperament but may take too optimistic a viewpoint because of familiarity with the breed.	May alter considerably when kept as a single pet.
House-training.	Quick to average, influenced by owner's dedication and weather conditions.	Should be house-trained but may lapse initially in unfamiliar conditions.	May lapse in house-training through time spent in kennels.	May have never been house-trained. May be difficult to train in adult life. Has probably been used to having access to kennel run throughout daylight hours.
Suitability as pet in average domestic situation	High/medium/low according to breed and inherited characteristics.	Probably good. May be mentally disturbed for weeks/months through changing homes.	Unknown. May be a delinquent which may or may not reform even with	May be unhappy as a sole pet. May be claustrophobic and orientated only to other dogs.

Behaviour faults to watch for.	Biting, snapping when restrained, excitability, furniture gnawing.	May be no faults, but may be almost untrained. May be aggressive over food and feeding bowls, towards other animals or certain categories of people, especially men and children.	May be none at first but behaviour patterns will emerge as the dog becomes confident in your home. Close observation of reactions and caution is advised.	May show phobias and fears, timidity or aggression at removal from supportive pack situation and complete change of environment. May have not had urban lead training or familiarity with traffic.
Activities with your dog.	Beauty shows right up to Championship Show level. Agility Competition. Obedience Competition. Sponsored walks, swims, water rescue in appropriate breeds.	All Kennel Club shows if dog is Kennel Club registered.	Exemption Shows. Agility, Obedience, etc.	Unlikely to be suitable for top-class shows, probably not suitable for competitive obedience.

OBTAINING A MONGREL DOG OR A CROSS-BRED

	Mongrel Puppy from 6½ weeks	Cross-bred Puppy	Mongrel Adult from Rescue Society
Purchase price.	Low. Average £10.	Low. £20–£30.	Average £10 donation.
Maintenance costs.	High in first year then levels out according to size.	High in first year then levels out according to size.	Average. Medical history unknown; there may be hidden illness or disability.
Precautions on purchase.	Make sure the puppy is weaned and can eat solid food. See the dam and/or sire if possible. Buy from the premises where the puppy was born. Do not buy a puppy which has made a long journey or changed ownership already, as risk of infectious disease is increased when puppies are moved between dealers.	Find out the breeds of the parents and how/why the cross was made. Take veterinary advice on the suitability of the cross. See also advice for mongrel puppy.	Consult with kennel staff about the suitability of the dog for your family. Have they tested its reactions to children, old people, men/women, ethnic races?
Possibility of breeding.	Not advisable. Consider neutering of both sexes.	Possibility of breeding back to one of its component breeds but very little chance of selling a whole litter.	Consider neutering of both sexes to curb desire to wander as dogs and bitches may have had mating experience.

OBTAINING A MONGREL DOG OR A CROSS-BRED (continued)

	Mongrel Puppy from 6½ weeks	Cross-bred Puppy	Mongrel Adult from Rescue Society
Vaccinations necessary.	Full course as advised by veterinary surgeon.	As mongrel puppy.	Full booster course unless rescue society has given current vaccination.
Insurance for veterinary fees.	As for pedigree puppy.	As for pedigree puppy.	Enrol at once if under 8 years old.
Health status to be expected.	Problematical. Long term worming routine will be necessary. Check for fleas/lice etc. and get veterinary advice about de-fleaing treatment for young pups.	Skin and coat may give problems through crossing of coat types.	Probably average health but early neglect or ill-treatment may pre-dispose to ill-health in middle to old age.
Feeding.	As pedigree puppy.	As pedigree puppy.	Feed small meals frequently until you can assess the state of the dog's digestive system. May be compulsive eater and/or coprophagic.
Suitability as pet.	Unknown quantity. Will require supervision and good fencing as parents may have been habitual vagrants.	May be difficult to train. Looks may favour one parent but behaviour traits may mimic the other.	Can be very successful but may be difficult to convert into well-mannered pet.
Temperament.	May be hyper-active.	Inherited behaviours may be in conflict, e.g. guard-dog crossed with gun-dog.	Long term kennelling can alter the temperament, encouraging barking, hyper-activity or aggression.
House-training	Average to short time to house-train.	As mongrel.	May be difficult to house-train.
Behaviour faults to watch for.	Extreme submission or aggression. Tendency to wander. Scavenging. Excess barking.	As mongrel puppy.	Probably chronic escaper. May have nervous or aggressive reaction to other dogs or even to familiar people when they are handling certain articles, e.g. brooms.
Activities to undertake with your dog.	Exemption Beauty and Fun Shows. Obedience tests. Agility. Sponsored walks.	As for mongrel puppy.	Exemption Beauty and Fun Shows. Agility competitions. Sponsored walks. Obedience tests.

CHAPTER 3

TRAINING AND DOG BEHAVIOUR

How dogs learn

Rewards

Punishment

Training

Behaviour modification techniques

Behaviour problems

There are three main reasons for studying dog behaviour and dog training methods. First, the owner that understands these matters, will get much more pleasure from pet ownership. Second, dogs that are properly trained and do not have behaviour problems will fit into the community at large without causing friction. Third, there is no doubt that dogs appreciate leadership and like to know their status, so training and the correction of inappropriate behaviour will make dogs happier and more contented.

It is not generally realised just how commonly behaviour problems in dogs occur. This is partly because many dog owners put up with bad behaviour either because they do not see it as a problem or regard such behaviour as simply being characteristic of dogs.

Furthermore, many owners do not appreciate that something can be done to prevent or cure unacceptable behaviour. For example it was found that two-thirds of male dogs presented at random at veterinary surgeries had one or more undesirable hypersexual traits. Some dogs had four or five such traits and yet the owners had not complained or sought advice!

There is no doubt that all dog owners need to understand how to train their dogs and how to prevent, and if necessary cure, inappropriate behaviour.

This chapter sets out the basic principles that need to be appreciated, studied and applied. But first the reader is recommended to read thoroughly the section of Chapter 1 which deals with the motivation and intelligence of dogs, paying particular attention to the pack concept and body language.

How Dogs Learn

An understanding of how dogs learn is necessary before they can be trained to become well-mannered and properly integrated into society. Learning can be defined as "a change in behaviour resulting from previous experience". In technical terms dogs are said to learn by "instrumental conditioning", which simply means that behaviour is determined by the result it brings. If a response of an animal to a command is followed by a reward then the animal will tend to repeat the response. Conversely if punishment follows a certain action then that action will tend not to be repeated. That is simple enough and of course applies to children and even ourselves.

However, in the case of dogs it is very relevant to appreciate that they can only establish whether their performance was right or wrong if it is rewarded or punished virtually *at the same time* as the action is being carried out. It is no good rewarding a dog five minutes later for sitting on command as it will perceive the reward as applying to its very latest action which could have been wrong.

Dogs learn quickest if the reward or punishment is given within half a second of responding to a command and this means in many cases that the situation will have to be "set up". Rewards will need to be readily at hand not wrapped up and in a tin that is hidden away.

Similarly, the method of punishment must have been thought out in advance. In many cases it pays to have an appropriate object readily available to throw, since finding one and approaching the dog will delay the adminstration of punishment.

Thrown objects can be very effective in "set-up" situations, as the dog does not know where they have come from, and it gets immediate punishment, while it is performing the crime.

Rewards

The best reward is undoubtedly a coveted titbit and in training sessions a ready supply will be needed. Failing that, lavish praise and petting will bring instant satisfaction to most dogs.

Punishment

Essentially two forms of punishment are used.
1. The administration of a painful stimulus.
2. The withdrawal of something pleasurable — particularly sending the dog to its bed and ignoring it (social isolation).
If punishment is used it is essential to follow these rules:
● It must be given immediately.
● It must be strong enough to disrupt the undesirable behaviour but not cause suffering.
● The dog should be given a chance to "escape" into a behaviour that will bring a pleasant reward.
● Shy and nervous dogs should not be punished.
● Do not punish puppies that are between seven and 14 weeks of age.
● Hitting and slapping will be confused with play by most big dogs and can therefore be quite counterproductive.

● Finally, if in doubt do not use punishment. It is better to turn about and ignore the behaviour or to apply social isolation.

Training

Dogs can be trained much more effectively if the following modern teaching techniques are used:
● Reward the dog very quickly for a correct response.
● Give a delectable food reward *and* verbal praise.
● Learning is quickest if the response is rewarded every time.
● To perpetuate the response reward only intermittently, but remember if no rewards are given the behaviour may be forgotten (extinguish).

Behaviour Modification Techniques

Essentially five techniques are used, namely:
● To rely on extinction
● Counterconditioning
● Systematic desensitisation
● Punishment
● Flooding

Extinction

If a behaviour is never rewarded it will be repeated less frequently and will eventually stop. Often owners do not appreciate that they are encouraging a behaviour to continue by continually and unwittingly rewarding the dog. Once this is pointed out the behaviour will often cease very rapidly.

Counterconditioning

This means training the dog to behave in an approved way in response to the stimulus which brought about an inappropriate behaviour previously. For example a dog should learn that it is more rewarding to sit quietly by their owner than to pull frantically on the lead, barking hysterically when another dog is met.

Systematic desensitisation

This is a technique that is used to break down an anxiety or fear response. For example dogs that are fearful of thunderstorms can be taught to sit quietly and receive rewards as progressively louder recordings of thunderstorms are played. This is not a system for amateurs and is generally not suitable for owner application as it requires close co-operation with other people.

Punishment

There is no doubt that correctly applied punishment following the rules mentioned will effectively stop many undesirable behaviours.

Flooding

This is a technique that is sometimes used to overcome phobias or bad habits such as sheep chasing. The idea is to expose the animal to the stimulus but allow no escape. The method needs to be applied with great care in animals and preferably under veterinary supervision to ensure that suffering is not caused.

Behaviour Problems — prevention and treatment

The majority of behaviour problems encountered by dog owners fall into five major categories: aggression, destructiveness, disobedience, phobias and sexual.

Puppy owners are advised to spend some time and effort preventing problems arising since there is no doubt that prevention is better and more certain than cure.

If an adult dog has been obtained there may be no alternative but to try to overcome the problem. The behavioural methods which are generally the most effective are outlined in the following table in answer to the question, "What if my dog . . . . ?".

This is a format that is used elsewhere in *The Doglopaedia*, see particularly Chapters 4 and 7. These are guidelines only, and if you are in doubt or if the method described does not seem to be having an effect consult your veterinary surgeon.

In relation to the prevention of behaviour problems it should be noted that puppies go through two very significant periods in respect of subsequent behaviour. If things go wrong at these times then problems that are difficult to correct can occur later.

1. *The critical period of socialisation.* This period starts at three weeks of age and ends at 12-13 weeks in most puppies. It is essential that they encounter as many different types of people and experience as great a variety of noises and situations as possible during this period. They are then more likely to be better adjusted later in life.

2. *The critical period for sensitivity.* This period lasts from eight to twelve weeks of age. Any experience which provides acute fear during this time may make a dog anxious, shy or very fearful of similar situations for the rest of its life, especially if it already has an inherited tendency for nervousness. Punishment *must* be avoided at this time and puppies should not be isolated from social contact for prolonged periods during this stage of their development.

PROBLEM	TREATMENT	PREVENTION
...is aggressive towards other strange dogs	Use counterconditioning. Teach the dog that it is more profitable to sit quietly rather than to attack other dogs by using modern techniques. Regularly practise dominance exercises and give the dog planned training periods each day during which it is taught basic commands. Avoid possible confrontation situations during the training period. If a fight does break out ignore the dog and walk away — on no account pick it up as that could be construed as praise.	Ensure that puppies are "socialised" with other dogs as they grow up. Do not play rough games or "tug of war" games with dogs especially large dogs. From an early age praise good behaviour with other dogs. Avoid overly aggressive dogs by crossing the road well in advance. This behaviour is often reinforced unintentionally by some owners who for example stroke or pick up growling dogs.
...is aggressive towards other dogs in the same house	If its aggression is towards other dogs in the same house it is important to enhance the hierarchical system by giving support to the more dominant dog and withdrawing privileges from the underdog — this is not very British but it often works!	Establish a proper hierarchical system from the start and immediately discourage any signs of unrest. The owners must ensure that *they* are the pack leaders.
...is aggressive when groomed or when a wound is dressed	Use systematic desensitisation. Find an area that can be groomed or touched and reward good behaviour. Gradually move to desired area step by step over a few days. Do not go too quickly and risk a set back.	Groom the dog regularly from an early age. Make it fun and reward good behaviour. Be dominant.
...has learnt to be aggressive	Stop rewarding aggression and rely on extinction. Be dominant. Encourage some other acceptable behaviour. Do not play rough games with dogs that have a tendency to be aggressive. Avoid situations where the dog's aggression may come to the fore.	Do not play tug of war or rough games with big dogs especially guard breeds like Boxers and Dobermanns — they do not need to be taught their job. Be dominant. Have regular basic training sessions.
...jumps up	Apply counterconditioning methods. Be dominant and have regular basic training sessions. Do not slap dogs with rolled up newspapers as this could be construed as play. Do not use word DOWN to discourage behaviour as that could confuse the dog. Say NO sharply followed by SIT, and if obeyed give lavish praise. Greet dogs from a crouched position and while sitting in the car with the door open rather than getting out first. Discourage the behaviour forcibly and stand away so that the dog has no support. 'Set up'' the scene and have someone else administer immediate punishment from behind the dog. Possibly give the dog something like a glove to carry off and thus distract it.	Recognise that this is undesirable behaviour and do not think that it is nice for your dog to show its pleasure at seeing you in this way. Show disapproval of the behaviour and encourage desired behaviour.
...is disobedient	Rely on extinction principally. Be dominant, instigate regular basic training sessions if necessary using a Flexi-lead.	Start obedience training early — as soon as puppy is obtained. Never use punishment inappropriately. If a dog does not respond to the command "come" don't punish it when it eventually does come.
...pulls on the lead	Be dominant, start regular training periods. When teaching the dog to heel turn suddenly and frequently. In the early training session do not take the dog on the lead towards its favourite walk. Persevere and reward.	Be dominant. Start training the dog to walk to heel *properly* right from the start.

PREVENTION AND TREATMENT OF SOME COMMON BEHAVIOUR PROBLEMS — "WHAT IF MY DOG . . . ?" (continued)

PROBLEM	TREATMENT	PREVENTION
. . . is destructive	Do not punish bad behaviour as it is always too late. Adopt a training programme in which the dog is left for progressively longer periods starting with very short times. Reward lavishly good behaviour. Give the dog a cue and go through the same ritual each time it is left. Be dominant and do regular basic training exercises. Ensure that the dog is well-fed and has a comfortable place to lie when it is left. In bad cases consider using a cage to confine the dog. Consider "booby trapping" the environment so that the dog is instantly punished by falling objects if it opens a door or drawer for example. Tidy up before you leave the dog to reduce temptation. Possibly "set up" the situation and use the thrown object as a punishment.	Do not isolate young puppies for prolonged periods. When the dog is left on its own give it a cue that you will return i.e. leave a radio or a small light on. Go through the same routine each time the dog is left. Make sure that the dog has water, and is comfortable and warm. Reward good behaviour on return, do not punish any bad behaviour. Do not encourage dogs to become mouth orientated by giving it too many chew objects as a puppy. Remove temptations. Do not punish young puppies by social isolation.
. . . is sick in the car	Use counterconditioning. Check that the dog is not being sick to draw attention to itself or to get comfort and praise. Feed the dog in the stationary car and let it go in and out and chase a ball around the car so that it regards the car as fun. Start with short journeys and gradually build up rewarding no sickness and ignoring sickness.	During its socialisation period ensure that puppies encounter as many different situations as possible, including the car. Don't be *oversympathetic* if puppy is sick.
. . . is shy	Use systematic desensitisation. Introduce the dog to acceptable situations and people and gradually build up rewards for good behaviour. Do not use punishment in shy dogs. Ignore shyness preferably building the dog up by giving it some privileges, but don't overdo it. Do not allow visitors to force themselves on the dog — let the dog set the pace.	Ensure proper socialisation as a puppy. Make sure that the dog meets a full range of people including children when it is young. Do not punish young puppies during the fear period.
. . . licks people's hands excessively	This is a sign of submission. Build the dog up by giving it some privileges and stop dominance exercises, at least temporarily.	Do not make puppies mouth conscious. Discourage such behaviour from the outset. Do not overdo punishment, use rewards preferably in dogs that tend to shyness and where parents have a history of shyness.
. . . shows the hypersexual tendencies of mounting people and inanimate objects	Use counterconditioning. Instant punishment of inappropriate behaviour. Remove temptations. Possibly seek veterinary advice about special medication or possibly castration.	Discourage such actions forcibly right from the start. Be dominant and regularly practise dominance exercises. Give the dog an adequate amount of exercise.

Note: For dominance exercises see Chapter 1, Part II.

Basic Training

It is most important that dogs are trained to respond promptly and properly to the commands illustrated below if they are to fit without friction into the community at large.

The behaviour modification techniques described earlier in this chapter should be used to establish and maintain the behaviour. Contrary to popular belief simple training can start from 12 weeks of age; there is no need to wait until the dog reaches adolescence.

(a) Down

Fig. 27 **Basic training**

DOWN
● Give the command with a short sharp voice and insist on instant response. Do not use the word to stop dogs jumping up. It is useful to accompany the command with a downward gesture of the arm.

(c) Heel

(b) Stay

HEEL
● Constant changing of direction during training sessions will help ensure that the dog does not pull ahead. Harnesses tend to encourage dogs to pull on the lead. It is easier to train dogs to walk to heel as a special task rather than while taking it on its favourite walk.

STAY
● A useful command that can help to ensure that the dog does not run across the road when separated from the owner for example. Say in a sharp tone coupled with a hand held out palm first.

(d) Come

(e) Sit

COME

This command is most useful since it can prevent accidents occurring. Training can begin on a long lead to ensure the dog's attention. Never scold a dog that has answered the command to come even if it was doing something very wrong when it was called. The word should be used in an encouraging way and accompanied by a beckoning gesture.

SIT

● Ensure that the dog's bottom is properly on the ground and that the response is instantaneous.

Tips

● Set aside a few minutes initially each day and subsequently once a week to rehearse and reaffirm these commands to ensure that your dog responds promptly and properly.

● Basic training classes can be fun and are of help especially if the dog has been obtained at an older age.

● Obedience training can be interesting and rewarding. There is the chance not only to achieve something personally but also to make many friends with a common interest in dogs.

CHAPTER 4

PART I

SIGNS AND SYMPTOMS OF ILLNESS

> Observing dogs for signs of illness
>
> Pain
>
> The significance of the signs of illness
> "What if my dog...?"

Introduction

Early recognition and treatment of illness is important, not only to save pain and suffering, but also because treatment is likely to be more effective.

The object of this chapter is to help the owner to recognise, identify and to describe accurately the signs of pain and illness in their pet and to know when to seek veterinary advice. The observant owner will then be able to supply an accurate and detailed history should veterinary treatment become necessary. An accurate history can be a crucial factor in helping the veterinary surgeon to arrive at a correct diagnosis and is thus a prelude to effective treatment. Your veterinary surgeon may appreciate having the history in writing.

TIPS ON OBSERVING DOGS FOR SIGNS OF ILLNESS

- The concerned owner will spend time observing the normal habits, reactions and detailed appearance of their dog when in full health, so that any alterations which may be indicative of the beginnings of illness will be noticed quickly.

- Any small change in behaviour or any unusual physical sign should mean that the dog is kept under extra close scrutiny for a few hours, or a few days, until either more positive signs develop or the dog has returned to normal. A dog under observation for illness should not be given strenuous exercise nor should it be taken to training class, a dog show or into any situation which may cause it stress.

- It may not be beneficial to seek veterinary advice in the very early stages of discomfort, as the vet will usually want some positive signs to develop before treatment can be started. The discerning owner should know instinctively when this stage is reached.

- Dogs, like humans, may have days when they feel "off colour" for no obvious reason. If these episodes occur often in your dog, a note of days, times and surrounding circumstances should be made. Veterinary advice should then be sought in order to interpret the information collected in this way.

● Dogs may show signs of depression and illness in response to worry or grief affecting the owner or the household in which it lives. Human alterations in behaviour may be subtle, but the devoted dog recognises mood changes in its owner. The dog will return to normal when its owner is feeling happier and on no account should they be given anti-depressive drugs prescribed for human use.

Signs and Symptoms

Most canine illnesses are shown by a combination of signs and symptoms.

Signs of illness are: objective evidence that something is wrong which is readily apparent to an observer, e.g. diarrhoea or coughing.

Symptoms of illness are: a change in sensation of bodily function experienced by the patient, e.g. the pain caused by trying to put an injured foot to the ground. Although dogs are at a disadvantage in being unable to describe their symptoms they are nevertheless able to indicate in a number of ways what they are experiencing, but it is necessary to learn how to interpret these indications correctly.

It is important for the owner to keep an open mind about the nature of an illness during the early stages.

Not all cases of a particular illness show all the signs and symptoms associated with that illness. Furthermore, many signs are common to a number of different diseases. Jumping to the wrong conclusion too early may prevent help being sought at the right time and delay the start of proper treatment.

The significance of the various signs of illness shown by dogs will be found under the section of this chapter headed "**What if my dog**...?". Suffice to comment here on temperament and behaviour changes and temperature taking.

Temperament and behaviour changes

Dogs are creatures of habit. Any marked changes not associated with changes in the household may be indicative of illness. However, allowance should be made for jealousy, resentment and pining, as well as undue persecution by a puppy, kitten or child, or the onset of heat, whelping or false pregnancy in bitches.

Temperature taking

The normal temperature of a newborn puppy is 98.6°F and the normal adult body temperature of 101.5°F is not achieved until the pup is about four weeks old. It is not wise or helpful for an inexperienced owner to take the dog's temperature unless specifically requested to do so by the veterinary surgeon — thermometers can be broken in the rectum all too easily! Furthermore,

· readings need skilled interpretation, as any form of excitement can cause the temperature to rise by two to three degrees when the dog is in normal health.

Pain

Pain is probably the most significant symptom of illness or injury and it is important to understand the ways that dogs indicate that they are suffering from pain in a particular area or organ.

Symptoms of pain in specific areas as indicated by tell-tale "signs"

Area of pain	Signs that indicate pain is felt
Head pain (headache)	Half closed eyes coupled with persistent pressing of the top of the head into furniture, owner's lap or the flank of other dogs; gentle shaking of the head or vacant staring
Eye pain	Pawing at eyes; rubbing eyes on furniture or on the carpet.
Ear and mouth pain	It is not always easy to distinguish between the two as the nerve pathways are very close. One ear may be carried low and the head inclined to the affected side. There may be drooling or excess saliva, reluctance to eat hard food or to take food from the hand. Dogs with mouth pain may yawn frequently, and ear pain is usually accompanied by head shaking.
Throat pain	Retching, drooling, stretching neck towards the ceiling (sore throat) and difficulty in swallowing shown by gulping.
Abdominal pain	Continual glancing round at the site of pain, biting and licking at the area. Lying in a curled up position, reluctant to leave its bed. The dog may hold itself in a hunched up position when standing, or may take up the "prayer position" (down on forelegs with hindlegs standing). In some cases dogs with abdominal pain will show persistant straining to pass a bowel movement.
Limb and joint pain	Dogs quickly adapt to carrying a limb which is giving them pain when weight is put on it. When the problem is in the foot or, in case of severe injury, the limb is usually carried high, but sometimes it is only partially elevated and the toes will be dragged along the ground. In other cases the dog will put the foot of the affected leg to the ground, but will not put full weight on it. In such cases the dog's movement should be watched carefully, paying particular attention to the head and pelvis. A nodding action of the head or rump will be seen when the sound foreleg is put to the ground. Lameness associated with foot dragging is often indicative of nerve damage. A dog with arthritic pain in the joints will sometimes give a grunt or cry when settling into or rising from its bed. It is a useful diagnostic measure to know if the dog's pain eases when it has been moving about for a while, or whether exercise makes the pain worse. It is not always easy to decide which limb is lame, especially if more than one leg is affected. Bilateral hind leg lameness from severe hip dysplasia may not show on movement.
Spinal pain	Sometimes a dog will appear lame when the actual site of pain is in the spinal column. Other signs of back pain are a resentment to touch or accidental knocks, trembling while standing, wasting of the upper thighs, humping of the centre back, difficulty in assuming normal defaecation position, collapse of the hind quarters and incontinence.
Anal gland pain	Dragging the anus on carpet or grass is the dog's reaction to pain around the rectum. The dog may also turn round to inspect its back end frequently and suddenly.

Symptoms of pain in specific areas as indicated by tell-tale "signs" (cont.)

Area of pain	Signs that indicate pain is felt
General internal pain	Being unable to settle down when all normal wants have been fulfilled may indicate internal pain or mental trauma.
"Hind end" pain	Frequent whirling round is the dog's response to "hind end" discomfort from a burr or matt of fur in the region, or from blades of grass which have not been passed properly with a bowel movement and which are still protruding from the anus. As with anal gland pain the dog will also turn round suddenly and frequently to inspect the affected area, often with a cry.

Two general signs of pain that are frequently shown by dogs are:

Crying   Dogs do not cry by means of tears, but they will utter a vocal cry at a sudden injury (such as being stepped on) or when an external injury or a painful internal organ is touched. Unprovoked crying or vocalisation may indicate internal pain. Some dogs are much more stoical than others and will endure considerable pain without any vocalisation.

Aggression   Any radical change in temperament may be a reaction to pain. A sudden tendency to aggression may be reversible when the pain is alleviated, so give the veterinary surgeon a full history before concluding that the dog has become vicious.

"What if my dog...?"

Introduction

This section seeks to answer the questions which worry dog owners when their pet shows signs which may indicate that it is ill. Each topic begins with the words "**What If My Dog**...?" and it is hoped that the details given will help owners decide whether:

● The sign is normal and no action is required
● Some simple "treatment" is needed
● First aid action is indicated
● Veterinary help should be obtained and, if so, how urgently it is needed

Use the Index of Diseases and Conditions, the diagram opposite, or the list on page 76, to identify the relevant number.

> HISTORY TIP: Throughout the book are HISTORY TIPS highlighted in colour. These show information which will be important for the veterinary surgeon to know when making a diagnosis. Usually this information can only be supplied by the observant owner and so you have a very important function to perform in contributing towards the restoration of your pet to perfect health. The history which you supply can be crucial in making a correct diagnosis and rapid recovery.

WHAT IF MY DOG......?

1. eats grass
2. vomits
3. refuses to eat
4. is eating too much
5. is eating well but remains thin
36. is eating with difficulty
52. has a depraved appetite
53. is salivating excessively

6. is drinking excessively

7. sneezes
8. has a discharge from its nose
9. has a dry and crusty nose
10. has a nose which has turned brown or grey

37. has bad breath

12. has eyes that look abnormal
13. is blind

14. is shaking or scratching its ears
49. appears deaf

15. is holding its head on one side

21. had noisy abdominal sounds
20. keeps breaking wind

23. has diarrhoea
24. is passing blood in its faeces
25. is constipated

22. is biting its tail or scooting or rubbing its bottom on the ground

26. is eating its own faeces

39. has a lump or swelling
40. is wounded
41. is licking itself excessively

42. is weak and lethargic
43. has collapsed and is comatose
48. is staggering and wobbly on its legs

44. is in pain

45. is loosing weight or is looking thin

27. is not passing urine
28. is incontinent
29. is passing blood in its urine
30. has a discharge from its penis or vulva

31. is mismated
32. is found to be pregnant unexpectedly
50. is aborting

33. is pot-bellied

54. is over-sexed

35. is coughing
16. is breathing abnormally
47. is not breathing

17. is shedding hair
18. is going bald
19. is scratching

34. is limping

38. is having fits, convulsions or is twitching

46. is aggressive
51. is nervous and excitable

"WHAT IF MY DOG...?"

1 eats grass
2 vomits
3 refuses to eat
4 is eating too much
5 is eating well but remains very thin
6 is drinking excessively
7 sneezes
8 has a discharge from its nose
9 has a dry and crusty nose
10 has a nose which has turned brown or grey
11 has runny eyes
12 has eyes that look abnormal
13 is blind
14 is shaking or scratching its ears
15 is holding its head on one side
16 is breathing abnormally
17 is shedding hair
18 is going bald
19 is scratching
20 keeps breaking wind
21 has noisy abdominal sounds
22 is biting its tail, scooting or rubbing its bottom on the ground
23 has diarrhoea
24 is passing blood in its faeces
25 is constipated
26 is eating its own faeces
27 is not passing urine
28 is incontinent
29 is passing blood in its urine
30 has a discharge from its penis or vulva
31 is mismated
32 is found to be pregnant unexpectedly
33 is pot-bellied
34 is limping
35 is coughing
36 is eating with difficulty
37 has bad breath
38 is having fits, convulsions or is twitching
39 has a lump or swelling
40 is wounded/cut/burnt/grazed
41 is licking itself excessively
42 is weak and lethargic
43 has collapsed and is comatose
44 is in pain
45 is losing weight, or is looking thin
46 is aggressive
47 is not breathing
48 is staggering and wobbly on its legs
49 appears deaf
50 is aborting
51 is nervous and over-excitable
52 has a depraved appetite
53 is salivating excessively
54 is over-sexed

1. What if my dog eats grass?

Many dogs will eat small amounts of coarse couchgrass regularly, only for it to be vomited, covered in frothy saliva, a few minutes later. It is thought that the grass is eaten to relieve an excess of digestive juices which accumulate in the stomach when it is empty. If this habit causes inconvenience, it may help to give two or three small meals a day rather than one large meal.

Fine grass may be grazed by some dogs and digested. This will act as roughage in the diet.

- Grass eating is seldom harmful, provided the grass has not been sprayed with a toxic chemical. If grass eating is accompanied by prolonged or persistent vomiting, and particularly if the vomit contains blood, veterinary advice should be sought quickly.

2. What if my dog vomits?

Dogs vomit easily and occasional incidents are to be expected and are unimportant.

- Vomiting is part of the defence mechanism of the body, enabling the stomach to get rid of an excess of food, water or unsuitable or decayed matter before it passes further into the digestive system and causes harm.
- Prolonged or persistent vomiting, particularly if the vomit contains blood, requires immediate veterinary attention.

There are three main types of vomiting listed here in order of the frequency with which they occur.

True Vomiting

This involves movement of the muscles of the abdomen, chest or diaphragm (i.e. heaving) in order to eject the contents of the stomach.

The main danger of repeated or continuous vomiting is dehydration (loss of body fluids), so that the volume of circulating blood is decreased and the dog goes into a state of shock very rapidly. Dehydration can be recognised by picking up a fold of skin on the dog's back between your thumb and forefinger. If the fold remains "tented" when you release it, dehydration is indicated.

It is wrong to allow a vomiting dog to drink its fill of cold water, as this often leads to further vomiting, but it is also dangerous to withhold water completely. Instead, very small amounts of water should be offered every half hour (see Chapter 6 on home nursing).

In cases of persistent vomiting where the dog is not eating, it may be helpful to dissolve one heaped tablespoon of glucose in one pint of boiled water, and to offer this in small quantities in order to supply the dog with the energy it requires. This is an emergency measure for use where veterinary advice cannot be obtained.

> **HISTORY TIP:** If the vomit contains identifiable food, it may be helpful to trace the time it has been in the stomach. Note particularly whether the vomit consists of small food particles with a quantity of frothy saliva; or large quantities of recently drunk water plus yellow bile and stomach fluids.
> Make a note of how much water is given and when. Record how long it is retained.

Regurgitation

The second type of vomiting is regurgitation — a more passive action used to bring up sausage-shaped boluses of something recently eaten. When freshly eaten food is regurgitated the dog may eat it again at once, and this behaviour is so frequent as to be normal in some dogs, particularly when they bolt their food in competition with others or when persuaded to eat when they are not hungry.

It is normal for some bitches to regurgitate their own partially digested food for puppies to eat as they reach weaning age.

Persistent regurgitation in an older puppy or an adult dog may indicate some obstruction or malformation in the oesophagus and this condition warrants prompt veterinary advice.

> **HISTORY TIP:** Note how much of the food given is being regurgitated and the time in relation to feeding.

Retching

The third type of vomiting is retching, an involuntary spasm of vomiting, possibly accompanied by a cough. There appears to be difficulty in swallowing food, which is then quickly brought back covered in saliva. The cause may be some obstruction in the mouth or throat, or retching may be associated with a cough or an acute sore throat. Veterinary advice should be sought at once if retching occurs frequently or is persistent.

The significance of true vomiting

Vomiting is associated with many serious diseases and conditions in the dog, particularly *Canine Parvovirus Disease, Haemorrhagic Gastroenteritis, Kidney Disease* and *Pyometra* in bitches. In these diseases vomiting will usually be accompanied by loss of appetite, depression and diarrhoea. Veterinary help is needed at once and must definitely not be delayed if there is blood in the vomit.

Vomiting may also be caused by eating unsuitable or decaying material, by eating poisonous substances or carrion or plant material which has been impregnated by poison; or by bad food, which irritates the stomach and intestines. In such cases the signs mentioned above may be accompanied by drooling from the mouth and signs of abdominal pain. Veterinary help is needed urgently.

> **HISTORY TIP:** If the dog is known to have eaten a poisonous substance, e.g. a garden chemical or slug bait, take the original container with you to the veterinary surgeon, as the manufacturer's analysis may be helpful in tracing an antidote to the poison.

Intestinal obstructions are a relatively frequent cause of vomiting in dogs, particularly puppies. Vomiting may result from stones, toys, bones, and stolen objects becoming lodged in the digestive tract. Twists in the bowel, or the telescoping of one part of the bowel into another, as can occur in young puppies, will cause vomiting. In such cases true vomiting may be accompanied by frequent retching and the dog will become progressively more ill. If you suspect that your dog has swallowed some toy or trophy such as part of a ball, or a bone, it is important to consult a veterinary surgeon *at once,* as surgery may be required and it is better done before the dog is exhausted by frequent attempts to vomit.

Projectile vomiting is used to describe a particular kind of vomitng action in which recently eaten food is ejected with force sometimes over a distance of several feet. It is seen most frequently in puppies from six to 14 weeks old, but may not be noticed until the puppy is separated from the rest of the litter. Vomiting of this type when only part of the food and liquid is retained is associated with failure of the stomach to empty its contents into the intestine, and is often associated with *Pyloric Stenosis* (a malfunction of the exit valve of the stomach). Seek veterinary help immediately as surgical correction may be possible.

> **HISTORY TIP:** An estimate of how much food and/or liquid is retained is helpful, as well as daily weighing of the puppy, in order to monitor growth and weight gain.

Travel sickness may occur in dogs as it does humans. Many puppies are nauseated and drool and vomit when travelling in a car, possibly from a disturbance in the balance centre of the brain, or perhaps from stress associated with changing homes for the first time.

It is helpful for someone to hold the puppy securely so that it is not so affected by the movement of the car. Putting the dog into a wire mesh crate, perhaps covered with a light cotton material, may be helpful. Perseverence on the part of the owner   taking the dog out in the car *before feeding,* making journeys rewarding by including a walk etc., almost always allow the dog to grow out of travel sickness. Ideally, puppies should be introduced to car travel before they are eight weeks of age and so before the "fear period" in their development. If the puppy is not acclimatised and happy in the car by that age it is better to leave further introductions and the possible use of the methods described above until after it is three months of age. It is not desirable to give medication intended for travel sickness in humans.

Unproductive attempts at vomiting can be serious. Sometimes a dog will be seen to try to vomit but will be unable to bring up any stomach contents. When this is associated with a rapid expansion of the abdomen (bloating) the condition is very dangerous indeed and needs veterinary help immediately.

3. What if my dog refuses to eat?

While inappetance may be the first sign of a major illness, it is also not uncommon for a healthy, well-fed dog to refuse a meal occasionally, often for the reasons listed below.

Common Reasons for Refusal of Food in Healthy Dogs

Puppies
- Young puppies may refuse milky meals at around six months old.
- Puppies which have been on a four meals a day regime will begin to refuse "breakfast" when the time has come to switch to three larger meals given at longer intervals.
- Puppies may refuse, temporarily, to eat newly introduced foods.
- Puppies will often not eat if they are overtired.

79

Adults
- Refusal of food is normal and sensible when a dog is exhausted by vigorous exercise.
- Dogs will often refuse food when they have other things on their minds, for instance a bitch in season nearby.
- Inappetence may be due to environmental stress; guard dogs will not eat when strangers are present. Pet dogs in boarding kennels may starve themselves for a few days.
- Most bitches will refuse food for a day, or part of a day, at certain stages of pregnancy, and usually for 24-36 hours before whelping. Appetite may be variable for a few days after whelping.

Persistent refusal of food, especially if accompanied by other signs of illness, needs careful monitoring. Veterinary help should be sought if inappetence continues for more than 24 hours in a young puppy, or 48 hours in an adult, provided none of the situations mentioned above are pertinent.

HISTORY TIP: Note particularly
- How long is it since the dog ate a full meal eagerly?
- Whether the dog refuses all foods, or is selecting a certain type of food.
- Whether the dog is capable of swallowing, by offering small pieces of a favoured titbit.
- Whether or not the dog is drinking normally.
- If the dog is still passing motions at normal times and frequency and record their colour.
- If vomiting has occurred record the frequency and type.

---

4. What if my dog is eating too much?

It is normal for dogs to "gorge feed" if they have the opportunity, and many dogs fill up their day by worrying for food which they do not really need. This habit is often intensified when there are other animals in the household.

The amount of food given to a house dog must always be in the control of the owner.

While there are recommendations based on breed and weight on many commercial dog cans and packs, these are only approximations, and only the owner can gauge what is right for their dog.

Obesity is caused by giving too much food in relation to energy expended and, as in the human world, once too much weight is put on, it is very difficult to take off again. Obesity is just as dangerous for dogs as for people so take care not to overfeed. If it is difficult to limit the giving of titbits, cut the main meal down to compensate for the amount given between meals.

A dog that is frantically hungry and never satisfied and/or is willing to consume normally inedible things such as paper, plastic, soap, cardboard or stones, may be suffering from a specific disease or condition, and veterinary help will be needed to diagnose the cause.

> **HISTORY TIP:** Note how long the condition has been apparent. What type of faeces are being passed (take a sample)? Note the stage of the oestrous cycle in a bitch. How much water is being drunk (take a urine sample as excessive hunger can be a sign of diabetes)? When was the dog last wormed, and what preparation was used?

5. What if my dog is eating well but remains very thin?

This is a normal situation in adolescent dogs of the larger breeds, especially where more than one dog is kept and there is continual activity. A dog which matures slowly is likely to have a longer life than one which is reared to make maximum growth as early as possible. Heavy worm infestations and a number of disease conditions can give rise to this sign. In either case it is best to seek veterinary attention since it is a waste of time and money to purchase medicines which may not be specifically for the particular problem.

> **HISTORY TIP:** If the dog's condition is giving real cause for concern and veterinary advice is sought, a faeces sample should be taken and an estimate made of the volume of faeces passed daily. Note their consistency and frequency. It may be helpful to provide a record of the food being given and if possible an additional list of what each item contains. This information is usually found on the can or bag.

6. What if my dog is drinking excessively?

It is always useful for owners to have a note of what is normal for their own dog — any departure from normal which is not brought about by outside circumstances will then give rise to special observation to see if it has significance with regard to illness.

Common reasons for increased thirst in healthy animals

- Polydipsia (excessive drinking) is normal in hot weather, after excessive exercise, after eating salt food or drinking sea water.
- The lactating bitch needs to drink a lot of water in addition to any milk given.
- Bitches with a false pregnancy may also consume more water.

Excessive drinking in other circumstances is a significant sign of illness which should always receive veterinary attention.

> **HISTORY TIP:** Make an estimate of how much the dog drinks during the day and whether drinking also goes on at night. Measure the contents of the water bowl and take into consideration any other water to which the dog has access. In bitches it is most important to know the date of the last heat.
>
> Be prepared to tell the veterinary surgeon about any change in behaviour and importantly let him know what medicines, if any, the dog is being given or has received lately.
>
> Excessive drinking may be associated with diabetes or kidney disease so it is useful to take a urine sample with you when consulting the veterinary surgeon.

7. What if my dog sneezes?

It is normal for some dogs to sneeze two to three times when they wake up. An occasional bout of sneezing in dusty conditions, when being exercised on very dry ground, or when aerosol sprays or powders are being used is also normal.

A paroxysm of sneezing, accompanied by distress, shaking of the head, rubbing of the nose, with discharge or bleeding from the nostrils and noisy breathing, may mean that a foreign body (a needle, grass seed, twig or blade of grass) is lodged in the nose.

Do not attempt any first aid but take the dog to the veterinary surgery at once since a proper diagnosis and complete removal of any foreign object is essential.

Sneezing, possibly with the addition of bleeding from the nostrils and perhaps with swelling and cuts on the face, may be caused by a blow to the nose, for example when the dog has run at speed into a hard object. Veterinary help will be needed to ascertain the extent of the injury.

Finally, it should also be borne in mind that sneezing may be a prelude to respiratory disease. If that is suspected, observe the animal closely for other signs that will indicate the need to seek veterinary help. Do not over-exercise such dogs.

> **HISTORY TIP:** Consider if the dog has been in an area where garden or agricultural sprays are being used, particularly where there is aerial spraying. Is anyone in the household using a more pungent perfume or aftershave lotion? Is a deodorant powder being used on carpets before vacuum cleaning? Many dogs have proved to be allergic to these powders.

8. What if my dog has a discharge from its nose?

It is normal for a dog to have a cool, moist nose, but a warm, dry nose does not necessarily indicate illness.

It is normal for a small drop of clear watery mucus to accumulate at the nostrils, and this discharge may become temporarily more profuse when the dog is excited. Remove any excess discharge with moist cotton wool. If the discharge continues to be profuse for some hours, or if it becomes thick and contains pus, seek veterinary help at once as there may have been an injury to the nose, some foreign object may have become lodged in the nostril, or the signs may be an indication that the dog is in the early stage of a major virus disease.

> **HISTORY TIP**: Note whether the discharge is worse at any particular time of the day or in special surroundings and whether the discharge continues at night, and/or when the dog is asleep.

9. What if my dog has a dry and crusty nose?

In some older dogs the black pigmented area of the nose becomes thickened and crusted, with deep fissures in which food particles can collect and cause infection.

If there is no sign of infection, the crusts may be softened with frequent applications of Vaseline or lanolin. If an infection is present, your veterinary surgeon will be able to provide a suitable dressing. Dogs that are suffering from, or which have recovered from, *Canine Distemper* often develop thick crusty noses and pads. This is not usually too harmful in itself, but veterinary advice may be needed since some other signs may need treating or some medicament may be required to prevent the dog starting to show nervous signs.

Collie Nose is an hereditary condition which affects mainly Collie and Shetland Sheepdog breeds. In affected animals the bridge of the nose becomes sore, ulcerated and weeping. Veterinary help should be sought promptly as a mild case can become very much worse, very quickly. Since the condition may be caused by exposure to sunlight, affected dogs need to be kept indoors during sunny weather and exercised only at night.

> **HISTORY TIP**: If the breeder can be contacted, it may be a good idea to ask if any of the dog's relatives suffer from *Collie Nose*, as it tends to affect families within a breed. The nuisance to the owner and the discomfort to the dog should be taken into consideration if further breeding from the line is contemplated.

10. What if my dog has a nose which has turned brown or grey?

There is a tendency, said to be inherited, for the black pigmented skin on the nose to fade to brown or greyish pink periodically. The cause is not known and no disease is involved.

"Pink nose" is often associated with the anoestrus period in bitches, with the black pigment returning as they come on heat. "Pink nose" can also occur in spayed bitches and in male dogs. This fading usually occurs in winter and the black pigment returns in warm weather. The condition does not respond regularly to the administration of extra vitamins and minerals or herbal cures. It is not a cause for concern, except for exhibitors in beauty shows. Seaweed and elderberry tablets, from herbal suppliers have apparently improved some cases of "pink nose".

HISTORY TIP: In some cases loss of nasal pigment has been attributed to the use of plastic feeding and water bowls. You may wish to experiment with a change to pottery bowls.

---

11. What if my dog has runny eyes?

A slight, clear discharge from the eyes is normal in many dogs, and in some breeds the shape of the face and eyelids make a slight overspill of tears inevitable. The discharge should be carefully removed with damp cotton wool once a day or as often as necessary.

Where there is a pronounced staining on the face which threatens to become sore or ulcerated, veterinary advice should be sought as it is possible that a correction to the drainage from the eye can be made. An unaccustomed smokey atmosphere, or riding with the head out of the car window, may also irritate the eyes and cause an excessive discharge. The latter habit is dangerous in more ways than one and should never be permitted.

If the discharge from the eyes is profuse, contains pus or is accompanied by persistent signs of pain, veterinary advice should be sought without delay, as any injury to the eyes could potentially inflict damage to the sight.

Persistent discharge from the eyes, associated with *conjunctivitis* and accompanied by other signs of systemic illness, may indicate that the dog is suffering from a major disease which requires prompt veterinary help. *Conjunctivitis*, with a pus-like discharge often crusting the eyelids, is caused by inflammation of the inside lining of the eyelids. The condition may be caused by a local infection, but it is also often linked with a major illness. Certain anatomical defects of the face and eyes will also cause chronic *conjunctivitis*. A dog's eyes are too important to risk delay or incorrect treatment, so veterinary consultation is always necessary and nothing but veterinary prescribed preparations should be used. Do not be tempted to use eye drops which have been prescribed for a previous condition.

Anatomical defects of the eye and face may be the root cause of runny eyes. Some breed standards actually call for a shape of eye or facial conformation which leads to an anatomical defect which will cause the dog pain. Some anatomical defects are inherited but some are acquired. Many cause an irritation of the eyeball which can become chronic and cause persistent runny eyes. Some surgical correction may be possible, but the veterinary surgeon is likely to require that the dog or bitch will not be used for breeding or showing subsequently.

Common ocular defects which cause runny eyes

Condition	Description	Breeds particularly affected
Distichiasis	Extra hairs on the margin of the eye lid which point inwards and irritate the surface of the eye.	Sheltie, Cocker, Poodle, Pekingese, Mini-Longhaired Dachs.
Entropion	In-turning eyelids which cause the eyelashes to rub on the cornea.	ChowChow, Cocker, Labrador, Retriever, Golden Retriever.
Ectropion	The lower eyelid is turned outwards, leading to inflammation of the conjunctival sac.	Bassett Hound, St. Bernard, Bloodhound.
Trichiasis	Facial hair causing irritation to the cornea.	Pekingese.

12. What if my dog has eyes that look abnormal?

Once more an accurate study of the normal eye helps the owner to appreciate any changes quickly. The following conditions will be noticeable to an observant owner:

Conditions which cause dogs' eyes to look abnormal

Sign	Comment
Dislocated eyeball (eye hanging out of its socket)	Generally due to trauma but may be spontaneous. An emergency see first aid section in Chapter 6.
Bulging eyeball (see also table of inherited eye defects)	May be a sign of glaucoma, an acutely painful and serious condition. Consult veterinary surgeon immediately. Note, however, that certain breeds like Pekingese and Cavalier King Charles Spaniels have bulging eyes normally.
Swelling of the eyelids and surrounding facial area	May be due to an allergy or an insect sting. Probably quickly alleviated by a visit to the veterinary surgeon.
Inability to raise upper eyelid (Ptosis)	Associated with conditions affecting nerves of the head and also possibly with generalised illness. If not already receiving veterinary treatment for the illness, an immediate consultation is necessary.
Hair loss around the eye	Bare skin around the eye rim can be an early sign of Demodectic Mange which may become generalised if neglected
An opaque patch on the surface of the eye	Possible causes are: A film over part or all of the cornea caused by inflammation (keratitis) or by a failure in tear production, (keratitis sicca − Dry Eye). A corneal ulcer, usually caused by a direct injury to the cornea, e.g. being struck by the end of a lead. An indolent ulcer, seen most frequently in spayed Boxer and Corgi bitches, possibly caused by low oestrogen levels in the blood. In all cases veterinary consultation is urgent as sight may be damaged if treatment is delayed.
Blue eye, almost overnight the whole of the cornea becomes an opaque pale blue	Seen mainly in puppies, following infection with Infectious Canine Hepatitis, or possibly about ten days after vaccination against this disease. The eye colour usually reverts to normal in time. See Infectious Canine Hepatitis Chapter 4 Part II. In advanced cases of glaucoma the surface of the eye becomes a blue-green colour. Dogs with such signs should be taken without delay to a veterinary surgeon.

Conditions which cause dogs' eyes to look abnormal (continued)

Sign	Comment
Third eyelid prolapsed	In some dogs the third eyelid is always prominent and particularly noticeable because it is darkly pigmented. When the third eyelid is more prominent than usual in an individual dog, it is often because fat has been lost behind the eyeball through illness and poor condition. Severe dehydration can give the same appearance. If the dog is not already under treatment for illness, consult a veterinary surgeon without delay.
Enlarged Harderian gland (a red lump protruding at the inner corner of the eye) also known as 'Cherry Eye'	The Harderian gland is on the inner surface of the third eyelid. It can become swollen so as to protrude past the third eyelid. Veterinary attention should be sought without delay
Dilated pupils in daylight	This sign may be associated with several serious eye conditions and hereditary defects such as PRA. See "What if" No. 13.

> **HISTORY TIP:** Try to pinpoint the first time you noticed any change in the eye and whether at that time there was pain and irritation.

13. What if my dog is blind?

Many elderly dogs become partially or completely blind, but by using scent and hearing they can manage very well on familiar territory provided they are given a certain amount of consideration and unexpected hazards are not left in their path.

Loss of sight should not be a reason for having a well-loved dog destroyed when it is otherwise healthy. Sudden blindness in a young or middle-aged dog needs immediate veterinary help. In a younger dog, veterinary advice should be obtained promptly as treatment may be possible, but only if the condition is recognised early.

> **HISTORY TIP:** Note when the condition was first apparent. Check whether blindness is total or partial. Observe whether sight is worse in dim light or in daylight. It is useful to teach dogs to catch titbits since their sight can be judged periodically by their ability to perform in this way. Any change should be noted.

Inherited eye defects

A number of eye defects which can lead to total or partial blindness while the dog is still quite young are known to be inherited. A large number of breeds and crosses or mongrels deriving from these breeds may also be affected.

In order to stop the spread of these degenerative diseases by breeding from affected stock, the British Veterinary Association, in conjunction with the Kennel Club, have set up schemes to screen males and females used for breeding.

A special panel of canine opthalmologists has been convened to examine dogs and bitches for breeders and only members of this panel can give official BVA/KC certification of freedom from defects.

- Do not buy a puppy of the severely affected breeds unless you are given a copy of current eye clearance certificates for both parents.
- Do not breed even one litter from your pet until a clear certificate has been obtained through the official examination.
- Do not breed at all from your dog or bitch if any inherited eye disease is present.

Your veterinary surgeon can put you in touch with a member of the BVA/KC eye panel, and some breed clubs and canine societies arrange special events at which dogs can be tested.

The common inherited eye defects are listed in the table below.

Inherited Eye Defects

Disease	Sign	Breeds chiefly affected
Progressive Retinal Atrophy (PRA) — progressive destruction of the light sensitive tissue at the back of the eye.	Failing sight in dim light leading to total blindness. May start at any age so annual examination necessary. No treatment, no cure.	Collies, Shelties, Cockers, Mini-Longhair Dachs, English Springers, Irish Setters, Poodles, Golden Retrievers, Labradors, Briards, Tibetan breeds and cross-breds.
Hereditary Cataract — loss of transparency of the lens of the eye.	A bluish clouding of the lens causing blindness. Common in the older dog but in badly affected breeds can occur at less than 2 years of age. Surgical correction may be possible.	Staffordshire Bull Terriers, Afghans, American Cockers, Bedlingtons, Bostons, Golden Retrievers, Labradors, German Shepherd Dogs, Welsh Springers.
Collie Eye Anomaly (CEA) — a complicated eye defect very widespread in Collie breeds.	A canine opthalmologist can distinguish this defect in puppies of 6-8 weeks old. While the defect does not cause blindness, it can lead to other painful eye conditions. Affected puppies are acceptable as pets but should not be used for breeding. Do not buy a Collie puppy which has not been screened for CEA. The condition can not be treated but seek veterinary advice about management of affected dog.	Rough Collies, Smooth Collies, Border and Working Collies, Shetland Sheepdogs, and crossbreds.
Glaucoma increased fluid pressure within the eye.	A fixed cloudy, bulging, staring eye with wide-open pupil, usually only in one eye at first. Veterinary attention is needed immediately.	American Cockers, English Cockers, Welsh and English Springers, Beagles, Bassetts, small Poodles.
Lens Luxation — weakening or rupture of one or more of the ligaments holding the lens in place.	Probably suddenly failing sight will be the only sign the owner can recognise. Affected animals lose the ability to catch titbits and knock into objects in unfamiliar places. Surgical correction may be possible and veterinary advice should be sought before other complications set in.	Wire-haired and Smooth Fox Terriers, Jack Russell and similar terriers, Tibetan Terriers.

14. What if my dog is shaking or scratching its ears?

It is important to be familiar with the appearance of your dog's normal, clean ear so that, when you make your routine weekly inspection, you will be aware if any changes are taking place. A small amount of light-brown waxy secretion is normal and necessary to the health of the ear but there should be no unpleasant smell.

Many dogs shake their ears quite violently when arousing from sleep, and may also occasionally scratch the ears, but repeated and violent head shaking is a sign that something is wrong.

Signs of Ear Disease:
- Repeated scratching and head shaking.
- Head held with painful side downwards.
- Dark reddish brown waxy deposit in the ear.
- An unpleasant smell from the ear.
- Inflammation — heat, swelling and pain in the canal and flap.

Treatment
Any disease of the ears must be properly diagnosed and treated without delay, as a simple condition may aggravate rapidly into a more complex situation which may become difficult and expensive to treat, and which may create a smell which pervades the whole house. In addition, the acute pain caused by ear disease may make the dog irritable and inclined to snap when the ears are touched.

No attempt should be made to treat ear disease with proprietary remedies which may be inappropriate or useless for the particular condition affecting your dog. Always seek veterinary advice early as delay could mean that an operation will be required to cure the condition if it has become chronic.

> **HISTORY TIP:** Tell your veterinary surgeon if you have other animals in the home, especially cats. Your cat may need treatment too. Even though it is not showing signs of ear disease, your cat could be the source of infection for your dog.

Avoiding Ear Disease
- Keep the hair on the underside of ear flaps combed free of burrs and tangles.
- Dry the dog's ears after bathing.
- Remove excess hair from inside the ears by plucking or clipping, but be gentle. Ask your veterinary surgeon to show you how to do this. Failure to keep the vertical ear canal clear, clean and properly ventilated is often the root cause of otitis externa.
- Do not attempt to clean deeply inside the ear. Wipe the surface only with cotton wool damped with a weak disinfectant solution. Use only your fingers, never any kind of instrument or probe.

Possible causes of ear disease — Otitis Externa (Canker)
- **Earmites.** Tiny mites living within the ear can cause acute irritation which makes the dog scratch and so damage the tissue of the ear. Treatment requires the use of a product that contains an ingredient that will kill the mites. Cats in the same household may be the source of the infestation.

- **A fungus or yeast infection in the ear.** This leads to intense itching, a reddish brown discharge and an offensive smell. Specific medication from the veterinary surgeon is needed.
- **Foreign bodies.** It is common when dogs are running through long grass for the awns, or seeds, to lodge in the ear. Typically dogs that have a foreign body in the ear suddenly scratch violently, shake, and often hold their head to one side. Do not attempt to remove the foreign body. Take the dog at once to the veterinary surgery, where treatment can be carried out, if necessary, under a local anaesthetic or a strong sedative.
- **Allergy or an extension of skin diseases.** Diagnosis and treatment by a veterinary surgeon is obviously required when these causes are involved.
- **Bacteria.** Most bacterial infection is secondary to some other irritating cause. The correct selection of an antibiotic is necessary to obtain a rapid and complete cure.
- **Ear conformation.** There is no doubt that the structure of the external ear can be an important predisposing factor for the development of otitis externa. Long, loosely-hanging, heavily-feathered ear flaps prevent adequate ventilation, and excessively hairy ear canals, such as those occurring in Poodles and some Terriers, favour the retention of wax and debris — leading to inflammation.

15. What if my dog is holding its head on one side?

This sign usually indicates ear problems; see "What if" No. 71, but may also be caused by teething around the age of four to six months in a puppy, by toothache in an older dog (see "What if" No. 36), or by tonsillitis (see "What if" No. 35). Other causes may be: Otitis Interna (Inflammation of the Middle Ear) see Index of Diseases and Conditions or:

Aural Haematoma (a blood filled swelling on the ear flap).

Signs:	A hot and painful swelling of the ear flap increasing slowly in size over a period of two to three days, probably accompanied by head shaking.
Cause:	A fight injury, or self-inflicted injury caused by aggressive scratching, or violent head shaking or banging often associated with otitis externa
Action:	Consult the veterinary surgeon at once, as there is usually some underlying cause to make the dog injure its own ear and it is usually necessary for the swelling to be drained surgically.

> **HISTORY TIP:** Has there been any recent injury or happening which has involved the ear flap? Possibilities are a fight with a cat, or being caught in a thorn bush. Have the regular checks of the dog's ears indicated any signs of otitis externa?

Damage to the area of the brain controlling balance

Signs:	Unsteady gait, circling towards the affected side, involuntary movement of the eyes from side to side.
Possible Causes:	After-effects of epileptic fit. In this case the dog will return to normal within a few hours. Otitis externa leading to otitis media. Possibly poisoning, also brain damage due to trauma, or neoplasia (growths and tumours).

Action: Get a veterinary surgeon as soon as possible to diagnose the cause.

HISTORY TIP: It is important to recall any unusual behaviour or accident within the recent past.

---

16. What if my dog is breathing abnormally?

Dogs breathe through the nose when at rest, but through the mouth when running. Panting enables the dog to loose heat from the tongue and the lungs.

Deep compulsive panting when at rest is a sign of nervous apprehension, e.g. in a veterinary waiting room, or pain in the abdominal area.

Pregnant bitches may pant for up to 12 hours in the first stage of labour. Abnormal breathing is also associated with five important emergency situations.

- **Gastric Dilation and Torsion** — See "What if" No. 33.
- **Heat Stroke** — See First Aid section, **page 181.**
- **Airway obstruction** — See First Aid section, **page 180.**

- **Eclampsia** (Lactation Tetany)
  This condition occurs in bitches, occasionally in late pregnancy, but most frequently during lactation when the puppies are making heavy demands on the bitch.
  Signs: Anxiety, hiding from light, leaving puppies, uncharacteristic behaviour, stiffness, muscular pain, panting, collapse.
  Cause: Abnormally low calcium level in the blood stream. This can occur even if apparently adequate amounts of calcium are being given by mouth.
  Action: Contact veterinary surgeon immediately, day or night, as collapse, leading to death, can occur if the bitch is not treated immediately.
- **Chest Injury**
  Signs: Sudden onset, distress, cuts and bruises, shock, weakness, pain.
  Cause: A fall, road traffic accident, or fight with a larger dog.
  Action: Gentle transport to veterinary surgery.

Other types of **Abnormal Breathing** are:

Sign	Possible Cause(s)	Action
Snorting, reverse sneezing Very noisy snorting and inability to breathe properly, often occurring when the dog is first let out of the house or taken for a walk.	Believed to be brought about by a temporary spasm of the throat muscles possibly caused by excitement or sudden encounter with cold air.	None needed beyond soothing the dog, as the spasm soon passes and the dog returns to breathing normally. No treatment is required.

90

Sign	Possible cause(s)	Action
Roaring Occurs when the normal airway is obstructed and is seen most frequently in short-faced dogs but may occur in other breeds.	Elongated soft palate in shortfaced dogs may block the airway especially when they are being exercised in hot weather. In other breeds, collapse of the larynx can cause obstruction to the airway.	Veterinary consultation and diagnosis. Remedial surgery is often possible. A minor form of roaring will occur sometimes when dogs lean their heads on someone's knee or the arm of a chair. No action is required in such cases.
Shallow Breathing The inspired breath is not deep enough to expand the rib cage. Signs of distress and collapse are also usually present.	Pain on taking a deep breath, due to pneumonia, or fracture of the ribs after a fall or road accident.	Careful removal to veterinary surgery.
Wheezing Wheezy breathing possibly since birth and accompanied by exercise intolerance. The puppy may fail to eat and grow properly.	In short-faced breeds, collapse of cartilage tissue in the nose and narrowing of nostrils restricts air intake.	Veterinary consultation at once, as remedial surgery should be performed as early as possible.
Rapid Breathing A dog normally breathes at between 10 and 30 times a minute when at rest. Fast shallow breathing indicates something is wrong.	Pain, stress, fever, shock, heat stroke, haemorrhage, dehydration, poisoning.	Veterinary consultation.

HISTORY TIP: In all causes of abnormal breathing it is helpful to know if the onset of the sign has been a gradual (over four to six weeks) or a sudden occurrence. Was the abnormal breathing pattern seen at first only after exercise? Does it happen even when the dog is resting? Has the dog been involved in any accident or trauma?
Note: with all breathing problems it is better to seek veterinary advice early than regret it later.

17. What if my dog is shedding hair?

All dogs, with the exception of Poodles and Bedlington Terriers, shed dead hair from the coat. Sometimes the shedding is seasonal, but some heavy coated dogs which originated in a cold climate, for instance Labradors, shed all the year round if they are kept in a warm house. When a dog has started to moult, it is best to give it a thorough grooming out of doors to remove all the dead coat and allow the new hair to grow.
Other causes of hair loss are:

Post whelping and lactation in some bitches.
Cause: The cause of hair loss in these cases is simply the heavy demand made by the puppies on the bitch.
Action: Worming, to remove any internal parasites that may be present, and early weaning will help reduce hair loss and speed recovery to normal. Consult veterinary surgeon about vitamin supplementation.

Post infection/Chronic infections. Diseases that affect the digestive system so that nutrients cannot be absorbed properly can cause hair loss. Frequently the coat does not grow normally for weeks or months after such an illness. Hair loss is often associated with chronic debilitating diseases. Consult a veterinary surgeon about the need for a more easily digested diet and vitamin mineral supplementation.

Old Age. A generalised hair loss is to be expected in extreme old age, as well as greying or whitening of coat colour, beginning on the muzzle and gradually extending right through the coat.

Poor Diet. Dogs which have acute digestive problems, allergies, or which have been kept on a poor or unsuitable diet may show a sparse, harsh, dry coat. This will improve when the cause is remedied.

> **HISTORY TIP:** A photograph of the dog when in full coat may be of help to the veterinary surgeon when estimating the amount of hair loss.

18. What if my dog is going bald?

Symmetrical Bilateral Baldness is sometimes seen in older spayed bitches, particularly Boxers and Dachshunds. Typically, identical shaped bald patches appear on each flank. The cause of the condition is probably a hormone imbalance. Your veterinary surgeon will be able to help.

A more generalised progressive baldness may be associated with hormone deficiencies in entire animals, e.g. a lack of thyroid hormone. A veterinary consultation is certainly worthwhile as sometimes a few tablets daily will work miracles.

A few patches of baldness and dry skin situated on one area of the coat, typically on the spinal area, may be the result of an old scald or burn which was undetected at the time. It could also have been caused by some local skin infection or parasite infestation. Such areas should be observed closely and, unless they are showing signs of healing and new hair growth, veterinary advice should be sought so that the most appropriate medication can be given.

Large dogs often develop bare patches on their hocks and elbows through lying on hard surfaces. Your veterinary surgeon will give you some cream to help keep the skin supple but the dog should also, of course, be provided with soft areas on which to lie.

NOTE: *Chronic Demodectic Mange* may cause baldness in patches, particularly on the hocks and elbows. It is important not to let these lesions become chronic or erupt generally. Seek early veterinary help.

19. What if my dog is scratching?

Dogs, like humans, scratch because they itch. The nerve endings which transmit the itch sensation lie close to the surface of the skin. When the dog scratches the nerve receptors are damaged and no longer react. The mild pain which results is better tolerated than an irritation. A dog's strong nails and vigorous scratching action can cause considerable damage and open the way for bacteria to invade the broken skin, complicating the condition seriously.

Persistent scratching should not be allowed to continue. The main cause is parasites in the coat biting, sucking and causing damage to the skin. The most common parasites are fleas, lice, cheyletiella (the rabbit fur mite) and sarcoptic mange mites. Sometimes the cause is easily detected and can be treated simply but, if scratching persists, seek veterinary help. It is often cheaper in the long run to buy an effective anti-parasite treatment from the veterinary surgery. It is important to treat all other animals within the household with an appropriate remedy and also to take action to eradicate parasites from the dog's bed and the rest of the house.

Other causes of scratching include inflammatory conditions of the skin, caused principally by allergies or bacterial infections.

> **HISTORY TIP:** It will be helpful if you are able to decide if the scratching is becoming a compulsive behaviour. Will the dog stop scratching if you order it to do so? Does it scratch at only one area of its body or more generally? Is the scratching more intense at any particular time of day, in any particular surroundings, or when the dog is hot or cold? Is the scratching getting progressively more frequent and intense.?

20. What if my dog keeps breaking wind?

Breaking wind, stomach rumbles (Borborygmus), and flatulence are not usually associated with any specific major disease, and seldom seem to trouble the dog, although often cause considerable social embarrassment to the owner. Some possible simple causes are listed in the table below.

Possible causes	Comment	Action
Unsuitable diet	Some dogs cannot 'tolerate diets based on soya or other beans.	Take advice on a more easily digested diet.
Sudden diet change	The bacteria in the intestine need time to adjust when a radical diet change takes place, e.g. from a complete cereal diet to meat and biscuits.	Change diets gradually over 3 weeks.
Feeding household left-overs	Highly seasoned and spiced foods create digestive problems in dogs.	Avoid feeding spiced foods.
Scavenging	Dogs are attracted to the smell of decaying flesh and will eat putrid carcasses.	Keep the dog under stricter control.

Possible causes	Comment	Action
Constipation	Low fibre diets will contain very little residue, and faeces may be difficult to pass.	The addition of 10% bran to the diet will help.
Old Age	Lack of muscle tone in the digestive tract and a reduced ability to digest protein fat and carbohydrate.	Try giving 4 small easily digested meals a day. Your veterinary surgeon may advise you to use a diet specially formulated for elderly dogs.
Pregnancy	The digestive organs may be displaced and cramped by the full uterus.	Charcoal granules on the food or charcoal biscuits may help.
Enforced inactivity	A bitch nursing a litter or a dog on cage rest while recovering from injury inevitably lacks exercise.	Give 4-6 small meals a day plus a human digestive remedy such as Bisodol, Asilone or Milk of Magnesia tablets. Give one-quarter to a whole child's dose according to size of dog.

Breaking wind and flatulence may also be associated with *Pancreatic Deficiency*, see page 235 and other general digestive upsets.

HISTORY TIP: Experiment by giving the dog's largest meal earlier in the day. Change from dry to soaked biscuit, or vice-versa, or to boiled rice or bread as the carbohydrate element of the food, in an attempt to reduce fermentation in the intestine. Make only one change at a time and continue with that regime for two weeks. Observe the dog closely — does the flatulence seem to be causing any pain? If it still proves necessary to visit the veterinary surgeon, report the dietary changes you have made and the results.

21. What if my dog has noisy abdominal sounds?

It is not uncommon for adult dogs to have an episode of making audible internal rumblings, possibly accompanied by refusal to eat, gulping and sometimes vomiting of small amounts of bile and saliva. The most likely causes are digestive problems of unknown origin, possibly due to stress, over-eating, eating too rapidly or eating rubbish.

Treatment with children's antacid remedies will usually restore the dog to normal within a few hours. When calculating the dose to give, allow for the dog size in comparison to a child. If episodes occur more often than once in 14 days, or if digestive remedies fail to improve the situation, or if the dog shows signs of pain, seek veterinary advice.

22. What if my dog is biting its tail, scooting or rubbing its bottom on the ground?

This behaviour is common in dogs and it is almost always due to anal gland problems. The popular notion that worm infestation causes irritation around the anus is generally unfounded.

The anal glands situated on either side of the anus, should empty every time faeces are passed, depositing their contents on the faeces as a scent marker. This was useful to the wild or wandering dog, but is largely obsolete for the household pet. A diet containing more bulk may serve to make the anal glands empty more regularly.

Anal glands which become overfull and are not relieved may abscess and burst, causing a malodorous wound. This condition can be prevented by having the glands emptied periodically at the veterinary surgery. In skilled hands this service is quickly performed and needs no anaesthetic.

Other conditions which may cause a dog to bite at its hind end include:

Condition	Comment
Anal Furunculosis — Sore skin around the anus with open wounds discharging pus, originating from infected anal glands.	Almost exclusive to German Shepherd Dogs (Alsatians) and Belgian Shepherd Dogs. The anal glands can be removed surgically if trouble persists.
Anal Adenomata — Lumps (benign tumours) around the anus.	The surface of the tumour can become raw and ulcerated through pressure and contact with the ground. Seek veterinary advice at once as the area is unlikely to heal naturally.
Sore end to docked tail — Raw or calloused tail end.	The condition is caused by a lack of protective skin and hair to cover docked stump. The situation can develop into a chronic sore which can give discomfort and even alter the dog's temperament. It may be necessary for the tail to be redocked under anaesthetic if the condition does not respond to local medication.
Tail chasing — which seems to have no physical cause.	May be an attention-attracting behaviour, or a nervous aberration.

> **HISTORY TIP:** Try to observe how often scooting occurs. Is it a major behaviour pattern throughout the dog's day, or does it only occur after defaecation? Is scooting compulsive or will the dog stop when commanded to do so?

23. What if my dog has diarrhoea?

Diarrhoea is defined as the more frequent passage of liquid faeces. It is always worthwhile taking note of the frequency with which your dog passes faeces and their consistency, type and amount, so as to be aware of any changes from normal. If a change is seen, close observation should be kept on the dog for other signs of disease, as diarrhoea is a common indication of many illnesses, some relatively trivial, but some of a serious nature.

Amount of faeces passed by normal dogs

Normal faeces contain the elements of food not used by the body, together with digestive juices, bacteria and the discarded cells of the gut lining.

A dog which is not eating at all will still produce a small amount of faeces from body waste.

Average amounts of faeces produced daily: Miniature Dachs   70 gr.
Beagle   190 gr.
Newfoundland   500 gr.

These amounts will be doubled if complete dry diets are fed.

It is normal for an adult dog to pass faeces one to four times daily, and puppies defaecate two to six times daily.

Colour of normal faeces

The colour of faeces is affected by the type of food being consumed. The faeces will be pale when white meat is fed, dark if raw meat is given and dark red when the dog has eaten commercially prepared food.

Digested blood from the throat, stomach or small intestine produces a black stool. There may be streaks of fresh red blood on the faeces, in conditions where the lower bowel is damaged. Where as much as a teaspoonful of fresh red blood is passed with faeces, the veterinary surgeon should be consulted by telephone immediately as this sign is associated with the major canine diseases of *Haemorraghic Gastroenteritis* and *Canine Parvovirus Infection;* it may also occur in some cases of poisoning.

Diarrhoea is most frequently caused by digestive problems. The bowel looseness is likely to cease when the food which started the problem is withdrawn or if dietary changes are made gradually.

First Aid treatment
- Withhold food for 12 hours to rest the intestines.
- Water must always be freely supplied; diarrhoea cannot be "dried up" by withholding water.
- Begin feeding again using cooked eggs, or fish, with plain boiled rice — fed in small quantities.

If diarrhoea persists, or if there are other signs of illness, contact a veterinary surgeon without delay, since it may be caused by bacterial or viral infection, or an enzyme deficiency. It may also be associated with an endoparasite infestation. Diarrhoea merits even earlier veterinary consultation in young puppies, as they quickly become dehydrated.

HISTORY TIP: When giving the history of the case it is important to distinguish between the types of loose stool.
Is the dog passing:
- a greater number of stools than normal, but they are of normal colour and consistency?
- a normal number of stools but very loose or accompanied by quantities of fluid?
- stools containing jelly-like mucus?
- foul-smelling, pale, bulky, fat-laden stools?
- very loose or watery stools, uncontrollably?
- blood stained stools: how much and what colour?

NOTE: It can be helpful to take to the veterinary surgeon a small quantity of freshly passed faeces for examination. Pack the sample in a small carefully washed yoghurt pot or similar container and label with your name and the date.

Other causes of diarrhoea may be:

Over-feeding in young puppies.

Feeding liver and offal in large quantities.

Too much milk — more than the equivalent of one pint to a Labrador. Some dogs may react to even very small quantities of milk.

Lack of fibre in the diet may cause diarrhoea and constipation alternately.

Raw eggs.
Sugar and honey.
Onions.
Currants, sultanas and raisins.
Nuts.
Carrots and broad beans.
Decaying or putrid food.
Scavenging.
Sudden dietary change.

NOTE: Bitches that eat large numbers of afterbirths when whelping may temporarily have diarrhoea.

It is worth noting that diarrhoea may be associated with stress, particularly in dogs with a nervous temperament. The bowel of the dog reacts quickly to shock, fear and stress, and diarrhoea and failure to gain weight in an otherwise healthy dog may be due to nervous causes.

The tension of dog shows and obedience competitions, bullying by humans or other dogs, re-homing, and even too great a desire to please the owner by instant obedience to demands, have been known to cause chronic diarrhoea in dogs.

Action: A peaceful, less demanding life without stressful episodes may be all that is required to effect a cure.

24. What if my dog is passing blood in its faeces?

Occasional, very slight streaks of fresh blood on the outside of the stool are likely to come from a small broken blood vessel around the anus and are unimportant provided the dog is otherwise well. If even this small amount of blood is seen persistently, veterinary advice should be sought. Any quantity of blood greater than a small fleck is a reason to seek veterinary advice urgently, even if the dog is otherwise well.

Polyps in the rectum are protruding growths which may accompany constipation or straining. They are common and may be the cause of blood stained faeces. Although they are unlikely to be malignant, a veterinary surgeon should be consulted about their removal.

> **HISTORY TIP:** Be prepared to estimate the quantity of blood passed, its frequency and colour, fresh red or dark digested blood. Note also the colour and consistency of faeces. It can be helpful if a typical sample of blood-stained faeces is taken to the veterinary surgery.

25. What if my dog is constipated?

Constipation (difficulty and pain caused by trying to pass small, hard lumps of faeces) is not uncommon, especially in toy breeds. Constipation can result from the simple causes listed in the table below and may be cured by the administration of a small dose of liquid paraffin and some other simple actions, making a visit to the veterinary surgery unnecessary. However, if constipation continues and/or the dog is obviously in pain then veterinary attention should be sought.

Some Common Simple Causes of Constipation

Cause	Comment
Low residue, all meat diet	Change the diet to contain some carbohydrate e.g. add biscuit or rusk plus 10 per cent bran.
Feeding bones	Fine bone chips can impact in the colon to cause cement-like faeces which are difficult and painful to pass. Bones are unnecessary and cause many problems so they are best omitted from the dog's diet. Chicken bones and other bones that can splinter or be eaten whole must on no account be given to dogs.
Feeding meat sawdust	This meat product, although cheap, contain, large quantities of very finely ground bone and is, therefore, not recommended. Very hard, white faeces result.
Dog left indoors all day	House-training may override the urge to defaecate. Dogs should have the opportunity to go outside every four hours at least, during the day time.
Travelling by car, and attending dog shows	Dogs may refuse to pass faeces if their eating pattern is upset, little exercise is given or the surroundings are unfamiliar.
Matted fur beneath the tail	Hair matted with faeces can block the anus, making the passage of faeces impossible. The surrounding skin also becomes very sore. Long-haired dogs should be groomed thoroughly and regularly especially around the anal area and, when necessary, the fur on the hindquarters should be washed and dried. If severe matting has already occurred it may be necessary to have the dog clipped at the veterinary surgery. In some cases an anaesthetic will be required so that the job can be properly accomplished.

Some other relatively common causes of constipation include:

Enlarged prostate gland in older male dogs. Dogs suffering from this condition will strain to pass faeces which are narrow and ribbon-like because the enlarged prostate bulges into the rectum blocking the passage of faeces. If these signs are seen in older dogs then veterinary help should be sought since if left the persistent straining may lead to a perineal hernia. Medication can help.

Stricture (narrowing of the rectum) is possibly congenital but, more often, is caused by straining to pass sharp objects like splinters of bone. Typically, in these cases, stools may be passed but only after considerable straining, and they may contain small amounts of fresh red blood. Seek veterinary advice without delay.

FIRST AID TIP: Where constipation is caused by the simple causes listed, like inappropriate feeding, confinement in house, inactivity or travelling, medicinal liquid paraffin may be given at the dose of one dessertspoonful for a 30lb dog. Giving too great a quantity is not harmful but the excess will probably leak from the anus and may soil the dog's fur and its bed.

NOTE: When it seems that a dog or puppy is failing to pass any faeces, consider whether it may in fact not be constipated but consuming its own stools, or whether a companion dog may be doing this. See "What if" No. 26.

26. What if my dog is eating its own faeces? (Coprophagy)

Eating the faeces of other animals, especially horse and cattle manure, is a natural animal behaviour which is, however, quite unacceptable in the companion dog. Not uncommonly the desire to eat animal manure extends to the dog eating its own faeces. It is a natural and normal behaviour in bitches to consume the faeces of their puppies until at least weaning time. Puppies will sometimes imitate the bitch in this behaviour, so it is essential to keep a sharp watch on them to ensure that this behaviour never starts, as it can be difficult to cure. In this condition especially, prevention is better than cure.

As a first step the dog's diet should be checked to see that it is receiving sufficient amounts of the essential nutrients, especially vitamins. If necessary, relevant adjustments should be made but care should be taken not to overdose with vitamins and minerals, otherwise problems could arise.

Faeces deposited in the garden should be picked up and disposed of promptly. This is far more effective than sprinkling the faeces with pepper, disinfectant powder, etc. The dog should be called away from faeces passed while on walks, and should be prevented from eating other animal manure as far as possible.

Coprophagy is often associated with boredom, when dogs are shut into a small run for a long time, and may also occur when the dog is left alone in the house. It has been noticed that some types of food seem to encourage the behaviour, while feeding a complete dry diet may make the faeces less attractive.

If the habit has become established the behaviour control methods, described in Chapter 3, should be used to cure this most undesirable trait.

NOTE: If other signs of illness, such as diarrhoea or compulsive eating, occur it is wise to seek veterinary help initially before taking the actions mentioned above.

> **HISTORY TIP:** Be prepared to describe to the veterinary surgeon exactly how the dog is fed and how it spends its day. Take a fresh faeces sample to the surgery with you.

27. What if my dog is not passing urine, or is straining to pass small amounts frequently?

It is important to distinguish between straining to pass urine and constipation; the straddle-legged stance adopted by bitches for both acts can appear similar. Not passing urine may be a voluntary decision on the dog's part. Bitches in particular are capable of withholding urine for as much as 24 hours when off their home territory but, if they are given as much opportunity as possible to use a ground surface similar to the one they use at home, they will usually oblige in the end.

It is useful, as an extension of house-training, to train dogs and bitches to urinate at the sound of an undulating whistle, or in response to some special word. Long confinement in a car or a crate can inhibit both sexes from passing urine when they do get the chance, but patience on the part of the owner will eventually get results.

In all other circumstances, failure to pass urine, or difficulty in doing so, is always a serious emergency and must certainly not be neglected if it continues for more than 24 hours. Be prepared to consult your veterinary surgeon earlier if other signs are present. The pain of a full bladder which cannot be emptied is agonising.

> **HISTORY TIP:** Normal urine is yellow and clear, but certain drugs can alter the colour. Check with your veterinary surgeon if you notice any change in colour or smell of the dog's urine when on medication. If any urine is passed at all it is helpful to take a sample to the surgery at the time of consultation.

28. What if my dog is incontinent?

A distinction must be made between the puppy or adult which is not successfully house-trained and true incontinence, which is the dripping or dribbling of urine without the dog being aware of it. It is rare that a dog cannot be house-trained, but in some individuals it has proved impossible. For example, older dogs which have lived in kennels all their lives can be very difficult to adjust to life in a house and this applies particularly to Beagles and Fox Hounds which are surplus to pack requirements and are offered as pets.

Territory marking in the male dog and bitches on heat should not be confused with incontinence. During illness, and in extreme old age, overnight incontinence should not be unexpected. Such dogs can be kept clean and comfortable by making up a bed on a sheet of plastic, topped with thickly spread newspaper over which is laid a polyester fur rug which allows urine to pass through rather than making the rug wet.

Arthritic dogs may also have difficulty in rising from bed to urinate, especially first thing in the morning.

One of the most troublesome demonstrations of incontinence is the very submissive bitch which dribbles urine when excited or when greeting people. See Chapter 1 Part II.

Incontinence is not an uncommon sequel to ovariohysterectomy (spaying), particularly in large bitches, and when the operation is performed in middle age. The condition can often by treated satisfactorily by giving hormone medication; your veterinary surgeon will advise.

Incontinence in young puppies may be associated with a congenital defect in the urinary system which can often be corrected surgically. If your puppy drips urine constantly day and night, seek veterinary help promptly.

Incontinence is also associated with paralysis and with *Cystitis*.

Any disease which causes excessive drinking will also lead to the more frequent passage of urine, see "What if" No. 6.

Incontinence is not in itself a serious sign since there are many simple causes. However, if other signs are present, or if the dog shows signs of discomfort or pain on passing urine, or if the urine contains blood, it is wise to seek veterinary help without delay.

> **HISTORY TIP:** It is helpful to know if incontinence occurs every night, and/or during the day. Does urine dribble away all the time, or is the entire content of the bladder voided at long intervals? Can you relate any external circumstances to episodes of incontinence?
>
> Ask in advance at the surgery for a sterile container, so that you can take a fresh urine sample with you to the consultation, otherwise sterilise a small, well-washed bottle by boiling in water for five minutes, and allow to drain.

29. What if my dog is passing blood in its urine?

It is normal for a bitch on heat or a newly whelped bitch to have a blood-stained discharge from the vulva which will blend with the urine. In any other circumstances blood in the urine is a serious sign, so a veterinary surgeon should be consulted as soon as possible. It is helpful and saves time to take a urine sample with you, as it is often very difficult to persuade a dog or bitch to pass urine on the surgery premises.

> **HISTORY TIP:** Note:
> 1. Whether blood is present in the urine every time the bitch urinates.
> 2. Try to observe if blood is present in the first or last amounts of urine to be passed, or whether it is generally mixed with the urine.
> 3. Check whether the dog is having difficulty passing urine and whether urination is accompanied by pain before, during or after water is passed.

Blood in the urine is often associated with the following major diseases: *Cystitis, Leptospirosis, Warfarin Poisoning* (see index).

Other possible causes include: Growths and tumours in the urinary or genital tract (these are rare), injury to urinary or genital tract following trauma, most frequently a road traffic accident and stones (calculi) in the bladder.

30. What if my dog has a discharge from its penis or vulva? (or licks excessively at its genitals?)

It is normal for male dogs to have a small amount of whitish, mucoid discharge from the prepuce, and bitch puppies also often have a drop of mucus at the vulva.

It is normal dog behaviour for both sexes to pay attention to cleaning the genital area. Bitches coming into season will pay extra attention to the vulva, and they will also do this after whelping. Male dogs may lick their genitals more frequently after mating.

An excessive amount of discharge, a foul-smelling emission, the presence of lesions on the genitals, or an obsession with licking them is abnormal and such dogs should be taken to a veterinary surgeon so that the cause can be diagnosed. A cause of this behaviour, which can be dealt with at home, is failure of the penis to retract into its sheath after mating.

Action: Bathe the penis with cold water, lubricate it with Vaseline, handcream or the like and pull the sheath gently forward over the tip of the penis as it decreases in size. If the condition persists, seek veterinary help. Avoid over-enthusiastic use of disinfectants after mating.

NOTE: A copious discharge from the vulva also occurs in cases of open *Pyometra*, see page 48. If a bitch has a severe foul smelling discharge a few weeks after she has been in season seek veterinary help immediately.

HISTORY TIP: Dogs — It is important to relate the appearance of the sign to the last time the dog was used at stud. Before stating that the dog has never mated a bitch, consider if there is any possibility that the dog has escaped and had an opportunity for mating. It may be necessary to question other people who may have had charge of the dog within the past few months.

Bitches — The veterinary surgeon will want to know the date of the bitch's last season, if the season was normal, and if dogs are still paying the bitch attention.

---

31. What if my dog is mismated?
See Chapter 2 — The Bitch.

32. What if my dog is found to be pregnant unexpectedly?
See Chapter 2 — The Bitch.

33. What if my dog is pot-bellied?
It is normal for young puppies to show considerable abdominal distension after eating, but if the expansion is gross, consideration should be given to spreading the food intake over more but smaller meals. Adult dogs may also benefit from being fed two or more smaller meals a day, especially when high bulk, complete dry diets are used.

A pot-bellied puppy which is thin on the shoulders and hindquarters, with poor coat, is probably suffering from an overburden of *worms*, see section on Endoparasites, Chapter 4 Part II.

The most serious cause of abdominal enlargement is:

Gastric Dilation and Torsion (bloat)
This is a sudden enlargement of the stomach which is usually full of fermenting food and gas. The condition is complicated when the stomach twists, blocking both the entrance from the throat and the exit to the small intestine. Dogs of 40lb weight and upwards are most usually affected.
Signs: A sudden and noticeable enlargement of the abdomen, usually soon after eating. The stomach rapidly becomes grossly swollen and hard with a distension which is easily observed as it takes place very quickly. The dog is in great pain and distress, and has difficulty in breathing. There may be an attempt to vomit and pass faeces, but when torsion (twisting) has taken place nothing can pass.

Cause: No definitive cause has been found. Suspicion has fallen on violent exercise after feeding, copious drinking on top of dry meals, blockage of the stomach exit by indigestible material, excess fermentation in the stomach and overloading the stomach with one large meal.

Action: **This is one of the true veterinary emergencies.** Releasing the gas and emptying the stomach by mechanical means is imperative as this condition can be fatal within a very short time. Make contact with a veterinary surgeon at once, day or night, and be prepared to drive the dog to the surgery immediately.

Other causes of pot-bellied appearance which are not due to overfeeding are pregnancy and false pregnancy, *Pyometra* (pus in the uterus), some hormone disorders, and other major abdominal diseases which are accompanied by fluid retention (see Chapter 2, The Bitch). If in doubt seek veterinary attention.

HISTORY TIP. *Worms*   Take a fresh faeces sample with you to the surgery if you suspect the condition is due to worms in a puppy or young dog.
Bloat — When a dog is frequently subject to painful gross enlargement after meals, it is helpful to keep a record of the normal post-feeding enlargement, by measuring round the widest part of the abdomen with a tape-measure. It is then easier to assess whether the dog is enlarging more than normal and is in danger of bloating, so that rapid action to get veterinary help may be taken when needed.

---

34. What if my dog is limping?

Dogs limp because of pain or a "mechanical" problem in the leg. It is not always easy to find out which leg is causing pain but it helps to watch the dog moving across in front of you, as well as coming towards and going away from you.

A dog may often take the weight off the injured leg when standing still and, when moving, may nod or drop the head as the weight goes on to the sound foreleg. Similarly, the hindquarters will be dropped when the sound hindleg is placed on the ground. If a dog is holding its leg off the ground the problem is most likely to be in the foot. If it places its foot gently to the ground or drags the leg, the injury is likely to be higher up.

Very often an acute limp is easily diagnosed and can be cured by first aid. Look at the foot to detect impaled thorns, stone chippings, balls of tar, or snow wedged between the pads, which are common causes of limping in dogs.

Examine the rest of the leg for signs of injury, such as swelling, deformity, pain, loss of function or a break in the skin. In most cases it is sensible to seek veterinary advice promptly but if the dog is otherwise well, is eating, and the pain is not severe, then such an action can be delayed for 24 hours. It will be helpful to your veterinary surgeon if you have already managed to identify the painful area or locate some injury.

Other causes of limping may be:

Arthritis

Cause: Inflammation of a joint which may be caused by infection, a previous injury, or hereditary joint deformity.

Signs: Chronic pain, difficulty in rising from bed, reluctance to walk, but may ease after some movements are made.

Action: Many new products are available to veterinary surgeons which can ease the pain, but continual medication may be needed. In some cases, surgery may be required.

Bone Fractures

Cause: Usually the result of road traffic accidents or falls.

Signs: Severe pain of sudden onset; inability to put weight on the leg which may be visibly deformed.

Action: Contact a veterinary surgeon quickly for diagnosis and fixation of the fracture. Repair is usually good. See Chapter 6 for advice on care and transport to the surgery.

Dislocations

Cause: The displacement through accidental injury of one or more bones which form a joint.

Signs: Sudden onset of pain; limb cannot be used and may be noticeably different in length from the sound leg.

Action: Veterinary consultation at once as there may be internal bleeding or an associated fracture. Generally, correction of a dislocation is more likely to be successful if it is carried out without delay.

Sprains

Cause: Damage to a ligament or tendon by being overstretched or torn through wrenching or twisting.

Signs: Sudden pain occurring while running or playing, followed by inability to use the leg; swelling and tenderness when the area is touched. There may be swelling around the injury. The most common joints to be affected are the shoulder, the stifle, the carpus or the tarsus.

Action: Put a cold compress on the leg to reduce the swelling and pain. A prompt veterinary consultation is necessary to assess the extent of the damage and commence treatment.

Strains

Cause: Damage to the muscles. Muscles are most often torn or damaged by a sudden wrench or twisting movement, particularly in racing dogs.

Signs: Usually a sudden pain while running followed by swelling and loss of power.

Action: Complete rest of the limb and prompt veterinary advice for differential diagnosis and further treatment.

Interdigital Cysts (painful inflamed swellings between the toes)

Cause: Some dogs are subject to a succession of these cysts. The cause is thought to lie in the sweat glands in the foot. The cysts may become infected by bacteria and may contain grass seeds.

Signs: Lameness; red swollen area between the toes on the upper side of the paw.

Action: Veterinary consultation for immediate treatment and future prevention, which may involve long term treatment with antibiotics.

35. What if my dog is coughing?

It is normal for a dog to cough occasionally, particularly after a bout of barking, or after vigorous play. Any dog which suddenly begins to cough persistently should be segregated from other dogs, kept very quiet, and taken to the veterinary surgeon promptly. Even if the cough is occasional and not severe, if it persists for more than a week the cause should be investigated.

> **HISTORY TIP:** Do not take a coughing dog into the waiting room at the veterinary surgery, as many coughs are infectious. Telephone for a special appointment or leave the dog in your car and ask the receptionist's advice on what to do next.

Coughing is associated with the following major diseases and conditions (see Index of Diseases and Conditions):

1 Canine Distemper
2 Kennel Cough
3 Heart Disease
4 Respiratory Disease
5 Endoparasite Infection (worms)
6 Poisoning (Warfarin and Paraquat)

Other possible causes include:

Condition	Signs	Action	Comment
Breathing in of Irritants (fine dust, paint fumes, aerosol sprays)	Rapid and exaggerated breathing, watering eyes, depression.	Telephone veterinary surgeon for advice on first aid treatment.	Prevention is much better than cure.
Injury to Chest	Rapid breathing, bruising or pain over the ribs.	Seek veterinary help without delay.	Many road accidents cause some degree of lung haemorrhage.
Pharyngitis, Laryngitis and Tonsillitis	Depression, fever, loss of appetite, coughing and retching.	Prompt veterinary consultation as this condition responds well to treatment	It is as well to remember that *Tonsillitis* is often an early sign of a major infectious disease and it should not be treated lightly. Some breeds of dog seem especially susceptible to recurrent bouts of *Tonsillitis.*

36. What if my dog is eating with difficulty?

Decaying teeth and gum disease are common causes of difficulty in eating. The study and practice of veterinary dentistry is enlarging all the time and

much can be done to avoid discomfort and preserve the teeth without the need for extraction. Missing teeth prevent dogs getting show prizes. Seek veterinary advice promptly.
Other causes of difficulty in eating include:

Neoplasia (growth and tumours in the mouth)
Signs: Visible swellings around flews and gum line, offensive breath.
Action: Veterinary consultation as soon as possible with a view to removal of the growth. Treatment can be very successful.

Foreign Body Lodged in Mouth
Signs: Sudden onset of foul breath, gagging, retching, drooling or foaming at the mouth; pawing and rubbing the mouth.
Cause: Typically, a piece of bone or stick lodged across the roof of the mouth, between the upper carnassial teeth; cotton or wire wound around the teeth.
Action: It is best not to persist in trying to remove the obstruction, if it does not come away easily, but to take the dog to the veterinary surgery. A local anaesthetic or sedative may be needed while the obstruction is removed.

37. What if my dog has bad breath?

Mild cases of *Halitosis* (bad breath) are often associated with what the dog eats. For example, a large quantity of fish meal incorporated in a complete dry diet will give a characteristic fishy smell. Scavenging, and the eating of horse or rabbit droppings (see also Coprophagy, "What if" No. 26) will also render the breath unpleasant.
    Where the odour is persistent and very noticeable, it is wise to have the dog examined by a veterinary surgeon.
Other possible causes of bad breath include:

Periodontal Disease
Cause: Inflammation of gums associated with the accumulation of tartar deposit. This is by far the most common cause of loss of teeth in dogs.
Comment: Common in old age.
Action: Regular visits to the veterinary surgery for scaling can be enormously beneficial for the dog's health and comfort. Feeding hard crunchy food can help prevent the condition occurring.

Foreign body lodged in mouth
See "What if" No. 36.

Tooth decay
Signs: Difficulty in eating. Possible swelling and abcess formations over the root of the tooth. The upper carnassial tooth is most often affected and leads to a swelling in the cheek, often called a facial abcess, just below and in front of the eye. This can burst leaving a discharging painful sinus.
Comment: Tooth decay is most common in the toy breeds, and some may have lost nearly all their teeth by the time they are four years old. Such dogs can usually deal with hard foods despite having no teeth.
Action: While it is sometimes possible to fill or replace teeth which are

decayed it is hardly practical, and painful teeth are usually extracted, under anaesthetic by the veterinary surgeon.

Other possible causes:
Bad breath may be associated with the following major diseases: kidney disease and liver disease.

38. What if my dog is having fits, convulsions or is twitching?

It is normal for newly born puppies to twitch frequently when resting and older dogs may twitch and whimper during their sleep while dreaming. These twitching episodes are very different from a true fit or convulsion. A fit is a convulsive seizure, occurring typically while the dog is relaxed or asleep and never while the dog is active. The first fit which an owner observes usually occurs when a dog is between one to three years of age. A fit usually begins with a period of rigidity (tonic phase) which is followed by shaking and spasm of the muscles, which progresses to involuntary paddling with the paws (clonic phase). There may be involuntary passing of faeces and urine. The fit may last only a minute or two and the dog may recover quickly and appear perfectly normal. In other cases the fit may be more prolonged and the dog may appear dazed and disorientated for some hours after the convulsions have stopped. Sight seems to be the last sense to return fully. Dogs often eat ravenously after a fit. In severe episodes, one fit may lead very quickly to several more. Although it is unlikely that the dog will harm humans or itself while in a fit, it is wise to be cautious. The type of first aid treatment given to human fit victims is inappropriate for dogs, and no attempt should be made to force anything into the dog's mouth.

While the fit lasts, do not touch the dog, but remove anything lying nearby which could cause it injury and gently move the dog by using a blanket if it is lying in a dangerous place such as the top of the stairs. Turn off radios and the T.V. and keep the room dark and quiet.

> **HISTORY TIP:** Make a note of the progress and duration of the fit and the circumstances which preceded it. **There is no point in asking the veterinary surgeon to make an urgent visit to the dog,** as it will almost certainly be normal by the time help is obtained. Once the dog is out of the fit, report to the veterinary surgeon on the telephone. It will probably be wise not to attempt to make a surgery call the same day, as the dog is best kept quiet for some hours following a fit.

Puppies may react to severe pain, especially of an abdominal nature, by having convulsions. Veterinary diagnosis and treatment of the underlying cause will be needed.

Epilepsy, often showing for the first time at around two years old, is a relatively common condition in dogs, but this condition can often be controlled by medication so that the dog lives to a full lifespan. Since fits may sometimes be associated with brain tumours, previous traumas, inherited conditions such as *Hydocephalus* (water on the brain), *Canine*

Distemper and *Liver Disease*, always seek veterinary attention since an accurate diagnosis of the cause is essential before any medication is given.

Rabies. In other countries, a dog having a fit would have to be considered a possible rabies case, but this is extremely unlikely to be the case in Britain, unless the dog has only recently been released from a quarantine kennel, or has been bitten by a dog or cat which has been illegally smuggled into this country. If you have any suspicion that this may be so, tell your veterinary surgeon so that he can report the matter to the Ministry of Agriculture, Fisheries and Food, Rabies Division, immediately. Even if your fears may be unfounded, where this deadly disease is concerned it is better to err on the safe side.

> **HISTORY TIP:** It will be helpful to the veterinary surgeon if you can recall any traumatic incident in the dog's life, e.g. a fall, being dropped or hit by a car, which may have caused brain damage not perceived at the time. The breeder may also be able to contribute some information on the dog's early life and whether similar signs have been shown by related animals.

39. What if my dog has a lump or swelling?

Any lumps or swellings which do not disappear within a few days should be investigated by a veterinary surgeon. This is particularly important for the early recognition of abcesses and to identify tumours early in their development. It is common for the large breeds to develop swellings on their elbows or hocks; the risk of this can be minimised by ensuring that the dog has an adequate number of soft areas where it can lie.

Types of swelling include:

Abcess

Cause: Swelling beneath the skin caused by bacterial infection. Often the result of a bite or puncture wound.

Signs: Pain, heat and swelling developing over a few days probably with subsequent bursting and discharge of pus. Abcesses may occur anywhere on the body.

Action: Contact the veterinary surgeon promptly as the condition may need surgical drainage and medication with antibiotics.

Puppy Head Gland Disease (Juvenile Pyoderma)

Cause: Thought to be a temporary failure of immune system. Occurs in puppies of many breeds under four months old.

Signs: Sudden painful gross swelling around eyes and on head, which may spread to the whole body. The swellings eventually burst and drain pus. The puppy may, surprisingly, remain otherwise well and reasonably cheerful.

Action: Veterinary advice immediately for appropriate medication. With careful nursing the puppy is likely to recover but there may be subsequent scarring.

Salivary Cyst
Signs: Sudden appearance of a large swelling under the tongue, and at the angle of the jaw causing drooling and sometimes displacing the tongue to one side of mouth so that it protrudes.
Action: Seek veterinary advice at once; surgery may be required.
Cysts
Sign: Smooth slow growing swelling under the skin, anywhere on the body.
Action: Urgent veterinary advice if the cyst ruptures or starts to bleed. Otherwise keep the cyst under observation for any changes.

Interdigital Cysts
Signs: Painful swellings between the toes.
           See "What if" No. 34.

Papillomas and Warts
Cause: Unknown but may be due to a virus infection. Often occurs on smooth-coated dogs.
Sign: Painless dark coloured projections from the skin (tags), usually small.
Action: Seek veterinary advice if the wart is increasing in size rapidly, otherwise, mention the wart at the next routine consultation.
Comment: A number of warts caused by a virus infection sometimes occurs in the mouths of young puppies.

Ulcers
Cause: Various.
Sign: A red, ulcerated area occurring on any part of the body.
Action: Seek veterinary advice without delay.

Haematoma (blood or fluid filled swelling)
Cause: The result of an injury to blood vessels, or to drainage of fluid post-operatively. The ear flap is a common site. See also "What if" No. 14.
Signs: Soft swelling and distortion of the area — sometimes painful, but not usually so to the touch.
Action: Consult your veterinary surgeon as surgical treatment may be required. A post-operative haematoma may require a support bandage which the veterinary surgeon will show you how to put on.

Tender area at an injection site
Cause: A local irritant reaction to a component in the injection.
Signs: Pain and swelling and possibly heat. If the injection has been given into a leg muscle, possibly lameness.
Action: Further treatment seldom required unless the dog is in a lot of pain but the matter should be reported to the veterinary surgeon.

Stings and insect bites.
Sign: Very sudden swelling which may be severe, and dangerous if the face and mouth is affected, especially in short-nosed breeds.
Action: See Chapter 6 but contact veterinary surgeon immediately if breathing or swallowing is impeded.

Bruising after injury
Sign: Pain and heat in the affected area which may also be grazed and
           bleeding.
Action: Seek veterinary advice if pain is severe.

Lumps and swellings may also be associated with urticaria and possibly
tumours, the most common being *Mammary Tumours* and *Testicular
Tumours* (see Index of Diseases and Conditions).

> **HISTORY TIP:** In the case of non-urgent lumps and swellings, make a
> note in the dog's record to remind you when the swelling
> was first noticed, where it is, and the size now (in
> centimetres measured with calipers). It is also a good idea
> to compare it in size and shape with a common object e.g.
> a golf ball, a coin etc. Subsequent measurements will
> provide vital information on the rate of enlargement, a
> possibly crucial factor in deciding whether surgery will
> be necessary.

40. What if my dog is wounded/cut/burnt/grazed?

See Chapter 6.

41. What if my dog is licking itself excessively?

Licking is part of the normal cleaning procedure in dogs, to clean dirt off
coat or paws, to clean a wound, or to remove excess secretions.

Bitches will lick the vulval area when coming into season and during
oestrus. Stud dogs lick their genitals after mating.

Many dogs will attend to wounds on their companion animals and will also
clean the vulval and rectal area on puppies.

If a dog is seen to be licking excessively at one area of the body, check
for some unsuspected injury, insect sting, or thorn embedded in the flesh.
Continual licking can cause additional damage to the skin and so should be
investigated. Excessive licking may be indicative of:

Lick Granuloma
Cause: Often a self inflicted injury through boredom, frustration or
           nervousness.
Sign: A sore, thickened, red area of skin on a place the dog can reach
           easily, often a paw (carpus).
Action: Veterinary advice for medication, as constant licking can lead to
           an intractable sore. Also re-think the dog's day and lifestyle to
           improve its outlook and provide more activity and interest.

42. What if my dog is weak and lethargic?

It is normal and sensible for short-faced dogs, elderly dogs and pregnant
bitches to be lethargic in hot weather, but general weakness and lethargy
accompany many serious illnesses. There will usually be other more
prominent signs, but if you feel that your dog is less active than it should
be, it is always wise to seek veterinary attention.

Lethargy and Obesity may be associated and be a consequence of each other — see Chapter 5 Part II.

Other causes of lethargy include:
Diabetes Mellitus
Anaemia
Heart Disease
Hypothyroidism
(See Index of Diseases and Conditions.)

A bitch which is experiencing a false pregnancy, see Chapter 2, will often appear to be lethargic, as she has the instinct to remain with her imaginary puppies.

> **HISTORY TIP:** Dogs can become acutely depressed when some element that they particularly value is removed from their lives. Where there are no other clinical signs of illness, try to relate this behaviour pattern to any deprivation of person, activity or location which is causing the dog to sulk or pine.

43. What if my dog has collapsed and is comatose?

The terminal stages of any serious illness or death from extreme old age will include collapse.

Any disease or condition which makes breathing difficult may cause a dog to collapse temporarily. Heat stroke, which frequently occurs when dogs are confined in stationary cars, causes collapse — see section on First Aid, Chapter 6.

Short-nosed dogs (Boxers, Pekes, Pugs, Bulldogs) taking violent exercise may faint through lack of oxygen. A few minutes rest, plus dousing the head with cold water will generally restore the dog to normal, but the rest of the walk should be controlled on the lead. It is wise to take the dog to the veterinary surgeon to be checked if the problem arises on more than one occasion.

When a dog which has been previously healthy, and is not stressed for air, collapses suddenly, ensure that mouth and nose are clear of discharges and obstructions, keep the dog warm, and seek veterinary advice urgently

A condition associated with Cavalier King Charles Spaniels causes them to spin round and collapse momentarily unconscious, usually while walking on the lead. No satisfactory explanation has been found, and the dogs usually recover quickly, but the episode is likely to be repeated.

Other causes of collapse include:

Hypoglycaemia (low blood sugar) causing malfunction of the central nervous system. The condition is seen most frequently in puppies of the toy breeds, or in hard-working gun dogs.
Cause: Irregular feeding times, distress, exhaustion.
Action: Feed something sweet at once, a Mars bar or the equivalent is ideal.

"Slipped Disc" (dislocation of the cushioning disc between the vertebrae). This condition occurs most frequently in short-legged, long-backed breeds, Dachshunds and Pekinese predominantly.

Sign: Intense pain, weakness and unsteadiness in the hind or all four limbs or absolute paralysis of hind limbs. Alternatively there may be no pain, but complete loss of all sensation and power below the injured area. There may also be loss of bladder control.

Action: Keep the dog still, transport the dog to the veterinary surgery on a flat board to avoid causing it pain.

Hypothermia. Following exposure to intense cold.

Action: Apply gentle warmth, keep the dog loosely covered, until you reach the veterinary surgery. Give warm milk if the dog is able to swallow, do *not* give brandy or other spirits.

Shock. Following road accident or serious haemorrhage.

Signs: Cold, limp, lifeless, with rapid shallow breathing. Lips and gums and eye rims (conjunctiva) very pale.

Action: Seek nearest veterinary surgeon immediately. Give nothing by mouth, cover the dog loosely and keep warm.

Collapse may also be associated with the following major diseases:
Diabetes Mellitus, particularly following an overdose of insulin
Heart Disease
Kidney Disease
Poisoning
(See Index of Diseases and Conditions for relevant page number.)

HISTORY TIP: Be prepared to tell the veterinary surgeon the exact circumstances surrounding the collapse, i.e. relationship to feeding time or exercise, any trauma which occurred, the dog's behaviour just before the collapse, and the time it took for the dog to return to normal.

---

44. What if my dog is in pain?

Some dogs, especially the Bull-breeds and Hounds, are very stoical about pain and although they may be badly injured or very ill they will give little, if any, indication of the site of the pain.

Other dogs, usually of the smaller breeds, can be very babyish and make a great fuss over a mild inconvenience, so it is important to know your own dog's character.

If a minor accident, such as stepping on a paw, appears to have caused pain which has not subsided within a few hours, seek veterinary advice.

Occasionally pain may appear generalised and difficult to locate. If pain is persistent, always seek veterinary diagnosis. Dogs may show signs of pain before other signs become apparent.

Where the location of the pain is obvious, e.g. in teeth, ears, abdomen or from an abcess, consult the relevant "What if".

Other causes of severe pain may be: **Arthritis, Canine Parvovirus, Cystitis, Haemorrhagic Gastroenteritis, Infectious Canine Hepatitis, Leptospirosis and Poisoning.** (See Index of Diseases and Conditions.)

Another cause of severe and sudden pain is Cramp (Myositis)
Cause: Inflammation of muscles, often following strenuous exercise
especially when a dog which has been hot becomes quickly chilled,
e.g. through jumping into cold water.
Signs: Acute pain, probably vocalisation at least once, muscle tremor.
Action: Protect dog from any danger, if in water take steps to bring it to
land. Massage of the affected limb, keep warm, rest. Consult the
veterinary surgeon if pain persists.

45. What if my dog is losing weight, or is looking thin?

Young adolescent dogs in the larger breeds often remain very thin, although
they are well fed. Dogs of this age, particularly where two are kept together,
often burn off all the food they are given through constant activity. This
is good and will help ward off obesity in middle age. It is better to make
no strenuous attempt to artificially fatten or cram a dog just to appease
criticism or in order to compete in the show ring, provided it only looks thin
and is not actually losing weight.

Male dogs will lose weight dramatically when they are close to a bitch in
season, and many dogs will lose weight in boarding kennels although they
appear to eat well. Nervous anxiety will lead to lost weight very rapidly and
the dog will not utilise its food intake properly until the cause of its distress
is removed.

Bitches may lose weight when feeding a large litter, as they cannot process
enough food through their bodies to maintain their own weight as well as
producing enough milk for the puppies. They will usually recover quite
quickly if they are given increased amounts of high quality food after the
puppies are weaned. Worming two to three times at three weekly intervals
after the puppies are weaned may help the bitch regain her normal weight.

If there is any doubt whether a dog is being fed sufficient food of good
nutritional quality, consult Chapter 5 Part I and/or seek veterinary help.

Where an adequate diet is provided and none of the above circumstances
apply, but the dog still loses weight, this is an indication that disease is
present. Since the cause of the weight loss may be obscure, and associated
with many major disorders, professional help should be sought.

> **HISTORY TIP:** Before going to the surgery, write out the dog's menu
> giving weighed quantities of all the food eaten and milk
> drunk. If you are using a commercially formulated food,
> take a package or label with you, so the veterinary
> surgeon may see the manufacturer's analysis of the
> contents. It can also be helpful to take fresh faeces and
> urine samples with you when you go to the surgery.

46. What if my dog is aggressive?

Aggression, even in the smallest dog, is always dangerous, as it is a
cumulative habit, and a dog which shows aggressive tendencies usually
becomes increasingly fierce, unless the cause can be found and some strategy
used to correct this fault. See Chapter 3.

47. What if my dog is not breathing?

Lay the animal flat on its side, open its mouth, pull the tongue forward and check that there is nothing obstructing the throat. See Chapter 6. Contact the veterinary surgeon urgently and take the dog to the surgery quickly if it is possible to do so.

48. What if my dog is staggering and wobbly on its legs?

During the recovery period from an anaesthetic, or during convalescence, hind leg weakness is to be expected, as it is in very old dogs.

During the recovery stage from a fit, gait may be uncertain and wobbly. In any other circumstances, lack of a firm and steady hind leg movement is abnormal and, as this sign may be associated with serious conditions, veterinary help should be sought promptly.

Other possible causes of staggering gait include:

Slipped Disc (disc protrusion). See "What if" No. 43.

Cerebral Haemorrhage (stroke, C.V.A.)
May occur in older dogs. This condition has been observed to occur more often in winter, and may be triggered by turning an old dog out into a very cold atmosphere.
Signs: Confusion, dilated pupils, lack of response to owner, head tilt, circling, sudden blindness. Any combination of these signs may appear suddenly, but may gradually improve.
Action: Veterinary advice as soon as possible to confirm diagnosis and as medication may be needed.

German Shepherd Syndrome
This breed in particular is associated with a condition of increasing weakness in the hind legs of older dogs, with a tendency to collapse when turning corners, and to drag the hind paws which may become grazed. Pain is not a sign in this condition. Consult the veterinary surgeon to obtain advice on how best to cope with the problem and to prevent secondary complications developing.

Wobbler Syndrome
Inherited or congenital damage to the vertebrae results in pressure on the spinal cord causing ataxia (a wobbly gait) and poor position sense in young animals. The Wobbler Syndrome is seen particularly in Great Danes and Dobermanns but other large breeds are also affected.

Consult a veterinary surgeon as soon as any signs are noticed, as rest and medication may bring about an improvement, although it is likely that eventually surgery may be necessary.

Hypertrophic Osteodystrophy (skeletal scurvy)
This is a complex condition that affects rapidly growing puppies of the larger breeds, and particularly Boxers, Dobermanns and Afghans.
Signs: Pain and swelling of the joints of the legs, staggering gait, unwillingness to walk, acute pain on being touched.
Cause: The cause of this condition is obscure and many different factors may be involved including relative lack of vitamin C and an excess of vitamin A. More recently the condition is being associated with

114

cramming growing puppies with food and with an excess of vitamins and minerals in an effort to put weight on what should naturally be a lean, lithe frame.

Action: Veterinary consultation promptly for accurate diagnosis, probably via X-ray, and medication to relieve pain. Subsequently a balanced and moderate diet must be devised and the pup allowed to grow normally.

> **HISTORY TIP:** Be prepared to lead the dog up and down for some time so that the veterinary surgeon may have the opportunity to observe the gait. Make a note of whether the staggering gait is consistently bad or whether the dog is better at some times of the day or before or after exercise. Be prepared to tell the veterinary surgeon about the onset of staggering — was it sudden or progressive?

49. What if my dog appears deaf?

Congenital deafness is often associated with white coat colouring, and is known to occur in Dalmatians, Bull Terriers, White Boxers, Cocker Spaniels, Border Collies and several small Terrier breeds.

Deafness in puppies does not become apparent until about five weeks of age, and breeders should test each puppy individually at this time. Deafness may not be recognised in situations where affected puppies can copy the actions of other litter members.

Congenital deafness cannot be treated and it is usual for affected puppies to be painlessly destroyed by a veterinary surgeon, as acute hearing is of vital importance to a dog for self-preservation, interaction with other dogs, and obedience to its owner's commands. It is no kindness to a dog to attempt to rear a deaf puppy and furthermore such dogs could be the cause of serious accidents involving people.

Elderly dogs often become progressively deaf, but as by this age they have learnt to comply with their owner's wishes, and they are not violently active, deafness is not such a handicap to them provided the owner bears their disability in mind. It is worth asking the veterinary surgeon's advice to check that there is no underlying disease causing the deafness and which could be treated.

Loss of hearing in adult dogs may be associated with growths in the ear canal, or disease of the various parts of the ear, so when there is any indication that the ears are being affected in any way it is important to seek advice promptly

An avoidable cause of progressive deafness may be:

Carbon Monoxide Poisoning

Cause: Inhalation of toxic fumes from solid fuel boilers, or from a leaking car exhaust system, causing a lack of oxygen to reach the lungs and blood stream.

Signs: Excessive sleepiness, bloodshot eyes or, in extreme cases, collapse with blue-tinged tongue and mucous membranes.

Carbon monoxide poisoning can occur at low level where a dog is kept at night in an airtight boiler room where the atmosphere is tainted by fumes from the boiler, and also where a dog is made to ride in a car boot, or on the floor, without adequate ventilation.

In an acute situation, carbon monoxide poisoning will kill a dog in a very short time.

Action: Acute situation: See Chapter 4 Part VI and 6.

Mild condition: Take steps to improve the dog's location in house and car and have boilers serviced regularly. The latter action will also of course avoid danger to humans.

> **HISTORY TIP:** Test the dog with an ultrasonic (silent) whistle and low frequency sounds to see if anything at all can be heard. Be prepared to say when you first noticed signs of deafness and whether you can associate this sign with any trauma or ear disease which may have since cleared up. Test the dog's response, in the quiet of your own home before going to the surgery, to loud and soft noises, close to and far away, and in each ear. Be prepared to tell the veterinary surgeon the results and your conclusions.

50. What if my bitch is aborting?

Canine pregnancy lasts from 61 to over 70 days, so an early whelping is not necessarily an abortion which is, incidentally, not a common condition in bitches.

Where an abortion does occur in a breeding kennels it is always a good idea to have the bitch, and any dead foetuses which are salvaged, tested for the presence of any infection which may affect other bitches. Since the bitch will often eat the expelled foetuses, it is not always possible to know when an abortion has occurred.

Causes of Abortion may be: *Hormonal Imbalance*; *Bacterial Infection*; and in imported bitches, *Brucella Canis Infection*. The latter is an important cause of abortion in the USA and a few cases have now occurred in the UK. It is important to have this cause investigated, as it is infectious to other dogs, including any stud dogs used on the affected bitch.

Abortion is also more rarely associated with accidental injury to bitches and also to fighting between bitches.

> **HISTORY TIP:** It is important to be able to tell the veterinary surgeon the day the bitch's heat started, the day of mating, whether one or more services were given and at what intervals, whether the bitch escaped during heat, whether the pregnancy was normal before the abortion occurred, and whether previous pregnancies were normal. It may be helpful also to ask the breeder about the whelping record of your bitch's dam.

51. What if my dog is nervous and over-excitable?

Variations in temperament are inevitable in any litter. A tendency to nervousness may be inherited, from sire to dam or earlier ancestors, or it may be learned from the dam in very early life.

A confident puppy may become nervous through lack of understanding in the home to which it was sold, and a "rescued" dog may have become nervous through past experiences.

Dogs which have been in road accidents or similar traumatic happenings may be nervous in the same surroundings for many years afterwards.

Nervousness at dog shows may occur when a young male is benched next to a mature, very dominant dog, so that the younger animal is in a stress-inducing situation for many hours.

Some dogs show exaggerated fear of some specific noise, e.g. thunder, but this fear will be frequently found to be generated by the humans the dog is with. Dogs are very quick to pick up tension and fear from their owners.

For programmes to improve difficult behaviour patterns see Chapter 3.

Puppies. Puppies go through a "fear period" between the ages of eight and 12 weeks, when the puppy is very sensitive and impressionable about new experiences. Great care should be taken during this time to make the puppy feel secure and protected while behaviour training starts.

Failure to allow a puppy sufficient rest and quiet away from the stimulation of human attention is a common cause of development of nervous temperament.

Hyper-excitability can be induced in *adolescent dogs* by encouraging them to play roughly and in physical combat with owners. Great care must be taken in this respect especially in the case of guard dogs like Rottweilers, Dobermanns and Boxers.

Clinical causes of nervousness and excitability may include:

Onset of oestrus and/or whelping in the bitch.

False pregnancy and the frustrations of guarding an invisible litter.

Hyper-sexuality in the male. See "What if" No. 54.

Nervousness may also be associated with:

The secondary stage of **Canine Distemper; Diabetes;** and, in other countries, **Rabies.**

HISTORY TIP: It will be helpful if you try to associate episodes of excitability with particular happenings in the household, or with the presence of particular people. Some people's voices, or manner with dogs, creates over-excitability in dogs, whether they mean to or not.

---

52. What if my dog has a depraved appetite?

It is normal for the wild or free-running dog to eat decomposing bodies and the faeces of other animals, and sometimes their own faeces. Pet dogs will also do this if they have the opportunity. See "What if" No. 26.

Puppies will explore the edibility of practically any substance, and may eat leaves, earth and stones, paper etc. This habit is usually grown out of by the time the puppy is nine to ten months old.

When an older dog chooses to eat earth, gravel, stones etc. regularly, it is as well to check with the veterinary surgeon that there is nothing wrong. If you happen to notice your dog eating rubbish or decaying matter, giving it a dose of liquid paraffin (one teaspoonful to one tablespoonful) can often prevent a digestive problem occurring.

117

> **HISTORY TIP:** Try to recall when the behaviour started, and look for other signs of illness, e.g. compulsive drinking. It can be helpful to take fresh faeces and urine samples with you when you go to the veterinary surgery.

53. What if my dog is salivating excessively?

It is normal for dogs with loose lower lips to exude more saliva than those with tight mouths. It is also normal for a dog to drool when eagerly awaiting food, and stud dogs will drool in the presence of an in-season bitch. Fear and anxiety give rise to drooling and over-production of saliva is a frequent prelude to car sickness. Where none of these explanations applies, excessive and continual salivation should prompt a visit to the veterinary surgeon.

Excessive salivation may be associated with problems in the mouth which may cause difficulty in eating. See "What if" No. 36, and also the following major diseases: **Neoplasia** and **Poisoning**.

54. What if my dog is over-sexed?

Sex drive in the dog is expressed in mounting behaviour, territory marking, roaming, excitability, and aggression to other dogs. Males of the small breeds and mongrels up to medium size tend to hyper-sexuality more than males of large and giant breeds, which are often reluctant to mate even when required for stud work.

It is normal for a healthy, young male dog to have a vigorous sex drive, especially if he is kept with or near entire bitches coming into oestrus.

Many adolescent males go through a short period of hyper-sexual behaviour at puberty (six to 14 months), but in most dogs this behaviour is short-lived.

It is a common error to believe that the dog "needs a bitch" at this time and that being used at stud will cure the behaviour — it is in fact more likely to encourage this undesirable tendency in the pet male. It is far preferable never to use a companion dog at stud and not to keep him with brood bitches unless there is the prospect of regular stud work for him.

For corrective treatment of hyper-sexuality in the male see Chapter 3.

Your veterinary surgeon may also be able to help with medication and, if necessary, eventually with castration, but where mating behaviour has been learnt, or even if it has not, the dog may still "go through the motions" when extremely stimulated, but will not, of course, be fertile. It is a mistake to assume that castration will cure all hyper-sexual activity since that is not the case and castration may cause the dog to increase in weight and change its character in other ways.

> **HISTORY TIP:** Note whether the hyper-sexual behaviour is regular or intermittent. If the trait occurs irregularly try to observe some pattern in the episodes of hyper-sexual behaviour. Does it occur, for instance, after boisterous play with children or adults? Are the episodes linked with visits to specific places?

CHAPTER 4

PART II

THE MAJOR INFECTIOUS DISEASES

Canine distemper
Infectious canine hepatitis
Leptospirosis
Canine parvovirus infection
Kennel cough
Rabies

The most important infectious diseases of dogs are:

Canine Distemper
Infectious Canine Hepatitis
Leptospirosis (two forms)
Canine Parvovirus Infection
Infectious Canine Tracheobronchitis (Kennel Cough)
Rabies

Dogs can be protected against all these diseases and a vaccination programme should be discussed with the veterinary surgeon, ideally before a puppy is bought. Prevention is far better than cure. If an adult dog or older puppy is being acquired, and its vaccination status is not available on a certificate signed by a veterinary surgeon, it will be wise to consider with the vet the protection which should be given.

Reputable boarding kennels will require to see up to date vaccination certificates given (within the previous 12 months) for the first four diseases mentioned above and probably for *kennel cough* too. *Rabies* vaccine is used in the U.K. only in newly imported dogs and in dogs for export.

Canine Distemper

Cause:	A virus infection, usually complicated by secondary bacterial invasion.
Transmission:	The virus is transmitted from dog to dog usually by inhalation of particles in the air which have become contaminated by discharges from dogs suffering from the disease.
Incubation period:	Usually seven to 21 days.
Major signs:	Initially, a cough accompanied by high temperature, lethargy, lack of appetite, reddened eyes, runny nose, noisy breathing and, possibly, also diarrhoea and vomiting. Subsequently, usually after some weeks, nervous signs — a nervous twitch (*chorea*), fits or paralysis — may develop often accompanied by thickening of the pads and the nose (*hyperkeratosis*).
Action:	Veterinary consultation immediately. If distemper is suspected do not take the dog into the waiting room but

119

	ask the receptionist where the veterinary surgeon would like to see the case.
Prevention:	Primary vaccination with modified live vaccines when puppies are six to 12 weeks of age and subsequently booster doses annually is usually advised.
Disinfection:	Thorough cleaning of the house or kennel is required. First with detergents to remove grease followed by disinfection, using chlorine derivatives particularly. Subsequently the affected areas should be opened to the air and, where possible, sunlight and left unoccupied by dogs for as long as possible.
Comment	• *Canine distemper* used to be rife nationwide before effective vaccines were introduced more than 25 years ago. Now the disease is mostly confined to unvaccinated populations in large cities. Thus dogs in more rural surroundings do not receive a natural boost to their immunity by exposure to infected animals and therefore booster vaccinations are most important.

• Good nursing is an essential part of treatment.

• Dogs that develop nervous signs are most unlikely to make a full recovery.

• In some cases the primary signs may be so mild as to go unnoticed. In others treatment may appear to bring about a recovery, but there is always the possibility that nervous signs may develop later, sometimes much later, often accompanied by *hyperkeratosis*. The latter signs earned this stage the name 'hardpad', once thought to be a separate disease but now known to be a sequel to distemper.

Infectious Canine Hepatitis (also known as Rubarth's Disease, or Canine Viral Hepatitis)

Cause:	This highly contagious disease is caused by a canine adenovirus (CAV-1). It has no connection with hepatitis in man.
Incubation period:	Five to seven days, but it may strike suddenly, and the dog may pass from apparent health to acute illness within 24 hours.
Transmission:	Dogs catch the disease by swallowing material contaminated with faeces, saliva or urine from infected dogs.
Signs:	Puppies in their first year of life are most commonly affected but all ages of dog are susceptible. The major early signs are generalised illness and lack of appetite, with pale conjunctivae and gums, greatly raised temperature, vomiting, diarrhoea, abdominal pain. Yellowing of the whites of the eyes (*jaundice*) may occur. Some 20 per cent of dogs which are recovering from *hepatitis* show a blue clouding over the whole of the cornea of one or both eyes (*blue eye*). In most cases this clouding will disappear within a few days without additional treatment but, if it persists, veterinary advice

should be sought. A similar clouding of the eye may be seen in some puppies after vaccination against *infectious canine hepatitis* when live CAV-1 vaccines are used.

Action: Urgent veterinary consultation taking precautions not to transmit the disease to other dogs.

Prevention: Have puppies vaccinated early. A number of different types of vaccine are available — your veterinary surgeon will advise which is the most suitable for your dog in your area. Booster doses may be needed.

Disinfection: Normal cleaning routine. Segregation of sick dogs. NOTE: Dogs suffering from this disease will shed the virus in their urine during the progress of the disease and possibly for several months afterwards. Some may become permanent carriers of the disease.

Comment:
- If a kennel has continual problems with ICH, blood testing of older stock will help to identify carriers.
- This infection has been linked with puppy mortality in breeding kennels.

Leptospirosis

This is a disease caused by a group of bacteria called Leptospires. Dogs can be infected by two of these: *Leptospira icterohaemorrhagiae* and *Leptospira canicola*. Both these organisms can be passed onto children and adults.

Leptospira icterohaemorrhagiae

Incubation period: Five to 15 days.

Transmission: This bacteria is carried by rats, and is transmitted to dogs which kill rats or play with dead vermin. Dogs may also be infected by rat urine on the ground, in ponds or water bowls, or on fallen fruit etc. which may be eaten by dogs. The disease is particularly prevalent amongst dogs on farms, at ports and in mining areas.

Signs: High temperature, severe thirst, increased frequency of urination, abdominal pain, depression, possibly ulceration of the mouth, coated tongue, diarrhoea containing blood, jaundice and persistent vomiting.

Action: Urgent accurate veterinary diagnosis, probably assisted by laboratory tests. This is a very serious disease.

> **HISTORY TIP:** Does the dog take exercise around barns, junk yards, or play in rural streams where rats may be found?

Prevention: Keep dogs away from rat-infested water and do not leave drinking bowls outdoors over-night. Take steps to rid your premises of rats, but put the poison where dogs cannot get at it. Do not neglect vaccination against *leptospirosis*, and the annual boosters.

Comment:
- Leptospires excreted in the urine of the dog during this illness, and possibly for months after apparent recovery, can infect other dogs and also humans, where the illness is known as *Weils Disease*. Particular attention should

121

be paid to hygiene when attending to a sick dog, and especially when clearing up urine.

Leptospira canicola (also known as Lamppost Disease, and Stuttgart Disease)

Incubation period: Five to 15 days.

Transmission: Dog to dog via sniffing at urine (hence lamppost connection).

Signs: Similar to those described under *Leptospira ictero-haemorrhagiae* except that jaundice is much less frequently seen and less marked. Mild cases with few signs occur quite frequently. This infection can cause damage to the kidneys which may become critical later in life.

Action: Immediate veterinary consultation, especially in puppies. Segregate patient from other dogs.

Prevention: Most of the dogs which recover will excrete bacteria in their urine for up to a year. It must be a matter for consideration whether such dogs should be kept on the same premises as young puppies. Prompt vaccination of puppies at eight to 12 weeks of age, and regular annual boosters are necessary.

Disinfection: Recovered patients should be kept in the same kennelling/living space for at least six months, as eradication of the disease by disinfection may be difficult.

Comment: ● **It should be remembered that this infection can be passed on to man. Great care must be taken when nursing dogs with this disease.**

Canine Parvovirus Infection (CPV)

Cause: A small, but very tough and persistent virus. This disease has only been recognised in dogs since 1978.

Incubation period: Five days.

Transmission: Dog to dog, via virus excreted in faeces, and also via virus carried on human clothing, footwear and objects which may have been contaminated by an infected dog. Infection occurs through ingestion of virus particles. The virus may remain viable for up to one year in a house where there has been a case, and may be almost permanently present in kennels where there have been successive outbreaks. Disinfection is exceptionally difficult.

Signs: Two forms of canine parvovirus are recognised:

Canine Parvovirus Myocarditis.

Where the dam of a litter has not been vaccinated and has not been infected by the disease, she will have no protection to pass on to her puppies. Canine parvovirus, which always seeks out the cells of the body which are multiplying most rapidly, will concentrate in the heart muscle of newly born puppies which are exposed to the virus. The heart muscle is weakened or completely destroyed. The effect is not usually seen until the puppies become active, at four to ten weeks, when seemingly healthy pups will suddenly collapse and die after play or feeding. The whole litter is usually affected, although some individuals may survive longer than others; none of them should be sold as sound puppies.

This form of CPV is now becoming rare, as most breeding bitches will have some antibody to the infection either through previous exposure to the disease or through vaccinations.

Intestinal form of Canine Parvovirus Infection

This is the most common form of CPV. It affects dogs from four weeks of age right into old age, but most severely in their first year, when the disease can be quickly fatal. The signs seen in this form of the disease are: depression, severe protracted vomiting, abdominal pain, refusal of food and water, and very profuse diarrhoea, often with considerable blood content. Mostly CPV infection is rapid in resolution, and if the dog is going to survive it will be noticeably better within four to five days of the start of the illness. When puppies are badly affected by CPV, growth may be stunted and the puppy may be bald for up to a year.

Action:	Immediate consultation with the veterinary surgeon, initially by telephone, if possible, in order to avoid transmission to other dogs.
Prevention:	Consult your veterinary surgeon about a course of vaccinations to protect against CPV and do not neglect annual boosters.
	When a dog is suspected of having CPV, not only should it be kept in isolation, but all members of the owners household should avoid dogs also, as the virus can be carried on shoes and clothing.
Disinfection:	It is very difficult to eradicate CPV from a home or a kennel. Sodium hypochlorite (domestic bleach) and formalin are the only disinfectants active against CPV. Where a single puppy has died of CPV on domestic premises, it is wise to wait at least six months before introducing another puppy.

HISTORY TIP: Since protective vaccination will not take effect until antibody obtained from the dam of the litter has waned, it is helpful if the breeder has had the dam blood tested to determine antibody level just before or after whelping. Your veterinary surgeon then has some basis from which to decide when the puppy will respond satisfactorily to vaccination. It will also be important to know if the puppy has been hand-reared from birth, as then it will have received no protective antibodies at all.

Comment:	● CPV destroys the cell lining of much of the intestine, so that the badly infected dog has no means of absorbing fluid and nourishment. Fatalities are often due to dehydration, and intravenous drip therapy, to replace fluid loss, as an in-patient may be necessary. Consequently treatment can be expensive.

Infectious Canine Tracheobronchitis (Kennel Cough)

Cause:
A complex package of viruses and bacteria which may vary in content at each outbreak, so making it possible for susceptible dogs to have kennel cough more than once during the season (May to November), or to have kennel cough every year.

Transmission:
While this disease is mainly transmitted from dog to dog where a number of animals are gathered under one roof, e.g. at a dog show or in boarding kennels, it is possible for the singly owned pet dog to suffer from kennel cough too. Dogs become infected by breathing in infected airborne particles. The infective agents are carried in the air in a manner similar to the way human colds or influenza are spread. Peak time for infection is the summer, when dogs which do not normally mix with others are gathered in boarding kennels.

Signs:
The most important sign is a protracted harsh cough which sounds as though the dog has a bone stuck in its throat. Affected adult dogs usually remain relatively cheerful and continue eating. In puppies however the disease may be complicated by a secondary pneumonia which can cause death.

Action:
Consult the veterinary surgeon, but do not take the dog into the waiting room, or allow it to approach other dogs. Cancel attendance at any gathering of dogs (shows, training classes) for six weeks.

Prevention:
Keep your dog away from any dog which is heard to be coughing during the summer season — do not believe the common excuses of "he has been pulling on the lead", "just ate some grass", etc.

A vaccine, which is put straight into the nasal passage where the disease enters, protects against infection with the bacterium *Bordetella bronchiseptica* which is considered to be the major cause of *kennel cough*. Protection will last for about six to nine months. In relation to this disease primary and booster vaccination against canine distemper and adenovirus infection is most important. In some situations veterinary surgeons may advise the use of a combined vaccine that not only stimulates immunity to those infected but also gives some protection against infection with canine para influenza virus, one of the viruses which is involved in causing *kennel cough*.

Consult your veterinary surgeon about the use of vaccine, particularly if the dog is going into boarding kennels, or to dog shows, and especially if you are also planning a litter during the summer. Remember immunity takes some time to become established so consult your veterinary surgeon at least two to three weeks before you are due to go on holiday.

Comment
- While this disease is trying and can be long lasting, it is seldom life-threatening except possibly in the case of very young puppies.
- Even after the cough seems to be cured, it may be reactivated by excessive exercise or stress.
- Problems arise because dogs may be infectious to others before they show signs and after they have apparently recovered. Chronic carrier dogs may also exist.

Rabies

Rabies is a fatal infection transmitted through the saliva of many animals. Foxes are the most important carriers of infection in Europe, followed by dogs and cats and small rodents.

Transmission:
The virus is present in the saliva of affected dogs and is transmitted through the bite of an infected animal, or through saliva entering a wound already present on the skin. The virus travels via the nerves to the brain, where is sets up inflammation (encephalitis) causing the typical nervous signs. It then returns via the nerves to enter the salivary glands and other organs.

Incubation Time:
The time between infection and positive signs being shown may be very long (several months) but since most animals bite other animals around the head and mouth, the virus usually reaches the brain quite quickly, and the incubation period may be as little as two to three weeks.

Major Signs:
Rabies in animals takes two forms — dumb or furious rabies. Both are demonstrated in obvious personality changes, wild or ferocious animals may become affectionate and seek human company, while normally quiet animals in the furious form will become exceedingly savage and make unpredictable attacks on humans and animals. The facial expression changes, the eyes become staring and the jaws fixed and paralysed, drooling copious saliva. Dogs tend to hide away from light and are extremely dangerous to approach. Death is usually preceded by paralysis and coma and dogs seldom survive for more than 15 days once the signs have been noted. Although affected dogs may develop difficulty in swallowing they do not go into spasms at the sight of water so the term "hydrophobia" does not apply to the dog as it does to man.

Prevention:
- We are fortunate in Britain that our island situation enables our government to take effective measures to keep rabies out of the country, by our quarantine regulations and by efficient detection by Customs and Excise at ports and airports.

There are penalties of imprisonment and very heavy fines for those found attempting to smuggle cats, dogs and other pets into the country.

It is every right thinking citizen's duty to report to a veterinary surgeon or to the police where there is any suspicion that foreign visitors or immigrant workers have brought pets with them into the country, or where people who have been abroad for holidays have taken pets and brought them back, or seem to have acquired pets while they were away.

No dog in this country will show signs of rabies unless it has been in a country where rabies is endemic, or it has been bitten or licked by an illegally imported dog.

Action: If a dog is suspected of having rabies avoid touching it, barricade it by some means into a small room and tell Police or a veterinary surgeon immediately — day or night.

There is no treatment for rabies, but if possible affected animals are kept under very strict confinement on Ministry of Agriculture premises for observation as rabies can only be positively proved by laboratory tests on the brain of the dog after its death.

In-contact animals will also have to be kept in confinement for the full quarantine period of six months.

Precautions: Rabies vaccines are only available in this country for dogs which are being exported to countries where rabies is endemic and for the use in imported dogs when they are in quarantine kennels. MAFF will issue to your veterinary surgeon a specific dose for each dog due to be exported.

Comment: **Help keep rabies out of Britain by obeying the quarantine laws.**

Further reading: *Rabies — the facts you need to know*, by Henderson and White, (Barrie & Jenkins)

CHAPTER 4

PART III

PARASITES

Roundworms
Tapeworms
Toxoplasmosis
Hookworms
Whipworms
Lungworms
Fleas
Lice
Ticks
Harvest mites
Mange mites

Endoparasites

Endoparasites are parasites which live inside the body as opposed to on its surface. A great variety of such parasites infest dogs but four are particularly common in all breeds of dogs in the UK, however kept. They are:

1) *Toxocara canis* — a roundworm
2) *Toxascaris leonina* — another type of roundworm
3) *Dipylidium caninum* — a tapeworm
4) *Toxoplasma gondii* — a protozoan parasite

Toxocara canis

Description: A round, white worm three to six inches long and pointed at both ends which infects, most frequently, pregnant nursing bitches and young puppies. Adult worms are passed by puppies with or without accompanying faeces. Often several worms are passed at one time coiled up like a spring or in a loose hank.

Life cycle: The release of hormones during pregnancy activates roundworm larvae which may be lying dormant in the tissues of the bitch. Some will migrate to the uterus and into the developing puppies, while others will continue their lifecycle in the intestine of the bitch.

Larvae already within the puppy at birth develop into adult worms by the time the puppy is two weeks old.

The puppy will also receive more toxocara larvae via the bitch's milk, from being licked by the bitch and from her coat where traces of faeces may remain. Additionally, the bitch will take into her body eggs, larvae and adult worms when she cleans up the faeces of her puppies. Within the puppy, ingested toxocara eggs hatch into larvae which burrow through the gut wall and migrate via the liver to the lungs, where they undergo further development. As they pass through they may cause respiratory problems. Some of these larvae are distributed by the blood to other tissues where they remain dormant. Other maturing larvae are coughed up, swallowed, and pass down into the digestive system where they mature into adult worms, which lay thousands of eggs within the intestine. These eggs, with or without adult worms, pass out in the faeces, to lie on plants, grass or soil, sometimes for many months, until ingested by another susceptible dog, when they start the toxocara lifecycle all over again.

Signs: It may be taken that all baby puppies and nursing bitches have a roundworm burden, whether you see any live adult worms or not. A very heavy worm burden in puppies will cause breathing problems, coughing and possibly pneumonia, while the larvae are migrating through the lungs. Abdominal pain, diarrhoea, retarded growth, a pot-bellied, poor appearance, and harsh coat will be seen when the stomach and intestines are full of worms, which may eventually form a complete blockage of the digestive system. Badly affected puppies whine and adopt a characteristic straddle-legged position.

Action: In puppies especially, a heavy toxocara burden can be very debilitating, even life threatening, and because of the added risk that puppies are most likely to be handled by children, it is very important indeed that they are wormed early, at two and a half to three weeks old, and again at two week intervals until three months of age, again at six months old, and then twice yearly for the rest of their lives. If you have just purchased a puppy find out whether it has been wormed and if so with what. Discuss with your veterinary surgeon the need for further dosing.

If you have a litter of puppies, weigh the bitch, and each of her puppies, and obtain from the veterinary surgeon an effective wormer (vermifuge) at the right strength for each animal.

When you have carried out a worming for any infestation, or if you see worms in the faeces, be sure to pick up and dispose of the faeces properly. Worm infected faeces should not be put on to a compost heap, nor should they be dug into the garden, as many worm eggs can survive for years in soil. Burning, or putting into the WC, is the best disposal method. In kennels the number of eggs can be reduced by vigorous scrubbing with large quantities of hot water and detergent and, if practical, the use of a flame gun — the eggs are resistant to disinfectant.

Comment:
- Recent research has produced a vermifuge which is said to act on the encysted larvae in the bitch's tissues during late pregnancy and soon after whelping. This remedy is only available through veterinary surgeons, but if you mean to breed your bitch it is well worth making enquiries about this new development.
- Wormers purchased over the counter are not likely to be so effective and the old-fashioned remedies may cause purging and abdominal discomfort.
- With many modern wormers, you are unlikely to see any live worms passed, as they are digested within the animal and pass out unnoticed in the faeces. **Do not discontinue worming because you see no worms passed.**

Risk to Humans: The sticky eggs of *Toxocara canis*, too small to be visible to the eye, may be picked up from soil, grass or from an animal's coat or bedding, and may be subsequently swallowed — children run the greatest risk. Eggs that have been eaten in this way can hatch into larvae in the human gut but will not develop into adult worms. Instead, the larvae, which are very small, will travel around the body and become embedded in the body tissues, usually causing no problems at all. Very rarely, however, these migrating larvae may settle, by chance, in a particularly sensitive tissue such as the retina. In some cases where this has happened there has been impairment of vision. Sensible precautions will reduce any such risks to infinitesimal odds.

Precautions:
- Insist that any puppy you buy has been wormed at least twice, with an effective wormer, before it is eight weeks old.

- Continue with a worming programme as described earlier.

- Dispose of puppy faeces and post-worming faeces properly.

- Do not allow small children to handle very young puppies and nursing bitches, and do not allow dogs to lick children's faces or to share biscuits or ice-creams.

- Do not allow dogs to eat off crockery used by humans.

- Insist that children wash their hands and faces after handling a puppy.

- Keep long-haired pups well-groomed especially around the hindquarters.

NOTE: Freshly passed dog faeces are not a hazard in this respect, as the eggs of *Toxocara canis* need some time to mature outside the host before they are infective, so that while stepping in a pile of faeces is unpleasant, it is not dangerous. *Toxocara canis* cannot cause threadworm infection in children since that condition is due to another species of worm.

Toxascaris leonina

Description: A round, white worm very similar in appearance to *Toxocara canis*.

Life cycle: The life cycle of this worm is much more simple. Infection occurs by the ingestion of infective eggs. The eggs hatch in the stomach of dogs and the larvae develop in the wall of the stomach and intestine. They do not migrate as is the case with *Toxocara canis*. Thus infection of puppies in the womb or via the milk does not occur.

Action: Worming methods indicated for the elimination of *Toxocara canis* will be effective. Similar precautions should be taken in respect of the disposal of faeces etc.

Dipylidium caninum

Description: This worm is a segmented tapeworm which occurs in the small intestine of dogs. It can measure up to 20 inches in length. The worm has a small head which attaches to the wall of the intestine and a long, segmented body which contains maturing eggs in each segment. It is rare to see a complete tapeworm in faeces, but individual segments, loaded with ripe eggs, may be noticed which resemble cucumber seeds. When these segments have dried they resemble grains of rice, and may be noticed around the anus or on the dog's coat or bedding.

Life cycle: Fleas are a necessary part of the lifecycle of *Dipylidium caninum*. Flea larvae swallow eggs shed by dogs and these mature as the flea develops so that adult fleas are infectious for dogs. When a dog kills and eats a flea, the worm larvae are released in the intestine, where they will mature into adult worms.

Signs: Severe tapeworm infestation causes diarrhoea and poor growth in puppies.

Action: Your veterinary surgeon will prescribe a specific remedy for this tapeworm — be prepared to quote the weight of the dog or puppy.

Precaution: Maintain a regular campaign against fleas on the dog and around the home, see page ??.

Transmission to man: This worm can infect humans, mainly young children, who accidentally eat a flea containing infective larvae, but such cases are rare.

Toxoplasma gondii

Description: A very small parasite of cats which uses most mammals including dogs and humans as an intermediate host.

Life cycle: During a relatively short period of infection (because the cat develops an immunity) mature parasites in cats' intestines shed a large number of eggs. If these eggs are eaten by an intermediate host, such as a dog, the eggs mature and the parasite invades the tissues and forms cysts, mainly in muscles but sometimes in the brain. At this stage the intermediate hosts become immune and the cysts lie dormant. They may become active however if the dog is stressed by some other disease. If this occurs in pregnant bitches, puppies may become infected in the womb. Dogs may also acquire infection by eating muscles of prey animals that contain cysts. Cats become infected by eating animals such as mice which have cysts in their muscles and so the cycle starts again.

Signs: Most toxoplasma infections in dogs do not produce clinical signs or they are so mild as to go unnoticed. More severe infections may be associated with diarrhoea, muscle weakness and respiratory difficulty.

Action: None, since the infection can only be diagnosed by a veterinary surgeon.

Prevention: It is not really possible to prevent the disease since dogs can become infected in so many different ways which are not controllable. However, in homes where there are also cats it makes sense to remove all cat faeces from litter trays daily, so that they do not have time to mature and become infective.

NOTE: This infection can occur in man. If pregnant women become infected there is a possibility that the infection can reach the baby in the uterus causing abortion or pre-natal damage. It is most important therefore that pregnant women are extremely cautious about feeding raw meat to animals. They should avoid contact with cat faeces and certainly should not clean out cat litter boxes.

Other Endoparasites

A number of other types of worm can infect dogs in the UK. Details of these are given in the following table.

Other endoparasites that occur in dogs

Type of parasite	Scientific name	Life cycle/description	Signs in dogs	Comment
Hookworm	*Uncinaria stenocephala*	A thick, round worm only 2cm long which lives in the small intestine. Hookworm larvae may invade the skin causing a dermatitis between the toes. The main cause of infection is ingestion of larvae which hatch, in the open, from shed eggs.	Usually none but may cause diarrhoea and possibly anaemia as the adult worms live on blood.	Infection with this parasite is very common in Greyhounds especially those kept on grass runs. The infection can be cured by strict hygiene measures and regular worming with an appropriate product.
Whipworm	*Trichuris vulpis*	Worms 7cm in length with a thin front end and a bulbous rear end. They are found in the caecum. Infection is by ingestion of larvae which develop within the eggshell.	Mostly none but may cause intermitent diarrhoea with dark faeces.	The infection is common in Greyhound kennels. Treatment is difficult. Eggs shed on the ground can stay viable for several years making control difficult. Treatment is not easily accomplished.
Lungworm	*Filaroides osleri*	Adult worms are found in nodules in the trachea and bronchi which are about 2mm in size. The method of transfer is not fully understood. The tails of the worms can be seen, on bronchoscopy, protruding from the nodules.	Many infections go unnoticed but severely affected dogs have a protracted harsh cough particularly when exercised and may lose weight.	Mostly young animals are affected. The infection is more commonly found in dogs housed in groups e.g. breeding kennels. Treatment is very difficult and surgical removal of the nodules may be required.

Tapeworm	*Echinococcus granulosus*	A tapeworm, only 5mm in length that lives in the small intestine of dogs. Eggs shed by dogs are eaten by a great variety of intermediate hosts including man but particularly sheep in which the parasite develops into a hydatid cyst. Dogs become infected by eating carcasses of sheep or deer which contain cysts in their tissues, particularly the lungs and liver. Most commonly affected are working dogs which find dead animals on mountainous grazing land.	Few signs are seen in dogs except possibly loss of condition and occasional diarrhoea.	Dogs may harbour more than a thousand worms in their intestine. Hydatid disease in man is of consequence particularly in some areas in Wales. A national control scheme involving supervised worming of dogs, as is practised in New Zealand, is in force in some areas of the country. Regular worming of dogs is important. The feeding of raw offal should be avoided.
Tapeworm	*Taenia species*	Large tapeworms measuring up to 3 metres in length that live in the small intestine of dogs. A number of different intermediate hosts are infected by eating eggs shed by dogs. In the intermediate hosts, cysts develop in various areas depending on the species involved. Dogs become infected by eating the tissues of the intermediate host that contain cysts.	Most infections go undetected.	Tapeworms have little public health risk. Control is by regular worming and avoiding feeding raw offal to dogs.

Heartworms

Incidence: Heartworms are not a problem in this country except in imported dogs. An increasing incidence of heartworms is however being found in quarantine kennels.

Life cycle: The infection is spread by a mosquito not found in this country. The dog, bitten by a mosquito, has larvae deposited on its skin which eventually burrow into a vein. From there they travel to the right-hand side of the heart where they can live for several years, blocking the flow of blood, and eventually causing heart failure.

Signs: May be none for several months or years after the dog has been imported. Most frequent signs are a soft cough, fainting after exercise, listlessness and bloodstained sputum.

Action: Blood test by veterinary surgeon, medication, possibly surgery if heartworm is identified.

Precautions: Unnecessary in this country.

Transmission to man: Not recorded.

Prevention of endoparasite infections

Where meticulous care is necessary, for example in households with young children, a small sample of faeces can be taken to your veterinary surgeon for screening for the presence of worm eggs. This process is not costly and is worth having done periodically as many dogs can tolerate a light worm burden (less than ten worms in the gut), without showing any signs of ill health.

Giving Worming Medication

Using modern vermifuges it is not usually necessary to starve the dog before worming. The instructions given by the veterinary surgeon should be followed to the letter and, if the vermifuge has been given in bulk to cover several wormings, the dog should be weighed on each occasion to ensure the dose given is adequate but not excessive.

Not infrequently, puppies vomit soon after the worming dose has been given but, in general, if the vermifuge has remained in the stomach for 20 minutes, it will have served a useful purpose, and the puppy should not be re-wormed for at least seven days. Contact the veterinary surgery if you are at all doubtful about what you should do.

Ectoparasites

Ectoparasites are parasites that live on or in the skin. The major ectoparasites of dogs are:

(1) Fleas	(5) Mange mites *Sarcoptes scabei*
(2) Lice	*Demodex folliculorum*
(3) Ticks	*Otodectes cynotis*
(4) Harvest mites	Cheyletiella species

Details relating to these parasites are given in the table on page ?.

In general terms it can be said that ectoparasite infection is probably the major cause of skin disease in dogs. Unfortunately the signs of skin disease are not usually specific for any one infection and thus diagnosis and the correct selection of medication is far from easy. Unless the cause of a problem is very obvious, or it is a recrudescence of a previous infection, it makes sense to consult a veterinary surgeon about any skin lesion or signs of skin irritation in dogs. Very often diagnosis will entail the taking of samples for microscopic examination and the careful noting of the history of the case. With skin conditions particularly, owners should go to the surgery with the ability to give a full account of the signs that are being shown, when they started and whether their intensity varies daily, monthly, or not at all. It is also important to have noted whether or not the signs are aggravated by particular events or certain surroundings. It is also relevant to tell the veterinary surgeon any details that are known about other related and in-contact animals. Be prepared to tell the veterinary surgeon about the dog's diet, the condition under which it is kept (i.e. does it have its own bed? Is it allowed over the whole house? etc.) and particularly whether it has access to other dogs, cats, or any other animals. The more information the veterinary surgeon gets in these respects the easier it is for him to select the most appropriate medication so that the animal makes a quicker and more complete recovery. Finally don't forget to tell the veterinary surgeon if you or any of your family also have a rash or some skin problem, since some parasites can cause problems in both man and dogs.

ECTOPARASITE INFECTIONS OF DOGS

Parasite	Life Cycle	Signs Shown by Dog	Comment
Fleas Scientific name: Ctenocephalides species (dog and cat fleas) most commonly but also *Pulex irritans* (human flea) and *Ceratophylus* species (hedgehog fleas)	The life cycle of the flea is completed off the dog. Eggs are laid in the dog's bed, around the edge of carpets and in upholstered chairs. Dependent on the environmental conditions they hatch, within 2-16 days, into larvae which take 7-10 days to reach maturity and pupate. The adult fleas emerge from the pupae after a variable period of time dependent on temperature, moisture etc. Sometimes hatching is stimulated by vibrations, for example moving furniture. Fleas act as intermediate hosts for the dog tapeworm *Dipylidium caninum* — see page 130.	Thin, elongated, brown, wingless insects with 'long legs' which run rapidly over the skin and which jump when off the animal. They occur particularly around the neck and on the abdomen. The movement of the fleas causes irritation such that affected dogs will scratch frequently and bite at their coats with nipping movements of the incisor teeth. The majority of dogs show few signs even though they are harbouring a lot of fleas — others, however, become sensitive to the fleas themselves, or their excreta, and will develop a severe allergic dermatitis even though only a few fleas are present.	Flea droppings (dirts) are black, hard and the size of grains of sand. If they are placed on wet blotting paper the blood they contain will leach out and stain the paper red. Regular treatment of dogs, at intervals of 7-10 days, with baths, powders and sprays is required to overcome a severe infection and to prevent immediate re-infection. It is also necessary to vacuum carefully all the places 'where eggs may have been laid, to "treat" the environment with a suitable insecticide and to apply an insecticide to the dog every 3-4 weeks to prevent re-infection. Flea collars can be helpful in some cases where re-infection occurs regularly but they need using with care to avoid possible hazards.
Lice Scientific name: *Trichodectes canis*	Adult lice feed on the skin and lay eggs on the hair. These hatch into young lice which resemble the adults. Lice cannot exist off their host for more than a few days — infection is spread therefore by close contact between animals.	Light brown, fat, wingless insects with short legs that move slowly on the skin surface and which lay eggs (nits) that are stuck to the animals hair, particularly around the neck and ears. Dogs with lice will scratch frequently at the area where the insects are to be found. Severe infections may cause anaemia in young puppies.	Regular treatment of infected dogs with an insecticide is required and it makes sense to comb and wash away the nits. Since lice breed on an animal there is less need to pay attention to the environment than is the case with a flea infection.
Ticks Scientific name: Ixodes species	Dogs become infected by coming in contact with larvae which have hatched from eggs laid by adult ticks that have left their natural hosts (sheep and hedgehogs) and which climb on to blades of grass and shrubs.	Brownish-white, rounded insects which may, when engorged, be the size of a bean or pea. The insects lie attached to the skin by their heads which are firmly buried in the epidermis. The larval forms of some ticks may cause irritation to some dogs. Most dogs will, however, tolerate an adult tick or two without showing any signs. Indeed it is common for these parasites to be noticed only during routine grooming.	Adult ticks can be removed by first soaking them with a swab soaked in ether or surgical spirit. This has the effect of making the tick loosen its hold on the skin so that its mouthparts and head can be removed intact. If the head is not removed a local skin infection may result. If in doubt seek veterinary help. Dogs that are in close association with sheep, and which have ticks regularly, can be bathed in a suitable dip. Regular dipping is necessary to prevent re-infection.
Harvest mites (Chiggers) Scientific name: *Trombicula autumnalis*	Both the adults and immature forms are free-living but the larvae are parasitic. The larval mites occur most frequently in	Small, red larval mites, just visible to the naked eye, mostly seen in the inter-digital spaces and in a small pocket that is	The incidence of mites in different areas of the country is very variable. Seek

Mange Mites Scientific name: 1. Sarcoptes scabei 2. Demodex folliculorum 3. Otodectes cynotis 4. Cheyletiella species	The life cycle of all mange mites occurs on the host. The adults lay eggs which hatch into larvae in 3-7 days, these mature into nymphs which develop into adult mites. Mange mites do not survive long off the host.	1. *Sarcoptes scabei* causes sarcoptic mange. The mite is invisible to the naked eye and burrows superficially into the skin. The irritation caused by the mite is intense, causing much frequent and frantic scratching. The most commonly affected areas are under the thighs and fore legs and the edges of the ears in dogs of all breeds and ages.	1. Treatment needs to be repeated 3-4 times at weekly intervals in order to kill new generations before they are sexually mature. The dog's bedding should be destroyed and the places where infected dogs have been should be sprayed with an insecticide, since the mites can persist long enough off the host to infect another animal. Sarcoptic mange is readily transmissible from dog to dog and the mites can exist on people for a short while causing irritating spots.
		2. *Demodex folliculorum.* A microscopic mite which is a normal inhabitant of canine hair follicles but which, in small numbers causes no problems. However in certain circumstances, not fully understood, the mites multiply to cause severe dermatitis with hair loss. The condition is common in short-haired breeds and there may be an inherited tendency to the infection. Often the condition is localised but it may suddenly erupt over the whole body. A secondary bacterial infection may occur. Demodectic mange is a common disease in young dogs. Surprisingly the condition does not cause itching.	2. Dogs with skin lesions like pustules on the skin of the head, hocks and elbows should be taken to a veterinary surgeon without delay, since treatment is much more difficult once the condition has erupted more generally. Proper diagnosis and correct treatment applied meticulously is important if the disease is to be brought under control. Almost inevitably, occasional courses of treatment will be required throughout the dog's life as patches of infection recur from time to time. *Demodex folliculorum* does not affect people living with infected dogs.
		3. *Otodectes cynotis.* A white mange mite that is just visible with a magnifying glass and which is found in the ears of animals. The mite occurs naturally without usually causing much problem in the ears of cats. A small infection can however cause severe otitis externa (ear canker) in dogs.	3. Ear preparations which have activity against this mite are available through veterinary surgeons. It is prudent to treat both ears even though one may appear normal. Cats and other animals living in association with infected dogs should also be treated to help prevent re-infection.
		4. Cheyletiella species. A small parasite that is just visible to the naked eye. Mostly it causes few signs in dogs but heavy infections can cause marked skin scaling. The mites themselves, together with their eggs and the scurf they produce, have been called "walking dandruff" most frequently seen on the back.	4. Cheyletiella mites can cause an irritating rash in people. Treatment is relatively simple but should be under veterinary supervision. Medication needs to be prolonged because the mite has a long life cycle.

CHAPTER 4

PART IV

INHERITED DISEASES

General hereditary problems

Hip dysplasia

Eye conditions

The employment of increasingly sophisticated diagnostic methods in veterinary medicine has led to the identification of a number of diseases and deformities in dogs as being inherited, from immediate parents or from ancestors further back in the pedigree.

The mode of inheritance in many cases has yet to be determined and many breed clubs are co-operating with research projects aimed at eventually eliminating these conditions from the breed. Frequently it is not until dogs have been bred from, and disease has been recognised in their offspring, that it is realised that one or both parents are capable of passing on traits which are not apparent in themselves.

The passing on of genetic or congenital defects is to some extent the breeder's responsibility, but often not the breeder's fault, especially if this is the first time the defect has occurred in their strain of dogs. The ethical breeder will be aware of the particular problems which are common in their breed, and will do as much as possible to identify them and to breed away from such problems.

There is no breed which can be said to be totally free from hereditary defects. Mongrels and crossbreds suffer from the same conditions, but in these dogs eradication in the future is impossible because their ancestry is not recorded.

General hereditary problems

These include defects of the skeleton, malformations of the eye and the facial construction, and a tendency to conditions leading to blindness, heart disease, deafness, bleeding disorders and epilepsy, although some of these conditions may also arise from injury.

It is as well to remember that some inherited conditions are quite common and may cause trouble, suffering and expense later. It makes sense, therefore, to take newly purchased puppies to a veterinary surgeon to have them checked in this respect. Such problems as in-turning eyelids, umbilical or inguinal hernias, weak knee joints, incorrect undershot or twisted (wry) jaws or cryptorchidism, may not have been noticeable to you but will be readily picked up on a routine full examination. The vet will tell you whether the condition is likely to cause an immediate or long term problem and give advise about what can be done, usually surgically, to correct the fault. On occasion he may even advise you to contact, or return the puppy, to the breeder.

Hips

The British Veterinary Association and the Kennel Club (BVA/KC) jointly administer a scheme to evaluate Hip Dysplasia in dogs, (see page 10). Hip Dysplasia is especially important in German Shepherd Dogs (Alsatians), Briards, Golden Retrievers, Great Danes, Labradors, Old English Sheepdogs, Pyreneans, Rottweilers, and Rough Collies, but other breeds of medium to large sizes are also affected.

The dog's hips are X-rayed by your own veterinary surgeon, once only, after the age of 12 months. Your veterinary surgeon will give you all the necessary information. The X-ray is then sent to the British Veterinary Association, where it is examined and evaluated for normality by members of an appointed panel who have a special interest in orthopaedics.

The X-ray is assessed on nine different aspects of the hip joint, each leg being calculated separately. Each aspect of the hip is scored up to a maximum of six points — six being indicative of a high level of deformity, nine × six points equals a maximum of 54 scored for a really bad hip, or 108 for both. Low scores, e.g. two right and four left equalling six in total are very good Hip Dysplasia scores. 0 . 0 is absolutely normal.

In some breeds, normality has not been reached and may be difficult to achieve, so what may be a poor score in one breed may be acceptable in another. The breeder or breed club should be able to tell you the target score for your breed.

In all the breeds mentioned earlier puppy buyers should insist on seeing a BVA hip score for both sire and dam, and should in due course have their own pet X-rayed in order to contribute information on the progeny those dogs are producing. Dogs and bitches are capable of producing puppies with hip joints better or worse than their own, and correct rearing plays some part in determining the final state of the hips. However breeding from the best is slowly improving the state of the hip joint in those breeds where the BVA/KC scheme has been used for some years.

It is important that every hip X-ray should be sent to the BVA for scoring so that hips are evaluated on a nationwide standard. Local evaluation by individual veterinary surgeons may not be acceptable to stud dog or bitch owners, and does nothing to improve the standard within the breed. The extra expense of scoring by the official panel is always worthwhile.

Eyes

BVA and the Kennel Club also operate an official eye examination scheme to detect several eye conditions, among them those leading to painful blindness. The recommendation is that dogs and bitches should be examined annually for the whole of their lives, as many eye conditions can be late in onset, often after the dogs concerned have been used for breeding. This applies of course to those breeds which are principally affected by such problems and particularly the animals intended for breeding.

When a fault is found in the eyes of a dog which may have produced one or two generations of descendants, ethical breeders will want to withdraw that dog from their breeding programme, but obviously all those who have related animals will also be affected. It is only by this means that we can hope to eradicate the many eye diseases from which dogs suffer.

The official eye examinations are conducted by a panel of veterinary surgeons with post-graduate qualifications in opthalmology. Examinations are either held privately (your veterinary surgeon will refer you) or at examination sessions arranged, often in conjunction with shows, by breed clubs. Where numbers of dogs are examined at one time, the fee for each is reduced and, by special permission of the Kennel Club, dogs not entered at the show may attend for eye examination. No anaesthetic is required. The examination takes only a few moments and a report is given immediately.

Breeds most susceptible to eye problems include Smooth and Rough Collies, Border Collies and Shetland Sheepdogs. Puppies from these breeds should be screened at eight weeks old for a defect peculiar to Collies — *Collie Eye Anomaly*. Do not buy a puppy in these breeds with a view to using it for breeding until you have the examination verdict. Other eye diseases affect primarily American Cocker Spaniels, Bassets, Bloodhounds, Briards, Cavaliers, Cockers, English Springers, Golden Retrievers, Irish Setters, Labradors, Miniature and Toy Poodles, as well as other breeds.

CHAPTER 4

PART V

ZOONOSES

Definition
Simple preventive measures
Signs, treatment and prevention

Zoonoses is the term applied to diseases which are transmissible from animals to humans. Most domestic animals, including dogs, cats, birds, horses and rabbits, are capable of transmitting some disease, but the risk is minimal in respect of dogs if the simple hygienic precautions listed below are taken.

1. Keep pet animals healthy, have any signs of illness diagnosed and treated promptly by a veterinary surgeon. *Regular worming with tablets obtained from the veterinary surgeon is especially important.*
2. Groom your pet regularly and thoroughly.
3. Do not allow pets to lick children's faces.
4. Insist that adults, and particularly children, wash their hands after handling pets and especially so if sick dogs are being nursed.
5. Do not feed pets from household crockery.
6. Store pet food separately from human food; sterilise knives and chopping boards after handling pet quality raw meat.
7. Wash pet bedding frequently.
8. Treat dogs and the environment for fleas regularly.
9. Pick up excreta passed in the garden and dispose of it properly.
10. Wear gloves when gardening.

These rules, which should become a way of life in pet-owning households, go most of the way towards ensuring that your pet will never be a health risk to you or your children. Most human disease is caught from other humans, so do not be too ready to blame your pet until you have positive laboratory-investigated evidence that the pet is the vector.

Sore throats, tuberculosis, and fleas can be transmitted from humans to dogs, as can the diarrhoea-causing bacteria, *salmonella* and *campylobacta*. Again, hygienic precautions will prevent you infecting your dog.

Rabies is the most serious zoonosis. This disease is transmitted by the saliva of an infected animal. Rabies is kept out of Britain by strong and continuing campaign by government, by the vigilance of customs officials, by the general public, and by our sensible quarantine laws. We must hope that we never have to concern ourselves with the possibility of rabies either in wildlife or in our pets.

Details relating to some other zoonoses are given in the following table:

141

The signs, treatment and prevention of some zoonoses which occur in the UK

Disease in Animals	Transmitted by	Symptoms – Humans	Action to be taken – Dog	Action to be taken – Human	Prevention
Toxocariasis	Matured worms inhabiting the canine intestine. See Chapter 4 Part III.	Usually none, but migrating larvae may cause problems for example if by chance they end up in the eye.	Regular worming especially of puppies but also adults with remedy prescribed by veterinary surgeon.	None. Condition usually undiagnosed.	Regular worming of dogs. Prompt collection and disposal of animal faeces. Wear gloves when gardening.
Echinococcosis	See Chapter 4 Part III.	Hydatid cysts.	Regular worming with specific remedy in those areas where the disease is endemic.	Medical and possibly surgical treatment when disease is diagnosed.	Do not allow dogs to eat carcasses of sheep or cattle.
Leptospirosis	Via urine of dog suffering the disease. See Chapter 4 Part II.	Hepatitis. Jaundice.	Veterinary treatment.	Medical treatment.	Regular vaccination and boosters. Strict hygiene precautions when attending sick dogs.
Brucellosis	The casual bacterium may be excreted by bitches at whelping. The condition is very rare in this country among the public, although veterinary surgeons in large animal practice are at risk. The most likely source of brucellosis is unpasteurised milk.	Intermittent bouts of fever, headache, joint pain.	Positive identification by laboratory tests.	Medical treatment.	Avoid possible sources of infection. Always drink heat treated milk.
Sarcoptic Mange	Transfer of mange mite from infected dog.	Irritating rash as mite burrows below the skin on hands, wrists, etc. Can also be caught by human/human contact.	Treatment by veterinary surgeon. Clean dog's bedding and the environment.	Clean environment. Apply Benzl Benzoate lotion to affected skin.	Early professional diagnosis of any skin disease on dog.

Disease	Source/Transmission	Symptoms	Identification	Treatment	Prevention
Cheyletiella Infection (Rabbit Fur Mite)	Transfer of mite from rabbit to spinal and neck fur of dog – thence to owner – smooth-coated dogs most affected.	Very irritating rash often on chest and waist area where dog/puppy is held. Mite can penetrate clothing.	Identification of mite, and bath with shampoo provided by veterinary surgeon.	None necessary. Rash usually clears when mite is eliminated from dog.	Prompt attention to scurf-like deposits on dog skin.
Ringworm	The infection can be caught by direct contact with cats, horses and cattle.	Non-irritating eroded patches on skin, probably the wrists — not necessarily circular.	Positive identification as ringworm by laboratory tests, followed by specific treatments.	Treatment by doctor.	Avoid contact with animals which may be infected.
Salmonellosis	Salmonella organisms are shed in the faeces.	Food poisoning — diarrhoea and vomiting.	Laboratory tests to identify the bacteria and their likely source.	Laboratory tests to identify source of bacteria, i.e. human or animal carrier.	Strict hygienic precautions when handling animals and food.
Tetanus	A wound such as a dog-bite may become infected with the causal organisms.	Fever, lock jaw.	None.	Medical treatment of bites.	Keep anti-tetanus injections up to date.
Fleas	From environment where dog/cat fleas are breeding.	Typical irritating bite. Possibly a full blown allergic reaction in susceptible individuals.	Anti-flea treatment of dog and environment.	None necessary, but possibly the application of antihistamine creams.	Regular de-fleaing of all animals and environment.
Toxoplasmosis	For details see Chapter 4 Part III				

CHAPTER 4

PART VI

ACCIDENTAL POISONING

Risks
Signs
Common poisons
Dangers in the house and garden

All our houses, gardens and garages contain substances which can be poisonous to dogs, and the risk is particularly high in puppies during the "chewing stage".

Potentially poisonous material should be stored where the puppy cannot possibly reach it, and where it cannot be knocked down to the puppy's level by a cat or other animal. Some substances, especially mouse/rat bait, are cumulative poisons, although they may be declared safe on the container. Beware of rat poisons laid by local authority rodent eradicators, as they may be more dangerous than those sold to the general public. Do not allow your dog to nuzzle or play with carcasses of rabbits, birds etc. found in woodland, as they may have been baited with deadly poison in order to destroy foxes or other vermin.

Be safe rather than sorry. Never shut a dog, even temporarily, into a garden shed or garage where poisonous substances are kept.

Signs of poisoning

Among the signs of poisoning will be sudden, violent vomiting and/or diarrhoea, fits, foaming at the mouth, staggering gait, collapse, and coma, but all these signs may relate to other conditions not caused by poisoning. All will require immediate veterinary help.

> **HISTORY TIP:** If the dog's illness can be associated with access to a dangerous substance, or if the dog is found with a container or packet, take all the associated material, packaging, and any vomit with you to the veterinary surgeon, to help in identifying the cause of illness and the finding of a possible antidote.

The following table indicates some common poisons, their sources and how to prevent accidental poisoning from occurring.

144

Poison risks

Situation	Poison	Source	Prevention
The Garage	Engine oil Antifreeze (Ethylene glycol) Old lead paint Paint remover Wood preserver fumes Glue Tar and creosote (Phenol) Putty	Spillage on the floor and old containers. Spillage on the floor and old containers. Flaking paint, old paint tins improperly stored. Improperly stored containers. Improperly stored containers. Old pots and tubes of glue. Spillage and old containers. Old putty containers, old window frames.	Keep the garage clean and tidy with possible poison sources on high shelves. Keep dogs out of garages as puppies will sample almost any fluid and older dogs may walk in poisonous substances and then ingest them by licking their feet.
The Kitchen	Acrolein Detergents Disinfectants Carbon Monoxide	Vapour from overheated oil or cooking fat. Bottles containing concentrated detergents. Disinfectant containers and areas where disinfectants are used undiluted Leaking coal-gas appliances. Stoves burning Calor gas, oil or solid fuel without	Ventilate kitchens properly when cooking and keep young puppies in another room. Make sure that kitchen cupboards can be firmly shut and that containers are properly closed. Such substances may be swallowed and sometimes absorbed through the skin. Have such appliances checked regularly and only use them when ventilation is adequate. Do not provide dogs with beds close to stoves and allow proper ventilation of sleeping quarters.
The Bathroom	Various medicines intended for human or animal use	Old medicine containers.	Keep part used medicines in containers that can be properly closed, not packets. Throw out old unused medicines. Keep all medicines in cabinets that can be closed and locked.
Garden Sheds	Herbicides Arsenials and and Bipyricyl Diquat and Paraquat Insecticides/ Fungicides	Old containers that are not properly closed. Material spilt on the floor. Many of the older insecticides are quite safe but products containing organochlorines, organophosphorus compounds or carbamates can be very toxic for dogs.	Ensure that all such products are in properly sealed containers kept well out of reach of dogs. Sweep the floor regularly. Do not leave diluted products ready for use in places where they can be reached by dogs. Keep dogs away from plants that have been recently sprayed; they may eat them or even absorb the poison through the skin.
	Molluscicides (slug killers) (Metaldelyde)	The pellets are very attractive to dogs.	Do not use herbicides and insecticides near where dog's food is kept. Make sure that slug pellets are not used where dogs can reach them, or that they are accidentally spilt on the floor.

Poison risks (continued)

Situation	Poison	Source	Prevention
	Antu, Calciferol, Alpha – Chloralose, Crimidine Phosphorus. Thallium Warfarin, Arsenic	Rat and mouse poisons based on these compounds.	Take great care with the use and storage of such products. If in doubt, seek professional advice. Be careful of spillage and ensure that proper containers are used. Dispose of old material with proper care.
Other Rooms in the House and Conservatories	Plant poisons	Some house plants e.g. oleanders.	Make certain that house plants are kept out of reach of puppies. Train dogs not to go near house plants.
	Nicotine	Cigarettes or cigar ends.	Empty ashtrays regularly – do not leave full ash trays within reach of dogs overnight.
	Detergents	Dry powder carpet cleaners may cause inflammation of the skin.	Ensure such cleaners are properly vacuumed up as directed and keep dogs out of the room whilst they are being applied. It is probably better not to use such products where there are dogs in the house.
	Lead	Old toys, old paintwork, other lead objects.	Replace old paintwork with no lead-based paint.
The Garden	Fungi/toadstools Berries	Hedgerows e.g. Mistletoe berries.	Keep hedgerows clear. Keep dogs away from trees where mistletoe is growing and be careful if the berries are brought indoors.
	Laburnum	Laburnum trees.	It is probably better to forgo having such trees in the garden especially if a number of dogs are kept. Take care to keep puppies away from such trees or branches which have been pruned.
	Bulbs – Daffodils and Snowdrops	Garden beds.	Train dogs not to dig in the garden and take care when planting. Keep stored bulbs out of reach.
	Various herbicides e.g. Malathion, Paraquat, Sodium Chlorate	Garden sprays and weedkillers.	Keep dogs away whilst spraying and do not allow dogs access to sprayed plants until the spray has dried on the leaves. Cover or take water bowls indoors whilst spraying. Take special precautions if farm spraying is going on or if road verges are being sprayed.
	Cyanide	Products used to destroy wasp nests.	Be careful with use and storage of such products.

CHAPTER 4
PART VII

VACCINATION

Immunity

We are all under constant attack from the millions of micro-organisms which inhabit our world, so some means of protection is essential for survival. Healthy bodies are equipped with several defence mechanisms which are in operation all the time. The skin is a barrier to invasion by microbes; the mucous membranes in the nose trap foreign substances which are breathed in, and the cough reflex comes into play when throat and larynx are irritated and to prevent "germs" getting into the lungs. The acidity of the stomach will kill invaders which get that far, and the quantities of mucus produced by the small bowel acts as a barrier to infection. Other invaders will pass from the body in faeces and urine, while the liver will destroy toxins produced by bacteria. These defence mechanisms are similar in man and animals, and they work very well when health is good, but are not so effective when the body is in a run-down state, underfed or weakened, or when there is a state of mental or physical stress.

When an organism succeeds in passing these primary barriers, the body still has resources to use against the invader. *The immune system* comes into action to manufacture special and specific weapons — antibodies — to use against the organism making the attack.

Puppies

Puppies do have an immune system of their own at birth, but it is not fully developed. Thus nature has arranged for them to acquire some protective antibodies from their mothers. These are called passive antibodies since they have not been produced by the puppy itself. A modicum of passive "maternal antibody" passes to the puppy while it is still in the uterus, but most comes via the colostrum, the first milk from the dam. Antibodies to disease in the colostrum can only be absorbed by puppies for the first day or so after birth and that time can be much shorter. It is obvious therefore that when the litter is very large or the whelping is prolonged, the early puppies are going to have more opportunity to get colostrum than those born later, so the ability to resist disease may vary between the members of the litter.

The antibodies which the dam passes to her puppies will be to those diseases which she herself has encountered or been vaccinated against. If she has lived a very isolated or protected existence, never met other dogs, and has never been vaccinated, she will have no protection to pass on, and her puppies will be vulnerable to all the infectious canine diseases from their earliest days.

147

Although the normal dam will pass on protective immunity through the colostrum, this type of protection will fade quite soon — in fact the amount in the blood halves each week, so the puppy must develop its own antibodies either by encounter with disease or by vaccination if it is to be protected for the rest of its life.

Adult dogs

Most disease-causing organisms consist mainly of proteins. A healthy body is quick to detect proteins foreign to itself and to set about rejecting them by the production of specific antibodies to the invader. These active antibodies (i.e. they are created by the animal itself) are produced by specialised white blood cells found mainly in the lymph nodes and spleen.

The first time the body encounters a specific disease, or a vaccine, active antibodies may take as long as ten days to be produced, but next time that disease presents itself memory cells come into action and antibodies are "manufactured" very quickly, so that the disease does not have the chance to become established. This is why some diseases of man and animals occur only once in a lifetime. For example, measles in man is a once-only disease and once an attack has been survived there will be lifelong protection.

Antibodies tend to be very specific and destroy only the microbe (the antigen) which stimulated their production. A blood sample taken from the dog and processed at a laboratory will show if the dog has antibodies to a particular disease circulating in the blood, and sophisticated techniques can often reveal whether the antibody has been made in response to a recent infection or has been present for some time. Antibody levels wane with time, but another encounter with the right antigen will cause a quick resurgence of production.

Vaccines

Since we do not want dogs to have to endure an episode of disease to develop their own protection, we turn to the creation of active immunity by vaccination. This is the deliberate triggering of the immune response by the giving of a small, weak dose of the disease in order to stimulate the production of antibodies.

Essentially modern vaccines fall into four main classes:

1) *Attenuated living vaccines.* Fortunately bacteria and viruses can be modified to reduce their ability to cause disease but at the same time maintain their ability to stimulate the formation of active antibodies. This is achieved by a process called attenuation and is usually brought about by growing the organism in an unnatural host, e.g. in eggs, a different species of animal or in tissue culture. The amount of attenuation depends on how long the germ is maintained in the "artificial" system. The trick is to get the right balance to achieve maximum antibody production in the animal given the vaccine and yet not cause disease. The big advantage of live vaccines is that usually only one dose is required in adult dogs to stimulate immunity. Dogs injected with the ideal live vaccine will not shed organisms to other dogs — indeed that is the case with modern Canine Distemper vaccines. If this

is not so then organisms shed from vaccinated dogs may "infect" in-contact animals and if this happens on several occasions there is always a risk that the organism's ability to cause disease may return. Such vaccines are better not used where a good alternative dead vaccine, or a live vaccine that is not shed, is available.

2) *Killed vaccines.* These are made from "germs" which have been killed by heat or chemical agents such as formalin. Although the organisms are incapable of multiplying in the vaccinated animal they, nevertheless, stimulate the formation of antibodies. However, two doses are normally required and an additive, or adjuvant as it is called, may be needed to enhance the effect. By and large, the immunity produced is not so long lasting but obviously the safety factors in vaccines of this type are greater.

3) *Toxoids.* The lethal effect of some organisms is brought about by the fact that they produce poisonous substances called toxins. The body reacts to these by producing specific antibodies called anti-toxins, which are capable of neutralising toxins. This can be done artificially by injecting a toxoid which is a detoxified toxin. Toxoids are generally made by inactivating toxins either by heat or by chemical means and on injection they stimulate anti-toxin to be formed in the body. Two doses are normally required to stimulate immunity and booster doses may be needed over one, two or three years. Probably the most familiar example is tetanus toxoid.

4) *Mixed vaccines.* It is possible to make mixed vaccines provided that care is taken to ensure the compatibility of the antigens. Mixed vaccines may contain, for example, two live antigens, several dead antigens or even a combination of live and dead antigens. Such vaccines make it possible to establish an effective degree of protection against diseases with a minimal number of injections.

Booster vaccination

Protection created by vaccines is generally not as long lasting as natural immunity, so boosters are needed periodically, different intervals being advised for the different diseases. Dogs which are kept in isolated conditions, exercised only on their owner's land and never taken to shows or training classes, are *more* in need of booster protection than those dogs which live in towns and mix frequently with other dogs and hence get a degree of natural "boosting" from the low level of infection present in the environment.

Methods of administration

Vaccines are generally given by subcutaneous or intramuscular injection, but in certain circumstances, where there is a need to stimulate local protection, they are given by other routes. For example the vaccine used to protect dogs against Kennel Cough caused by the bacterium *Bordetella bronchiseptica* is given by the intranasal route. Administration by this route stimulates the production of "local antibodies" in the upper part of the respiratory tract within only a few days just where they are needed. This is followed later by the production of antibodies in the blood stream.

When to vaccinate

Obviously the aim is to stimulate the production of active antibodies, by vaccination, as early as possible in a puppy's life. Unfortunately this is not easily achieved, since not only does maternally derived antibody protect against disease, but it also prevents a proper response to vaccination. There is, incidentally, an "immunity gap" during which puppies will not be protected by maternal antibody and have yet to produce their own active antibodies in response to vaccination. Much effort has gone into devising vaccination regimes to keep this time of vulnerability to a minimum.

Canine maternally derived antibody declines at a fixed rate, halving every seven to eight days or so, thus its duration in a particular puppy will depend on the quantity it received from its mother, which in turn depends on *her* antibody level. In fact puppies, on average, acquire levels that are about 77 per cent of their mothers', provided they suck properly in the first 24 hours of life. Clearly then, the earliest age at which puppies can be successfully vaccinated will vary considerably although it will be roughly the same for animals from one litter. Orphan puppies which have had no colostrum can be vaccinated theoretically at birth but it is wiser to wait until three to six weeks of age to allow the immune system to develop properly.

The optimum times for vaccination against distemper have been plotted most carefully by scientific sampling, and this work provided a standard formula for vaccination times, *until* the advent of canine parvovirus.

In the case of Canine Distemper it was shown that:

at six weeks old, 30 per cent of puppies have no maternal antibody left;

at eight weeks old, 65 per cent of puppies have none;

at 12 weeks old, 98 per cent of puppies have none.

Thus if puppies are vaccinated against distemper at six weeks old, only one-third of them will be able to respond. From these figures the optimum timing for distemper vaccination was evolved. One shot at six to eight weeks, when about half the puppies will be ready for it, another at 12 weeks to take in the rest, and a booster shot when the puppy is one year old. It is more than probable that either the eight week or the 12 week shot will be wasted, because the puppy is still protected by maternally derived antibody or the early dose has already stimulated an active immunity, but this formula serves to protect the majority of puppies by the time they are being taken out. It is as well to remember however that there will still be an "immunity gap" during which puppies will not be protected by passive maternally derived antibody and yet are not capable of responding to vaccination. The regime referred to above ensures that this period of susceptability is kept minimal.

Canine Parvovirus disease or vaccine produces a higher level of antibody than distemper. A bitch which has a high level of CPV antibody should pass on a lot to her puppies, so they may have to wait a long time before they are ready for vaccination, perhaps up to 20 weeks. If the bitch has not much antibody to pass on, the pups may be ready for their own vaccination at six weeks. This wide variation causes a considerable dilemma and is the reason why several doses of vaccine are often recommended.

Veterinary surgeons need to calculate the optimum time for vaccination in the light of local disease conditions and the history of the kennel in which the puppy was born, possibly in conjunction with blood sampling.

Finally, in this connection it has to be remembered that there will always be a proportion of dogs (and humans) whose body fails to make any response to vaccine given to them.

A multiplicity of safe effective vaccines are available these days to protect dogs against the five major infectious diseases from which they suffer — Canine Distemper, Infectious Canine Hepatitis, Leptospirosis, Canine Parvovirus Infection, and Kennel Cough. Hopefully this article will explain the complexity of the situation and help the reader to appreciate the need for veterinary surgeons to consider a great number of factors before selecting which vaccine to use and recommending when it should be administered. There is considerably more to vaccination than simply "giving a puppy a jab".

(Acknowledgement: This article on vaccination, by J. M. Evans, was originally published in *Kennel Gazette,* the official journal of of the Kennel Club.)

CHAPTER 5

PART I

FEEDING DOGS

| Nutrient requirements |
| Choice of foods |
| Practical feeding |
| Tables and figures |

The food eaten by different dogs varies considerably yet the majority grow well and remain healthy. This is because dogs, like any other animal, have requirements for specific nutrients rather than particular foods and provided that these needs are met, the source (prepared petfoods, fresh raw materials or a mixture) is irrelevant.

Although the dog is a member of the mammalian order Carnivora, in a nutritional sense it is more accurately defined as omnivorous, since it is able to survive on a diet made entirely of materials of animal *or* vegetable origin. Like the cat it is equipped with strong, sharp teeth designed for tearing, cutting and chewing meat, but unlike the cat its long association with man has resulted in adaptation to a much more flexible and varied diet than one consisting largely of animal tissues.

The key to proper feeding is a 'balanced diet'. A balanced diet contains appropriate quantities of all essential nutrients, neither too little nor too much. It also embraces other important characteristics of foodstuffs often taken for granted — palatability, digestibility, concentration and safety. A food may appear to be suitable on paper because a chemical analysis shows that it contains all the essential nutrients but if it is not palatable enough to be eaten, or if the nutrients are bound in such a way to prevent their digestion and absorption, it is not the balanced diet it appears to be. Similarly the food must be sufficiently concentrated to allow the dog to take in enough to meet its particular nutrient needs, and should be free from any toxins, bacteria or parasites which might harm the dog.

Nutrient Requirements

Dogs need proteins, fats, minerals, vitamins and water. They can also utilise carbohydrate although it cannot strictly be described as essential. Most foods contain a mixture of some or all of these nutrient classes and therefore careful combination of different foodstuffs will result in a suitable diet. Nutrients are required in the diet in different quantities. As Table 1 at the end of Part I of this chapter shows, a dog needs 20 times as much protein as calcium, and 100,000 times as much protein as riboflavin (vitamin B2). Even so, if *any* essential nutrient is missing or present in insufficient quantity, the whole diet is inadequate.

Energy

In addition to providing specific nutrients, food also provides energy or calories. Energy is needed not just for muscular activity or exercise, but also for maintenance of body temperature and for processes necessary for life such as breathing and heart function. Even a sleeping dog uses energy.

There are many factors which affect energy requirements. Puppy growth, pregnancy and lactation increase the requirement, but for normal adult dogs the most important factor is body weight. Figure A shows that although larger dogs have a greater requirement, this is not strictly in proportion to their bodyweight. A range is shown to allow for other influences such as age, sex, level of activity and environmental temperature.

The energy requirements of every dog will change through its lifetime. Figure B gives a theoretical example of a typical Labrador Retriever bitch, showing energy intake and bodyweight through puppyhood, two litters, a period of working and into old age. While many dogs will not experience such large fluctuations, it is important that owners recognise that needs may vary and food intake be adjusted.

The energy in food comes from protein, fat and carbohydrate which are oxidised, or burned in working tissues to release energy. Each gram of protein and carbohydrate provides approximately 4 K/cals. while fat supplies double this amount. Excessive intake of any of these leads to the accumulation of energy as body fat, inadequate energy intake will result in poor growth (in puppies) and weight loss (in adult dogs).

Protein

Proteins are very long molecules made up of chains of many small units called amino acids. There are approximately 20 different amino acids, but since each combination produces a protein with specific characteristics, there is an almost infinite variety of proteins. Proteins are essential constituents of the cells which make up the body tissues, having several important functions in the regulation of metabolism (as enzymes and some hormones), in a structural role in cell walls and muscle fibre, in transport of essential materials and in the body's defence against disease.

The protein requirements of growing puppies and pregnant and lactating bitches are weight for weight considerably greater than those of normal adult dogs. This is because protein is necessary for the synthesis of new tissue, and for the production of milk. However, even adult dogs need protein to replace that which is broken down and lost from the body every day, mostly via the kidneys in the urine, but also in faeces and hair.

Protein quality is an important consideration in the selection of foodstuffs. This is governed by two factors, digestibility and the amino acid profile. Digestible protein is that part which is absorbed through the gut wall into the body and not lost in the faeces — the digestibility of protein in the dog can vary from as low as 50 per cent in some cereals up to 95 per cent for milk or egg protein. The amino acid profile reflects which of the 20 amino acids are present in the protein. This is particularly important as ten of these are essential to the dog. Essential amino acids cannot be synthesised in sufficient quantities by the body and therefore must be provided in the diet. Non-essential amino acids are equally necessary but can be synthesised if there are sufficient raw materials present (in the form of excesses of other amino acids and non-protein nitrogen). Milk and eggs contain the greatest proportions of essential amino acids, cereal the least. This does not mean that dogs should be fed entirely on meat, milk and eggs but that judicious mixing may be necessary if cereals form a large part of the diet.

Protein deficiency can result from either insufficient dietary protein or from a shortage of particular amino acids. The observable signs are non-specific — poor growth or weight loss, loss of appetite, rough and dull hair coat and increased susceptibility to disease. Table 1 shows that the recommended protein allowance is 22 per cent of the dry matter of the food. This is an extremely generous allowance and covers all stages of the life cycle including puppy growth and breeding. In fact, assuming a good quality protein is fed, ten per cent would probably be quite adequate for non-breeding adult dogs.

Protein which is surplus to the body's requirements is *not* laid down as additional muscle but is converted to fat and stored as adipose tissue. Feeding extra protein to produce 'body' will only produce fat.

Fat

Fat has several roles in the nutrition of the dog; it is a very concentrated source of energy, it enhances the palatability of many foods and it serves as a carrier for the fat soluble vitamins A, D, E and K. However, its most important function is as a source of the essential fatty acids, particularly linoleic acid. Essential fatty acids are used as part of cell walls, and are necessary for the synthesis of prostaglandins. A deficiency of linoleic acid results in a coarse dry coat, thick dandruff, skin lesions and in reproductive failure. Dogs with this deficiency usually respond quickly to dietary supplementation with corn oil which is a rich source of linoleic acid.

Fat is well-digested by healthy dogs. The Alaskan Huskies' traditional diet is seal meat which is two-thirds fat and these dogs thrive despite adverse environmental conditions and hard work. However any diet with a very high fat content may need additional supplementation with other nutrients — such diets will be eaten in smaller quantities, therefore other nutrients should be present in higher percentages to ensure that the daily requirements are met. It is important to note that diets containing very high levels of polyunsaturated fats may become rancid with the destruction of other nutrients, particularly vitamin E.

Carbohydrate

For many years it has been assumed that while dogs are extremely good at utilising carbohydrate as an energy source, it is not an essential dietary requirement. This is because dogs are able to synthesise their glucose requirement from dietary fat and protein if these are present in sufficient quantity. However recent work in the USA has indicated that some pregnant bitches need a dietary source of carbohydrate in order to produce healthy puppies. It is difficult to reconcile this with what we know of the dog's evolutionary history as the prey which formed the diet would contain very little carbohydrate. Whether this finding is confirmed or not is academic, as the majority of dogs are traditionally fed diets which contain large proportions of carbohydrate as biscuits or meal.

There are three major groups of carbohydrates in foods: sugars, starches and the indigestible polysaccharides like cellulose. Sugars are easily digestible and are palatable to dogs which tend to have a 'sweet tooth'. Starches are long chains of the simple sugar units. They are digested easily after the starch is degraded by cooking or crushing. Untreated starch is much more difficult to digest, and dogs fed on raw potatoes or uncrushed cereal are likely to suffer from diarrhoea and flatulence as the starch is fermented by the bacteria in the large intestine.

The indigestible polysaccharides can be collectively grouped under the title of 'dietary fibre' or 'roughage'. This passes through the digestive tract relatively unchanged, adding bulk. Because it acts like a sponge retaining water, it tends to reduce the incidence of constipation (by keeping stools soft) and diarrhoea (by mopping up surplus fluid). Although many benefits associated with the intake of high levels of dietary fibre have been described in man, these are mostly associated with diseases not commonly seen in dogs. In addition the action of fibre in the human gut is through a reduction of transit time (the time taken for food to pass through the digestive system) and the dog already has a much shorter transit time than man. It seems likely therefore that if there are any uses for dietary fibre in dog nutrition, these will be limited to the management of constipation, diarrhoea, obesity and possibly diabetes.

The incorporation of high levels of fibre in the diet of normal dogs may decrease the availability for absorption of other nutrients especially minerals. It will also markedly increase faeces volume, and not more than ten per cent of the dry matter of the food should be made up of dietary fibre (less than this when puppies are fed).

Vitamins

Although required in very small amounts, vitamins are necessary for normal health and function. A vitamin is an organic compound which plays an essential part in the regulation of various metabolic pathways and is broken down in the process. Vitamins are distinguished from other compounds with similar functions in that the animal is unable to synthesise replacements and must obtain a dietary source.

It is usual to describe the different vitamins by the major specific sign of deficiency. Thus vitamin A is popularly associated with sight, since deficiencies lead to an impairment of vision, vitamin E with reproduction, and so on. This is an over-simplification since deficiencies of all the vitamins have signs in common, particularly poor appetite, general loss of condition and poor growth. Table 2 shows those vitamins which are needed by dogs (note no requirement for vitamin C) with their dietary source, main functions, signs of deficiency and problems associated with excessive intake.

Vitamins are classified according to their solubility in either water or fat. This apparently arbitrary division has practical nutritional consequences. The water soluble vitamins are not retained in the body when given in excess, but are lost in the urine. As they are not stored, frequent intake is necessary. Conversely, the fat soluble vitamins A, D, E and K are retained when fed in excess of requirements, and while this means that daily intake of these vitamins is essential, there is a danger of accumulation following prolonged overfeeding. Vitamins E and K are unlikely to be toxic, but overfeeding of vitamins A and D has been shown to have serious results, principally malformation of the bones (vitamin A) and calcification of the soft tissues (vitamin D). It is understandable that owners who want to do the best for their dogs give generous vitamin supplements "just to make sure" but the outcome may be tragic. Most diets need no supplementation, but where this is necessary great care should be taken to ensure that the manufacturer's instructions are adhered to and that the same vitamin is not being given several times under different proprietary names.

Minerals

Dogs require about 20 minerals, but some are required in such small quantities that the absolute requirements have not been established. These 'trace elements' are present in most common foodstuffs and deficiencies are most unlikely. Minerals have three important functions:

(a) as structural components of bones and teeth (calcium, phosphorus and magnesium);

(b) as soluble salts which control fluid balance (sodium, chloride, in blood and extracellular fluid; potassium, magnesium and phosphorus inside body cells);

(c) in enzymes and other proteins (such as iron in haemoglobin).

Table 3 gives details of the minerals required by dogs. Again, many are toxic if given in repeated overdoses, and indiscriminate supplementation should be avoided. Some breeders believe that the larger breeds have special requirements for calcium and phosphorus as these are the principal mineral constituents of bone. However the greater total food requirements of these dogs ensure appropriate calcium intake, provided the diet is balanced.

Water

Water should be considered in conjunction with feeding. A shortage of water leads to illness and death more quickly than that of any other nutrient and a fresh supply of drinking water is an essential part of a dog's diet.

Water is necessary for many different functions in the body. It is used as a transport medium (blood), the route for elimination of toxic wastes (urine), for heat loss (evaporation), to allow the chemical reactions necessary for life (in digestion and within the body cells) and many other functions. Water balance is controlled within quite narrow limits, and since some water loss from the body is obligatory, daily intake is essential. Water is taken into the body in several forms; in fluid drunk, as a part of food, and in the water released when protein, fat and carbohydrate are broken down. It is lost in faeces, urine, by evaporation (mainly from the lungs), and in milk of the lactating bitch. The precise daily requirements of each dog depend on its particular situation and therefore a plentiful supply of clean drinking water should be always available.

Choice of Foods

There are many different ways of satisfying the need for nutrients. For dogs, these fall broadly into two categories — the use of prepared petfoods and of home-made diets. Neither of these methods is 'right' or 'wrong', each having different advantages and disadvantages.

Prepared petfoods

Prepared petfoods provide all the important aspects of a balanced diet — guaranteed nutrition, palatability, digestibility, suitable energy density and safety, in addition to convenience. They also offer variety without loss of consistency. Table 4 shows the main categories of prepared food, classified according to method of preservation, together with typical ingredients and characteristics. Most of the dogs in the population are normal adult dogs and the majority of foods are intended to meet the needs of this group, with more specialised foods for other stages of the life cycle such as puppy growth. This is a much less wasteful use of resources than formulating all foods to meet the most demanding situation. Foods for adult dogs can be divided into complete and complementary (which are intended to be mixed with other foods, e.g. canned food with biscuit, such as Pedigree Chum and Pedigree Chum mixer). This diversification is not as complicated as it may seem at first sight; the label should specify the intended role, give a guide to quantity and may also state how the food has been developed and tested.

Fresh foods

Considerable skill is necessary to put together a satisfactory diet from fresh raw materials. It is not enough simply to buy 'meat' whether best steak or 'pet mince' on the assumption that this is the natural diet of a dog. As a hunter, the dog did not restrict itself to the muscle meat of its prey, but ate the whole body, so obtaining minerals, vitamins and even roughage from the bones, brains, skin, gut and gut contents. Muscle meat alone cannot form a balanced diet as it contains inadequate amounts of calcium, phosphorus, iodine, copper and the fat soluble vitamins. It is possible to calculate that to meet its calcium requirement, a half-grown Labrador Retriever would need to eat seven times its own bodyweight in lean meat every day! Nevertheless, meat (including offals and tripe) is an excellent source of protein and, with careful supplementation, can form the basis of a reasonable diet. Table 5 shows the main groups of foods commonly used for pet feeding, with a summary of their nutrient content.

Other raw materials have different attendant problems. For example, cow's milk contains the milk sugar lactose in substantial quantities, bitches' milk contains little and many puppies lose the ability to digest it after weaning. When fed cows' milk, such puppies (and adult dogs) develop severe diarrhoea as a result of lactose intolerance. Eggs, when fed raw in substantial quantities, may cause a vitamin deficiency; this is because raw egg white contains a substance called avidin which binds biotin (a water soluble vitamin) and makes it unavailable. Heating destroys avidin and therefore eggs should be fed cooked. Mineral availability can be a problem when some cereals are fed, as one of their constituents binds to certain minerals, limiting their availability.

Although there are some materials which can be fed raw, cooking is advisable for most foods, particularly meats. Cooking will kill most bacteria and parasites and will improve the digestibility of some materials. However, over-cooking should be avoided as this will reduce the food value of proteins and destroy vitamins. Minerals and vitamins may be lost if the cooking water is discarded.

The same principles of hygiene should be employed in the preparation of food for pets as for the family. The list in Table 6 gives some reminders of basic principles. These include care in purchase, storage, preparation and feeding.

Supplementation

Most prepared petfoods, when fed as directed, require no additional supplementation. The larger manufacturers have large analytical laboratories which run continuous checks on the mineral and vitamin contents of their foods, in addition to facilities for long-term feeding trials. Home-made diets based on offal and fresh meats usually do require some supplementation, even when a good quality biscuit or meal is fed. The dangers of excessive supplementation have already been outlined, these are real dangers and should not be ignored.

Table 7 shows the various supplements available to dog owners. These range from proprietary vitamin supplements to herbal remedies, stopping just short of witchcraft. Some, such as garlic tablets and raspberry powders, have little scientific basis but are quite harmless.

Practical Feeding

Adult dogs

Most of the six million dogs in Great Britain are normal, healthy, non-working, non-breeding animals. These are by far the easiest to feed, having the least demanding nutrient requirements, and in general their problems are those of over-feeding rather than nutrient deficiencies.

Adult dogs will thrive on all diet types from complete dry foods, canned foods and biscuit, to home-made mixtures of fresh meat and meals. Sudden changes in diet should be avoided as this may lead to diarrhoea and if a new food is introduced it should be done gradually. Dogs left in boarding kennels or taken on holiday should be fed their usual food, if possible, as a change of diet will only add to the stress involved in travel and change of environment. Adults need to be fed only once a day, preferably at the same time, at the convenience of the owner. Some dog owners routinely fast their dogs on one day each week and while this practice is not recommended for every dog, it appears to have no ill effects on those involved.

The quantities of food required depend on several factors including temperature. Dogs living outside in the winter will require more food to maintain their bodyweight than in other seasons. In very hot weather water supply is the most critical factor since the dog relies on panting, with evaporation of water from the respiratory tract and tongue, to lose heat and maintain its body temperature within normal limits.

Dogs which are working also have higher energy needs than pet dogs of the same size, sex and age. This group includes police and army dogs, sheep dogs and, of course, sledge dogs. They are usually fed after a day's work, when they are tired, and should be given a palatable concentrated food, to ensure that their requirements are met. Extensive exercise increases food requirements, particularly in a cold climate.

Pregnancy and lactation

Just as a human mother-to-be is often mistakenly encouraged to 'eat for two', many dogs are overfed during pregnancy. In dogs the fertilised eggs are not attached to the wall of the uterus until two to three weeks after mating, later than in other mammals, and the additional demand for nutrients is negligible until the sixth or seventh week. In the last three or four weeks the foetuses grow very rapidly. The provision of energy and nutrients is extremely important at this stage, as the failure to supply sufficient food will firstly affect the condition of the bitch and eventually the puppies will suffer, being at best small, at worst malformed or dead.

If the bitch is a reasonable weight at mating, well-covered but not fat, no changes need to be made to her normal balanced diet until the fifth or sixth week after mating. Although approximately 40 per cent more food will be required during the final part of pregnancy, it is a good idea to scale this so that the amounts increase gradually. For example, a 20 per cent increase in the fifth week, 30 per cent in the sixth and so on, increasing by ten per cent every week, is a practical yet appropriate scheme, and experience has shown that this results in healthy puppies of good size and a bitch whose weight after whelping is little different from weight at mating.

It may be necessary to divide the allocation into several small meals towards the end of pregnancy as the uterus takes up more and more space in the abdomen, limiting the volume of the stomach. A fairly concentrated diet should be adopted for the same reason; a diet of canned or fresh meat alone would usually be too dilute and bulky and should be fed with a good quality biscuit or meal.

There may be some loss of appetite immediately before whelping. This is quite normal, but if it persists into lactation, veterinary attention should be sought as inappetence at this time may be associated with a variety of clinical conditions and, in any case, prolonged food deprivation will limit milk production. Lactation is arguably the most nutritionally demanding stage of a bitches' life cycle. Dogs' milk is very concentrated (having twice the energy, dry matter, protein and fat of cows' milk) and requires a considerable amount of food and energy to produce. It has been shown that at peak lactation, some bitches produce up to seven and a half per cent of their own body weight in milk every day. Even though the majority produce around four per cent, this is still a considerable output. During the third and fourth weeks after whelping, a bitch may need *four* times her normal daily intake. The exact quantity depends on the size of the litter and whether the pups have any other source of nutrients in addition to the bitch's milk. The food may need to be divided into several small meals, and again it should be concentrated and palatable. Some dogs may be left to determine their own intake, but others will overeat if allowed to eat to appetite and a careful watch of their intake and bodyweight will be necessary. An unlimited supply of fresh drinking water will also be necessary.

Weaning should be a gradual process. An abrupt separation of bitch and puppies may lead to mastitis in the bitch and a check in growth of the puppies. Puppies may be offered small amounts of soft foods from as early as two weeks of age, but only if they show an interest. Much will depend on the size of the litter and the milk supply of the bitch, and however early the puppies take alternative foods, the bitch's milk should remain the prime source of nutrients until the puppies are at least four weeks old. Gradual separation and withdrawal of the bitch will allow her milk supply to dry up without the use of medicaments and allow the puppies to adapt to their new food naturally. It may be advisable to cut the bitch's food down to half the maintenance level immediately after total separation, but if the bitch has lost condition during lactation she will need additional food to bring bodyweight back up to normal as soon as her milk supply has diminished and weaning is completed.

Puppies

Puppies have special feeding requirements. They require large amounts of food in relation to their bodyweight but have a stomach of small capacity. Very young puppies need two or three times as much food as an adult dog of the same weight (comparing for example a 7kg Boxer puppy with an adult Cairn Terrier, Figure 4) because they need to supply energy for maintenance and activity in addition to the materials for growth. It is very important to allow such puppies the opportunity to satisfy their needs, despite the small capacity, and for this reason the total food allocation after weaning should be divided into four or five meals spread as far apart as possible through the day. As the puppies grow this can be cut down to two or three meals and eventually the single daily meal of the adult.

159

Feeding

The question of exactly how much food is difficult to answer in general terms. The values in Figure 4 are derived from the National Research Council's recommendations, but these are intended only as a guide and individual puppies' needs will vary. It is now known that to cram food into puppies, or to allow free access to a palatable diet in an attempt to achieve very rapid early growth, may lead to bone disorders, especially in the dogs of larger breeds. On the other hand any puppy needs to grow quickly enough to fulfil its genetic potential for size before the bones lose their ability to increase in length. As with many aspects of nutrition it is a question of moderation and balance and it is ultimately the responsibility of the owner to assess the health and condition of their own dog, taking advice where appropriate from other owners and breeders and, of course, their veterinary surgeon.

Not all foods are suitable for puppies. Volume should be limited and therefore the food may need to be more concentrated than some of the foods available for adult dogs. Similarly many of the dry foods which are fed to adult dogs may be too hard for puppies to eat or be insufficiently digestible. In addition to larger quantities of food, puppies need a greater concentration of protein in their diet than adult dogs. Most of the canned foods will contain adequate levels of protein, and the proportion of biscuit can be adjusted. There are also specialist puppy foods which are designed to provide all the nutrients in a form which is easily eaten and digested.

Contrary to some schools of thought, milk is not an essential food for puppies as it provides nothing which cannot be obtained from other foods. However, for puppies which can tolerate it, milk may make a useful supplement to the feeding regime.

Any changes which are made to the diet should be made gradually to avoid stomach upsets. Overfeeding may also cause diarrhoea, because of the strain on the digestive system. A puppy, whatever its age, should be fit and lively, not fat and lethargic.

Old and sick dogs
There is often much that an owner can do to give nutritional support to dogs which are ill. For example, during convalescence the provision of an appetising food which is carefully balanced is essential to the proper recovery of the dog. There are proprietary diets for this but it is also possible to use the highest quality prepared foods or home-made diets, always remembering that fresh meat will need supplementation.

Specific illnesses require special dietary treatment. For instance diabetes requires consistant energy and carbohydrate intake; nephritis (kidney disease), a low protein diet with a protein of high quality; and some forms of heart disease, a low salt diet. All of these are likely to be needed in conjunction with other treatment and the veterinary surgeon will often give dietary advice when prescribing other therapies.

Old dogs suffer from a variety of different problems, each requiring specific nutritional support. Some of these may be contradictory, and this is why it is difficult, if not impossible, to design a diet which is suitable for all old dogs. Common problems of old dogs include the diseases listed above, in addition to obesity and constipation. As dogs become older their energy requirement decreases (partly through lack of activity, partly through a drop in metabolic rate) but often their intake remains unchanged.

Obesity, with all its complications (see Chapter 5 Part II) is a very unpleasant condition and it is worth making strenuous efforts to prevent it. Constipation occurs as the muscles in the intestines become more sluggish and it may help to add a little wheat bran to the food.

Some old dogs suffer a temporary loss of appetite. While it is inevitable that they will lose weight because of inadequate energy intake, it is possible to ensure that the vitamin and mineral intakes are kept up by careful supplementation of the food which is eaten, or by dosing with tablets under veterinary guidance in extreme cases where no food is taken.

For old dogs and sick dogs, the guidelines are the same as for every other group discussed earlier — provide a diet which is palatable, digestible and which has appropriate nutrient content for that dog. Look at the condition of the dog and, if in doubt, consult a veterinary surgeon. If prepared foods are used, it can be helpful to seek advice from the manufacturer.

Table 1 Recommended nutrient allowance for the dog*

Nutrient	Unit	Allowance per 100g DM or per 400 K/cals.
Protein	g	22
Fat	g	5
Linoleic acid	g	1
Calcium	g	1.1
Phosphorus	g	0.9
Potassium	g	0.6
Sodium chloride	g	1.1
Magnesium	mg	40
Iron	mg	6
Copper	mg	0.73
Manganese	mg	0.5
Zinc	mg	5.0
Iodine	mg	0.15
Selenium	ug	11
Vitamin A	IU	500
Vitamin D	IU	50
Vitamin E	IU	5
Thiamin (B₁)	mg	0.1
Riboflavin (B₂)	mg	0.22
Pantothenic acid	mg	1
Niacin	mg	1.14
Pyridoxine (B₆)	mg	0.1
Biotin	ug	10
Folic acid	ug	18
Vitamin B₁₂	ug	2.2
Choline	mg	120

IU = International Units
* Taken from the National Research Council (1974) Nutrient Requirements of Dogs, to allow for dogs at all stages of the life cycle.

Table 2 Vitamins

Vitamin	Dietary source	Main functions	Results of deficiency	Results of excess
Fat Soluble Vitamin A	Fish oils, liver, vegetables	Vision in poor light, maintenance of skin	Night blindness, skin lesions	Anorexia, pain in bones (malformation)
Vitamin D	Cod-liver oil, eggs, animal products	Calcium balance, bone growth	Rickets, osteomalacia	Anorexia, calcification of soft tissues
Vitamin E	Green vegetables, vegetable oils, dairy products	Reproduction	Infertility, anaemia, muscle weakness	n/k
Vitamin K	Spinach, green vegetables, liver, in vivo synthesis	Blood clotting	Haemorrhage	n/k
Water Soluble (B group) Thiamin (B$_1$)	Dairy products, cereals, organ meat	Release of energy from carbohydrate	Anorexia, vomiting, paralysis	n/k
Riboflavin (B$_2$)	Milk, animal tissues	Utilisation of energy	Weight loss, weakness, collapse, coma	n/k
Niacin	Cereals, liver, meat, legumes	Utilisation of energy	Anorexia, ulceration of mouth (black tongue)	n/k
Pyridoxine (B$_6$)	Meat, fish, eggs, cereals	Metabolism of amino acids	Anorexia, anaemia, weight loss, convulsions	n/k
Vitamin (B$_{12}$)	Liver, meat, dairy products	Division of cells in bone marrow	Anaemia	n/k
Folic acid	Offals, leafy vegetables	As B$_{12}$	Anaemia, poor growth	n/k
Pantothenic acid	Animal products, cereals, legumes	Release of energy from fat/ carbohydrate	Slow growth, hair loss, convulsions, coma	n/k
Biotin	Offal, egg yolk, legumes	Metabolism of fat and amino acids	Loss of coat condition (scaly skin, scurf)	n/k
Choline	Plant and animal materials	Nerve function	Fatty infiltration of liver, poor blood clotting	n/k

n/k = not known in dogs

Table 3 Minerals

Mineral	Dietary sources	Main functions	Results of deficiency	Results of excess
Calcium	Bones, milk, cheese, white bread	Bone formation, nerve and muscle formation	Poor growth, rickets, convulsions	Very high levels — bone deformities
Phosphorus	Bones, milk, meat	Bone formation, energy utilisation	Rickets (rare)	Symptoms of calcium deficiency
Potassium	Meat, milk	Water balance, nerve function	Poor growth, paralysis kidney and heart lesions	Muscular weakness?
Sodium/chlorine	Salts, cereals	Water balance, muscle and nerve activity	Poor growth, exhaustion	Thirst, high blood pressure (if intake maintained)
Magnesium	Cereals, bones, green vegetables	Bone formation, protein synthesis	Anorexia, vomiting muscular weakness	Diarrhoea
Iron	Eggs, meat (liver), green vegetables	Part of haemoglobin (oxygen transport)	Anaemia, low resistance to hookworm infestation	Weight loss, anorexia
Copper	Meat, bones	Part of haemoglobin	Anaemia	Anaemia in other mammals, hepatitis in Bedlington Terriers
Zinc	Meat, cereals	In digestion, tissue maintenance	Hair loss, skin thickening, poor growth	Diarrhoea
Manganese	Tea, nuts, cereals	Fat metabolism, many enzyme functions	Reproductive failure, poor growth	Poor fertility in other mammals, albinism, anaemia
Iodine	Fish, dairy produce	Part of thyroid hormone	Hair loss, apathy, drowsiness	In other animals, symptoms similar to deficiency
Cobalt	Organ and muscle meat, milk	Part of vitamin B_{12}	—	n/k
Selenium	Cereals, fish meals	Associated with vitamin E function	Muscle damage	Toxic

Dogs may also require molybdenum, fluorine, tin, silicon, cobalt, nickel, vanadium and chromium in very small amounts.
n/k = not known in dogs

163

Table 4 Prepared petfoods

Type of food	Feeding	Major ingredients	Comments
Dog biscuits/meal	Complementary — to be mixed with canned food or fresh meat	Cereals, some have mineral and vitamin supplementation	Cheap source of roughage and energy. May have low palatability
Dry complete foods	May be fed alone, only water required	Cereals, animal and vegetable protein concentrates, fats, vitamins and minerals	Cheap feeding regime, but may be problems with palatability and digestibility, particularly in loose mixed diets
Semi-moist foods	May be fed alone, only water required	Some cereals, protein concentrates, fats, vitamins and minerals to meet requirements	Higher water content leads to softer food which is more palatable
Canned foods	Mostly complementary — to be fed with biscuit	Meat, poultry, minerals, vitamins, some cereals or soya	Soft moist texture, very high palatability, even when mixed with biscuit. Canning process very effective preservation

Table 5 Fresh foods

Food	Source of	Seriously deficient in	Comments
Meat (lean beef, mince, chicken)	Protein, fat, some B vitamins, some minerals	Calcium, phosphorus, iodine, copper, fat soluble vitamins, biotin	
Tripe	Protein, fat	Calcium, phosphorus, many trace minerals, most vitamins	
Liver	Protein, fat, fat soluble vitamins, B vitamins	Calcium, phosphorus, other minerals	Excessive amounts of liver may lead to disease
Milk	Most nutrients		Some dogs cannot digest the lactose in milk
Eggs	Most nutrients		Raw egg white may lead to biotin deficiency (see text)
Bones	Calcium, phosphorus, magnesium, protein	Fat, vitamins, some minerals, essential fatty acids	Only feed large uncooked bones, not small or splintery ones. Restrict to one weekly as high ash content may cause intestinal problems
Bread/cereals	Carbohydrate (energy), some protein, some minerals and vitamins	Fat, essential fatty acids, fat soluble vitamins	High levels of phytate may restrict absorption of minerals

Table 6 Storage and preparation of fresh foods

Purchase
1. Make sure materials are fresh and have been stored in clean area. For meats check colour and smell.

Storage
1. Meats should be refrigerated or frozen. If meat is refrigerated, it should be used within one or two days of purchase. Frozen meat should be thawed slowly, used immediately and not refrozen after cooking.
2. Store dry materials in secure containers away from rodents and check for mites which will reduce food value. Do not keep indefinitely as vitamin potency will be reduced.

Preparation/serving
1. Cook meat to destroy parasites and bacteria. Do not reheat cooked meat after cooking. Cool before feeding.
2. Always use clean utensils and bowls which have been thoroughly rinsed to get rid of all detergent.
3. With the exception of dry foods, remove and discard uneaten food after 30 minutes.

Table 7 Dietary supplements

	Nutrient	Dosage	Dangers
Proprietary supplements	Minerals and/or vitamins	As directed	Toxic in excess
Yeast tablets	B group vitamins	As directed for man but scale to dog size by weight	None
Cod liver oil	Vitamins A, D, E	Less than one 5ml teaspoon per week for largest dogs	Toxic in excess
Vegetable oils	Essential fatty acids	One per cent of dry matter of diet (e.g. five per cent of meat diet)	Become rancid with time
Bone meal	Calcium, phosphorus	¼oz per lb meat	May cause malformed bones in excess
Seaweed tablets	Iodine	As directed	Little
Garlic tablets	?	?	?
Raspberry tablets	?	?	?

Feeding

Figure A   Factors determining energy requirements

Figure C   Growth of pups in utero

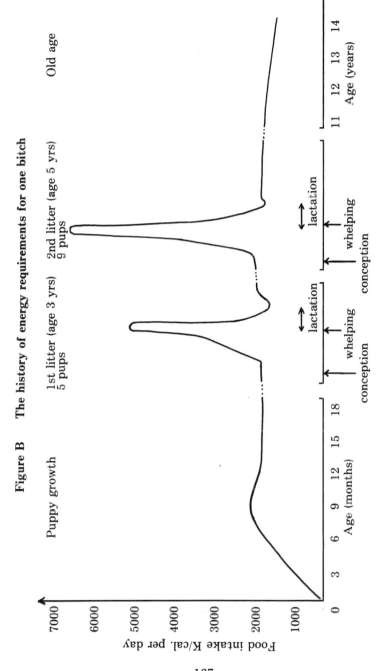

Figure B   **The history of energy requirements for one bitch**

Figure D   Energy requirements at different stages of life cycle

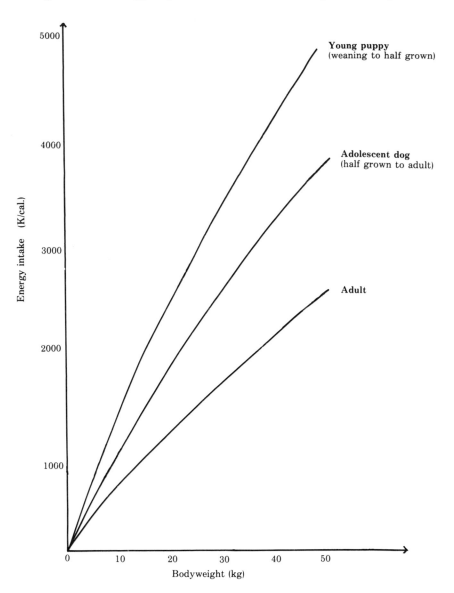

CHAPTER 5

PART II

OBESITY

The cause

Associated problems

Treatment

Prevention

Obesity is the single most common nutritional problem faced by both dogs and people in the developed world. Estimates vary, but approximately one-third of the populations of each species in these countries can be described as obese. The cause of obesity is quite simply eating more than is needed by the body, resulting in storage of the excess as fat in adipose tissue. There are many theories to explain why some animals eat more than others and why some appear to need less than others, but the fact remains that if intake exceeds requirement, for whatever reason, the result will be the accumulation of fat and a gain in bodyweight.

Why is obesity a problem? The definition gives the answer — obesity is an excess of body fat to the extent that normal bodily function is impaired. Unfortunately it is a problem which develops gradually so that the owner will often notice no change from day to day in the health and size of the dog — only approaching the veterinary surgeon when their dog has become severely incapacitated, as a consequence of its weight problem, yet not realising that the excessive weight is the cause of the disability. The major conditions associated with obesity are:
— orthopaedic problems (arthritis)
— congestive heart failure
— breathing difficulties
— reduced liver function
— reproductive problems
— diabetes mellitus
— impaired digestive function (flatulence)
— increased surgical and anaesthetic risk
— reduced resistance to disease
— heat intolerance
— skin disease
— reduced life expectancy

All these conditions (and more) have been attributed to obesity. Some result from the additional weight putting strain on some of the body's systems (for example locomotory problems, breathing problems), others to the insulating effect of a thick fat 'jacket' (heat intolerance). This list shows just how important the prevention of obesity is, and why it is worth slimming an obese dog rather than allowing it to waddle on in discomfort to an early death.

Obesity is easy to recognise. Not only is the behaviour of an obese dog

169

characteristic (see Table 1 at the end of this part of Chapter 5) but the visible signs are obvious. Conventional wisdom has it that a dog whose ribs are visible when moving is not obese; this is all very well for short-haired breeds but less useful for those with long flowing coats such as Setters and Afghans. If the ribs can be felt easily under the coat then it is unlikely that the dog is obese. Feeling other areas may also help, for example, fat may accumulate along the spine and around the base of the tail. If an owner is uncertain about the condition of his or her dog then a look back at old photographs might also help. A seriously obese dog should receive veterinary help immediately but if a dog is only showing a tendency to gain weight then a careful watch over its diet should suffice until the next routine visit to the surgery.

Treatment

The aim of any slimming diet is to reduce fat content of the body with as little effect as possible on the 'lean body mass' (muscles, organs). The lean body mass determines the resting metabolic rate (the rate at which energy is used) and therefore undue loss will not only weaken the body but reduce the amount of food needed to maintain the final bodyweight, increasing the risk of eventual further weight gain. It has been shown in man that too rapid weight loss results in excessive loss of lean tissue and therefore a slow but steady reducing regime is recommended.

It is not essential to buy special foods. Providing the total energy (or calorie) content of the diet is carefully reduced, the dog's normal diet can be used quite successfully. There are certain pitfalls and owners should be aware that some dietary components contain many more calories than others (Table 2). It may help to reduce the biscuit component of the diet as this will have a disproportionately large effect on energy density without significantly affecting total bulk. A sprinkling of wheat bran on top of the food is also reputed to have an effect in satisfying hunger, although the use of bran should be restricted as it does provide some calories.

The specially formulated 'slimming diets' available from veterinary surgeons do have certain advantages over home-made preparations. Not only do they contain all the nutrients required for normal health together with a large proportion of indigestible matter (to provide bulk without calories, rather like the 'high-fibre diet' for human slimmers) but their composition is controlled and constant. This makes adjusting the intake to achieve a reasonable rate of weight loss much simpler. These diets are only available from veterinary surgeons who will also provide advice, feeding guides and relevant literature.

Whatever the diet and its source, there are some guidelines which will help to increase the chances of success:

1. **Establish a goal**
   Decide how much weight needs to be lost (by consulting a veterinary surgeon, a breeder, or breed records, etc.). Don't forget individuals vary in optimum weight. Make a note of the current weight and the desired weight.

2. **Decide on a dietary regime**
   It may take several attempts before appropriate quantities are established, but the first step is to try one level (Table 3). Whether a prepared slimming food is used, or a modification of the dogs's normal diet, a fixed quantity should be decided on and fed for one week — *exclusively* — and then the dog reweighed. If the weight loss is not sufficient the diet should be adjusted (reduced by 20 per cent for example) for the next week.

3. **Weigh the dog regularly**
   It is necessary to monitor the dog's progress carefully. Some dogs will sit on bathroom scales, others may have to be held by owner and then the owner's weight subtracted. Once a week (preferably at the same time of day) is quite frequent enough as there will be some fluctuation in bodyweight from day to day. Keep a graph of body weight plotted against time.
   Figure A gives a hypothetical example of the progress of one overweight female Labrador.

4. **Aim for gradual weight loss**
   Gradual weight loss with retraining of appetite is more likely to result in permanent weight loss than a starvation diet followed by a return to the previous diet. For example, reasonable rates of loss are:

Size/breed	Weight loss
Small dogs, e.g. Cairn, Dachshund	less than ¼ kg per week
Medium, e.g. Beagle	¼ to ¾ kg per week
Larger, e.g. Labrador	¾ to 1½ kg per week

5. **Encourage exercise**
   Exercise alone will not result in sufficient weight loss for most dogs. However, as an adjunct to a decrease in food intake it can only help.
   NOTE: Do not *over* exercise grossly obese dogs as this may put intolerable strain on heart and lungs. Gentle exercise (e.g. walking) is the order of the day for dogs more than 25 per cent over their target weight.

6. **Make it easy for the dog**
   A reduction in calorie intake below expenditure must inevitably result in hunger. It is important that the owner of a would-be slim dog appreciates this — it is no good feeling sorry for your dog and offering snacks and titbits as a peace offering, this will only make the problem worse.
   There are certain manoeuvres which may appease hunger. These include the addition of materials which give bulk but are poorly digested. Dividing the food into two or three small meals may also reduce hunger. A long bone, stripped of its meat and fat will offer little in the way of calories but some satisfaction.

7. **Convince your friends**
There will always be people who cannot resist appealing eyes and a soulful expression, people who will believe that it is cruel to 'starve' a dog. If you live next to one of these people it makes it even more difficult to achieve satisfactory weight loss, for as soon as your back is turned, your dog will be fed biscuits and scraps and be beating a path to your neighbour's door for food. It is necessary to convince everyone who comes into contact with this dog that it is in its *own* interest that it should lose weight.

Prevention

By far the best way to eliminate obesity from any population is to prevent it rather than attempt to cure it. There are difficulties in this, however, particularly since the gradual onset means that owners slowly become accustomed to their dog's fatness and never see a sudden change. Nevertheless it is still entirely preventable. Glandular obesity, a defect which slows metabolism, is very rare and it is possible, with a sufficiently small food allowance to prevent even these dogs from becoming obese.

Each dog is different. Wide ranges are deliberately given on manufacturers' feeding guides to make allowance for this, and it is the responsibility of the owner to determine their dog's needs precisely. Fatty snacks and titbits which may just tip the balance from weight stability to weight gain should be avoided for all but the most active dogs.

Some dogs are more susceptible to obesity than others. These include bitches (particularly when spayed), older dogs, dogs of old and/or obese owners and dogs of certain breeds such as Labrador Retrievers, Dachshunds, Cocker Spaniels and Collies. Owners of dogs in these categories need to be particularly careful, but even dogs outside these groups can become obese if not properly fed. There is a well-known saying that 'fat babies make fat adults' and that may be true for dogs too. In man, the theory was that a fat child made excessive numbers of adipocytes (fat cells) which predisposed him to obesity as an adult, but this theory has now been largely discredited. It is more likely that the fat puppy gets accustomed to overfeeding and as a result begs for more food than thinner companions.

(*Acknowledgements:* The authors are indebted to Sandra E. Blaza BSc PhD, of The Waltham Centre for Pet Nutrition, for providing text for this chapter.)

Table 1 Characteristic behaviours of overweight dogs

Eating behaviour	* eats food very quickly and asks for more * begs for food at family mealtimes
Activity	* sleeps rather than plays * refuses to walk more than short distances * pants heavily if made to run * has difficulty negotiating steps and slopes
Effect of weather	* seeks shade, pants and sprawls out in warm weather

Table 2 Energy content of different foods

Food	Energy content K/cals. per 100g.
Canned dog foods	75-100
Puppy food (canned)	140
Dog biscuits and meals	340-390
Complete dry foods	330-370
Fatty mince	180-220
Liver	158-180
Dressed tripe	70-90
Green tripe	100
Milk	65
Bacon	400-500
Cheese	300-450
Chocolate	500

Table 3 Suggested feeding regime for obese dogs

Target weight (kg)	Energy allowance (K/cals.)	Canned slimming diet[1] (g)	Dry slimming diet[2] (g)	Canned + Biscuit (g) + (g)
less than 3	up to 150	up to 150	up to 45	up to 75 + up to 25
3-6	150-300	150-300	45-90	75-150 + 25-50
6-10	300-450	300-450	90-135	150-225 + 50-75
10-15	450-600	450-600	135-180	225-300 + 75-100
15-20	600-750	600-750	180-230	300-375 + 100-125
20-25	750-900	750-900	230-270	375-450 + 125-150
25-30	900-1000	900-1000	270-300	450-500 + 150-170
30-35	1000-1150	1000-1150	300-350	500-575 + 170-190
35-40	1150-1250	1150-1250	350-380	575-625 + 190-210
40-45	1250-1350	1250-1350	380-410	625-675 + 210-225
45-55	1350-1500	1350-1500	410-450	675-750 + 225-250
50-60	1500-1700	1500-1700	450-515	750-850 + 250-285
60-70	1700-1900	1700-1900	515-575	850-950 + 285-320
70+	1900+	1900+	575+	950+ 320+

[1] e.g. Obesity Diet (Pedigree Petfoods)
[2] e.g. Doggy Lo-Calorie (Leo Laboratories)

Figure A   The history of weight loss in one dog

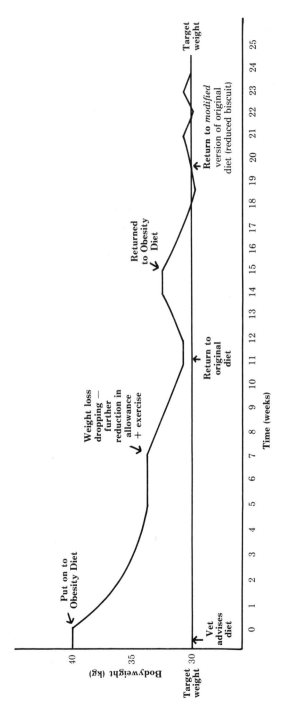

CHAPTER 6

FIRST AID AND HOME NURSING

Dog care and first aid kit

A first aid kit for the car

Emergency muzzling

Finding a veterinary surgeon in an emergency

Dealing with a road traffic accident

Table of common emergencies

Care of dogs before and after a surgical operation

FIRST AID

There will inevitably be times when your dog will need some first aid before being taken to a veterinary surgeon for treatment. First check the "What if" section of Chapter 4. If you are in doubt about what to do, telephone the veterinary surgery, and ask the nurse or receptionist if you are unable to speak to the veterinary surgeon at the time.

The following list of equipment, kept in a box labelled "Dog first aid kit", will be invaluable both for you and for anyone who may be taking care of the dog for you.

Your veterinary surgery can provide you with most of these items.

Dog Care and First Aid Kit

Tweezers, curved and straight scissors, nail clippers.
Strip of soft strong tape for emergency muzzle.
Conforming bandage which sticks to itself as layers are put on.
Disinfectant — T.C.P. is ideal.
Cotton wool.
Antacid emulsion for indigestion and flatuence.
Children's soluble aspirin as analgesic.
Liquid paraffin for constipation.
Meat tenderiser, soothes both wasp and bee stings.
Small nuggets of washing soda. (This acts as an emetic but should only
   be used on veterinary advice.)
Tube of antiseptic cream.
Roll of 2″ or 3″ wide adhesive plaster.
2″ and 4″ open weave cotton bandage.
2″ crepe bandage.
Small sterile container for urine sample.
Small jar or plastic pot for faeces sample.
Small empty bottle for giving liquid medicine.
Anti-flea spray, as advised by veterinary surgeon.
Environmental flea spray.
Shampoo specifically made for dogs.
Glucose powder.
Ear drops
Eye drops)as advised by veterinary surgeon.
Antihistamine tablets — as advised by veterinary surgeon for use after
   insect stings.
A small note book — in which to record the dog's weight and details of
   previous illness and treatments given. Most importantly the book
   should contain a note of the vetinerary surgeon's telephone number
   together with two alternative numbers for emergency use and the
   telephone number of a taxi company.

The prudent owner will also carry a few first aid items in the car, in order to be able to help his own dog or another which may be in distress.

When a dog travels in the car, *always* carry a bottle of water and a drinking bowl. In summer, a flask of ice can be invaluable. A strong blanket on which an injured dog can be carried is a necessity.

A First Aid Kit for the Car

Strong, washable nylon braid slip collar and lead.
Length of soft tape for an emergency muzzle.
Curved scissors, tweezers.
Small bottle of diluted antiseptic.
Large pad of cotton wool.
2″ crepe bandage, 2″ open weave cotton bandage.
3″ elastoplast.
Leg from a pair of tights to put over head if ears are bleeding.
Bottle of meat tenderiser to put on stings.
Roll of kitchen paper for blotting, cleaning etc.

Putting on a Emergency Muzzle

An important action when trying to cope with an injured dog is to put on an emergency muzzle so that helpers do not get bitten. However, do not muzzle dogs that are having difficulty with breathing. Even the sweetest tempered dog may bite when shocked, bewildered and in pain. Practice putting the muzzle on your own dog in a non-emergency situation.

Procedure:

1. Stand behind the dog, holding length of material in both hands.
2. Put centre of bandage/material on top of the muzzle, in front of the eyes.
3. Pass the bandage under the chin from both sides and cross over, bringing the bandage round to the back of the neck and tie behind the ears. In dogs with strong jaws it will be necessary to have a simple knot under the jaw rather than just crossing the ends under the jaw as described above. The real experts use a clove hitch on the muzzle.
4. For short-nosed dogs, a second length of bandage may be looped over the first and brought up between the eyes to anchor the restrainer to the mouth.

Fig. 28 **Emergency tape muzzle**

Fig. 29 **Clove hitch**

Finding a Veterinary Surgeon in an Emergency

Try: Police, Post Office, Yellow Pages, or a local breeder, kennel or pet owner.

Always plan to take the dog to a veterinary surgery. A vet is restricted in what he can do to help a dog in the road or at a private house.

Telephone first to be sure of locating a vet on duty.

It is as well to be aware that if you are helping an unknown, unowned animal, you may be required to pay some or all of the cost.

If an animal has been killed in an accident, call the police rather than a veterinary surgeon. It is a mis-use of veterinary time for them to be asked to act as undertakers.

Dealing with a Road Traffic Accident Involving a Dog

● Hold up the traffic.

● Restrain the dog, perhaps by throwing a coat over its head, while you assemble your thoughts and collect what you need for first aid treatment. *Comment.* Even a badly injured dog may run away from the scene, complicating your efforts to help.

● Loop a restraining lead over the dog's head. Protect yourself with whatever means possible, e.g. thick gloves. Put on an emergency muzzle *unless* the dog is having trouble with breathing.

● Gently move the dog to the roadside if necessary by lifting it onto a blanket and sliding it along. *Comment.* Many drivers will not take kindly to being held up for too long.

● If blood is being lost, inspect the wound to see if it contains any obvious large pieces of glass, stone etc. which can be easily removed; do not probe for smaller pieces. Apply a large pad to the wound with firm pressure, adding more pads if the blood seeps through. If there is debris in the wound, which can not be removed, bandage lightly to avoid driving it in; only use a tourniquet if blood is actually spouting from the wound. If that is not the case pressure bandages usually work and are safer.

● Locate veterinary surgery to which the dog is to be taken. If fractures are suspected, transport the dog on a board, keeping the spine as straight as possible.

● Keep the dog lightly covered and warm during transport to the surgery.

Common Emergencies
Wounds, cuts and abrasions

(i) *Minor wounds and grazes.* Allow the dog to lick and cleanse but be careful that it, or any companion animals, does not lick the wound excessively. This can be prevented by distracting the dog and teaching it not to lick (see Chapter 3) or by bandaging. For certain wounds, and where bandaging is difficult, it may be necessary to apply a wide collar (an Elizabethan collar) around the dog's neck to prevent it getting at the wound — your veterinary surgeon will advise.

If the dog cannot reach the wound or is not licking itself, cleanse the wound with soap and water, or salt water (one tablespoonful in half a pint), and dilute antiseptic, e.g. TCP. Subsequently apply a small amount of antiseptic ointment. This treatment should be repeated two to three times daily until healing has occurred.

(ii) *Severe wounds.* Seeping dark blood indicates that a vein has been cut. Clean the wound as above and apply a pad of lint (woven side to the wound) or a strip of bandage, cover with a layer of wet cotton wool and bandage lightly with a woven cotton bandage or a crepe bandage. Be careful not to apply the bandage too tightly. Check at regular intervals that swelling is not occurring below the bandage. Remove the bandage daily, dress the wound and re-bandage until healing takes place or is well on the way. A piece of Tubigauze (woven tubular bandage) may be used to help keep bandages in place.

Foot bandages may be kept clean by putting the dog's paw in an old sock which can be covered with a polythene bag when the dog goes outside. It is best to tape the sock and bag in place with Elastoplast rather than use an elastic band, since the latter can cause severe problems if left in place for too long and can be picked up and swallowed only too easily.

Bright red, spurting blood from a wound indicates that an artery has been severed. Provided that a large vessel is not involved, a pressure bandage, applied as described above, will usually suffice to control the haemorrhage. A second layer of cotton wool and bandage may be required if blood seeps through the first. Once the bleeding has stopped, treatment can continue the next day as described previously. If such methods fail to stop the bleeding then a tourniquet will need to be applied at a suitable point between the heart and the wound. Do not leave tourniquets on for excessive periods; check by feeling the skin below the tourniquet — if it is cold and blue the pressure must be released slightly. If it is necessary to apply a tourniquet, veterinary help must be sought since ligation of the artery may be required so that bleeding is controlled without adversely affecting the blood supply to the rest of the limb.

Cuts more than one inch in length may need suturing (stitches). It is wise to seek veterinary help without delay in such cases since if the wound is repaired early the chances of it healing quickly, by first intention, are greatly increased.

Wounds in the pads or the ear flaps present special problems in that walking or head shaking may well make the wound start to bleed again. Foot wounds may need suturing if deep and professional bandaging can save a lot of mess in the house. A length of Tubigauze, or a tube manufactured from a leg from a pair of tights, can be placed over the dog's head for 12 to 24 hours to prevent the ear flapping when the head is shaken; the ears should be folded over the top of the head. It is unwise for owners to attempt to bandage a dog's head since such bandages slip only too easily and obstruction to breathing can occur if the bandage is not correctly applied, especially in the case of the short-nosed breeds.

Comment
- It is important to ensure that hair is not getting into the wound — this may necessitate clipping around the edge with blunt edged curved scissors.
- Deep puncture wounds can lead to abscess formation since they often heal too quickly on the surface leaving infection to brew under the skin. If your dog has been in a fight with a cat it is wise to visit the surgery since a course of antibiotic medication may be needed to prevent abscesses forming.
- If you have any doubts about the severity of a wound, or if during healing the edges are very inflamed and sore and the surrounding area feels hot to the touch, seek veterinary advice without delay.

First aid and nursing

The following table provides hints to help you deal with some other common emergencies.

Emergency	Immediate Action	Subsequent Action
Bloat (stomach full of gas and greatly expanded in size).	One of the true great emergencies. VETERINARY SURGERY IMMEDIATELY.	See "What if" No. 33.
Corrosive or irritant liquid splashed in eye.	Bathe quickly with plenty of water at body heat. Restrain dog from rubbing eye.	Veterinary surgery at once. See "What if" Nos. 11 and 12.
Caught in wire or thorn hedge.	Pause long enough to *protect yourself,* e.g. with strong gloves, or by throwing a coat over the dog's head. Lift dog up to cut free. Don't forget to talk to the dog to pacify and reassure it.	Clean wounds as soon as possible and apply antiseptic ointment. Most wounds of this nature heal very quickly but veterinary attention will be needed if lacerations are extensive.
Dog fight.	A stick thrust through the collar and twisted, to momentarily cut off the airway, will give the opportunity to part two dogs. Be ready to remove them from each other immediately. Cold water via hose or bucket is effective, so is a sudden loud noise, a ringing door bell, or a shout by an unfamiliar voice. Screaming by owner only encourages fighting between guard dogs.	Fights may reoccur between protagonists. They may have to be parted for life. If your dog is habitually aggressive to other dogs refer to Chapter 3.
Drinking seawater.	Dogs have to find out that seawater is not good to drink. Carry fresh water for the dog.	Frequent and copious urination often follows drinking salt water.
Drowning.	Check airway, remove mud or debris from mouth. Hold dog up by hind legs to drain water out of lungs. If it is not breathing, lay it on its side and press intermittently on its chest or, having closed its mouth, blow gently up its nose until it starts to gasp.	Take dog to surgery. *On the way* start to dry the dog and keep it warm.
Electrocution.	*Switch off the electricity.* If this is not possible, do not touch the dog with your hands, but move it away with a wooden handled broom.	Pull the tongue forward in the mouth to allow the dog to breathe. Push down rhythmically on the ribs at about 5 second intervals to induce breathing. If this fails then mouth to nose resuscitation, as described under drowning, may be tried. Keep up artifical respiration while transporting dog to veterinary surgery.
Fainting.	1. Pull the dog's tongue forward to make a clear airway. 2. Wait quietly with dog while it recovers, applying ice or cold water to forehead and mouth if available.	A relatively unimportant and quite common occurrence in Boxers, Boston Terriers, etc. Report to vet if fainting occurs frequently. See "What if" No. 43.
Falls.	Dogs fall over cliffs when chasing seagulls, and also slip down gullies in rocky country. Leave one person to identify the place where the accident took place.	Contact Royal National Lifeboat Institution, Mountain Rescue, or Police.

Emergency	Immediate Action	Subsequent Action
Fits.	1. Protect dog from injury, e.g. falling downstairs. 2. Turn off radio and T.V., darken room. 3. Do not touch dog but observe behaviour and duration of fit.	Report to vet when dog has recovered, and make appointment for a full examination. A single fit is not a true emergency, dog is likely to be perfectly normal once active phase of fit is over. See "What if" No. 38.
Foreign body in eye, injury to eye.	Apply a cold wet pad as described under prolapse of eyeball if the dog seems to be in great pain. In any case prevent the dog from scratching the eye and rubbing its face on the ground.	Veterinary surgery without delay. See "What if" No. 12.
Fractures, sprains, torn muscles.	Restrain dog, make it lie down, restrict movement, confine in box or small space. Arrest any bleeding. Cover dog lightly and keep warm.	Contact veterinary surgery. See "What if" No. 34.
Heat stroke.	Cool the dog's body temperature by any means possible — cold water, ice, dunking in a stream, even surrounding it with packs of frozen food. *Note:* The commonest cause of heat stroke is leaving dogs in cars into which the sun shines, but it can also occur while driving, even in cold weather, through sunshine in a hatchback car.	Beware of cooling the dog too much and lowering the body temperature too far. Ten minutes application of cold should be enough. Take the dog for veterinary check even if it appears fully recovered.
Picking up stones and sand.	A dog can consume a large quantity of sand while playing with a ball on the beach, and diarrhoea may result. If you see your dog eating sand, or something unidentified on the beach, a dose of liquid paraffin that night and the next morning can help prevent problems.	Veterinary treatment to control diarrhoea.
Poisoning.	Take as much evidence as possible to the veterinary surgery, e.g. vomit, and packets, tins or plants which the dog has been chewing.	Take the dog to the veterinary surgery at once, being prepared to give the full history of the incident. See Chapter 4 Part VI.
Prolapse of eyeball.	Do not attempt to replace eyeball. Soak a pad of cloth in cold water, apply to cover eyeball and socket, keep cool and wet dressing gently in place.	Veterinary surgery immediately.
Scalds, burns (serious).	If caused by hot fat, wipe as much as possible off the coat with paper. Douse burn with cold water, do not apply ointments etc.	Get to veterinary surgery quickly.
Scalds, burns (minor).	Clip off hair around the place as the burn may be more extensive than you think. Apply cold water to ease the pain, then antiseptic ointment. Keep all burns and scalds scrupulously clean.	Observe area closely, especially for the next 5-7 days. If inflammation persists seek veterinary help.

181

Emergency	Immediate Action	Subsequent Action
Snake bite.	Britain's only poisonous snake is the Adder, found on heath land in summer. The marks of two fangs may be seen at the site of bite, on head or legs. Gross swelling begins immediately. Carry the dog if possible rather than let it walk, to avoid spreading the poison. If bite is on leg, put on a tourniquet above the bite, release it every 15-20 mins. Heroic treatment such as sucking out the poison is useless, but the wound may be cleaned with soap and water.	Veterinary Surgery at once.
Trapped under-ground.	In sandy country, dogs pursuing rabbits can become trapped in the burrows. Another dog is your best assistant, using its superb sense of hearing and smell. Carry a spade to dig the dog out, and water, as it will be dehydrated. Keep searching, the dog may survive for as long as 7 days underground.	Rest and care should be enough for complete recovery, but the dog may do the same thing again.
Wasp and bee stings.	If sting is visible, pull it out with tweezers. Apply meat tenderiser to area. Observe amount of swelling. Keep dog indoors and quiet.	Veterinary attention needed if swelling is acute in mouth and throat. If the dog seems in great pain your veterinary surgeon may be able to give you extra advice over the phone.

Note: Tips on first aid measures are also noted in the "What if" section of Chapter 4.

HOME NURSING

Since most owner nursing is carried out in relation to surgical operations, the information in this chapter is given with that in mind. However, much of the detail, such as the giving of tablets, will of course apply in other situations too. Some information on nursing is given in the "What if" section of Chapter 4 and reference should also be made to the relevant section there. *If in doubt consult your veterinary surgeon* — a short telephone call to the surgery will ensure that mistakes are not made and will help set your mind at rest.

Care of the dog before and after a surgical operation

Many dogs will need surgery under a full anaesthetic at some time in their lives. The care that you give the dog before and after the operation will contribute greatly to the successful outcome.

Dogs make much better surgical patients than humans, possibly because they are not apprehensive before the event. Many breeds have a high pain threshold and will behave entirely normally two to three days after surgery.

Small animal veterinary surgery has now reached a high degree of sophistication, but there is always some risk involved in a full anaesthetic.

Before surgery
If the operation is non-urgent ("elective" or "cold" are words used in this context), plan to have a few days free when you have plenty of time to devote to your dog after the operation.

If you are unable to keep close observation on the dog in the post-operative days, it may be wise to ask the veterinary surgeon to keep it as an in-patient. It is not unknown for dogs to burst their sutures, or to remove them, if they are left alone to their own devices.

Pre-operative starvation
Your veterinary surgeon or the veterinary nurse will give precise instructions on withholding food and drink, usually for 12 hours, possibly longer, before the operation.
It is very important that these instructions are carried out, as otherwise the dog may choke on vomit during the anaesthetic.
Tell the veterinary surgeon if a mistake has been made as it may be better to postpone the operation.
Tell the veterinary surgeon if your dog has ever had special problems in recovering from an anaesthetic, or if there is a known tendency in the breed to take anaesthetics badly.
If the dog is on medication, ask the veterinary surgeon when it should be withdrawn.

On the operation day
1. Arrive at the surgery at the time requested.
2. Provide a telephone number where you can be contacted all day.
3. Be aware that the hair will have to be shaved from around the operation site. If you hope to show the dog again soon, ask if as little hair as possible can be removed.
4. The dog will probably be given a "pre-med" tranquillising injection and you may be asked to sit with the dog while this takes effect.
5. You will probably be given a time at which you may telephone to enquire about your dog.

After surgery

Collection of the dog after surgery
Dogs vary in the time they take to recover from an anaesthetic. They should remain under skilled supervision until they are fully conscious and able to walk.

Before your dog is handed over to you, make sure you have all the information you will need. Never be afraid to ask!
1. Ask about food and fluid — what should be given and when.
2. Ask about medication — when should you start giving what is prescribed.
3. Ask about contacting a veterinary surgeon should the dog develop problems after it reaches home.
4. Ask about exercise.
5. Ask when you are to report progress and when the sutures (stitches) are to be removed. The cost of suture removal and post-operative checking are often included in the operation fee. You may wish to ask if this is so.

The journey home
1. Keep the car warm but well-ventilated, or you may pick up the anaesthetic the dog is breathing out. Fat dogs can give out anaesthetic gases for 48 hours or more.
2. Prevent the dog from rolling off the seat, possibly having someone to hold it upright.
3. Prevent post-operative shock with hot water bottle and blanket.
4. Be aware that the dog may relapse into a deeper sleep when in familiar surroundings. If you cannot remove the dog from the car at the journey's end, let it recover where it is under close supervision.

Post-operative care
1. The dog's first need will be to pass urine. Support may be needed to enable it to reach its usual spot and while it "performs".
2. Make up a comfortable bed on the floor so the dog cannot roll off. Use plastic protection as the dog may pass urine while in a deep post-operative sleep.
3. Unless instructed otherwise by the veterinary surgeon, after major operations offer small quantities of water/glucose solution (one tablespoonful of glucose to one pint of boiled water) or an electrolyte solution provided by the veterinary surgeon, every hour.
4. Give small amounts of easily digested food every three to four hours, unless instructed to the contrary.
5. Be prepared to support the dog to pass urine and faeces for 24-48 hours after surgery. If balance has not been regained by that time, tell the veterinary surgeon.
6. Be aware that the dog may have a slight cough, caused by intubation for the anaesthetic, for two to three days after surgery, and the throat may be sore making eating difficult.

Post-operative nursing
Veterinary surgeons often say, "Give me a ring if you are worried!". The following conditions will give reason for post-operative concern and should be reported to the veterinary surgeon.
1. Sinking deeper into unconsciousness.
2. Cold, clammy feel to the paws, pale gums and lips.
3. Still not fully conscious and only cautiously active within 48 hours post-operation.
4. Persistent retching and vomiting, dog not retaining even small quantities of water.
5. Failure to regain limb control in 48 hours.
6. Passing faeces with blood content — estimate how much.
7. Acute swelling and redness around wound site or unpleasant smell from wound.
8. Convulsions or seizure.
9. Allergic reactions, such as bumps or wheals appearing on skin, or acute swelling of face, mouth or throat.
10. Removal of the sutures by the dog.

Medication
Before you leave the surgery, make sure that the name of each drug is written on the container, together with its use, e.g. to stop vomiting, antibiotic etc. Enter the names of the medication in your dog's records, it may be invaluable to you later on.

If the tablets are supplied to you in an envelope, transfer them to a clean dry bottle, sticking the vet's envelope securely on the outside.

Make a chart for the dosage, marking off each time you give a dose.

If you have more than one pet, make sure the invalid is alone when you give the tablets, so that another dog does not snatch the tablet up if it should be dropped.

Control of water intake
Dogs which have become dehydrated during surgery will be very thirsty, but water in large quantities may make them vomit.

Romovo all water bowls, flower pots and vases, and prevent access to puddles, ponds, water butts etc.

Give fluid in appropriate quantity, one teaspoonful to one tablespoonful every hour by the clock. After two hours, if the dog is not vomiting, the quantity may be doubled, and thereafter increased cautiously until the dog is able to drink freely.

Fluid may be given in a hypodermic syringe (without a needle in place) if the dog finds it difficult to raise its head.

Dressings
If the dog has a dressing on leg or foot, it may be kept clean when the dog goes outside by putting the foot into a plastic bag, secured loosely by an elastic band. Remove the bag and the elastic band immediately on return to the house and put them in a safe place. Elastic bands are bad news for dogs! If the dressings are becoming soiled but are still in place, another layer of conforming bandage may be put on top. It is important not to allow dressings to become wet.

Sutures
If the sutures are well-positioned and not too tight, most dogs tolerate them well. The leg of a pair of tights makes a useful body stocking to keep dressings in place.

If the dog is inclined to worry about the sutures, try putting a bandage on a front paw to offer a distraction. An Elizabethan collar is another solution. Take a plastic bowl or bucket big enough to contain the dog's head; cut the bottom out of the bucket, and discard it. Make a row of holes around the edge which remains, and thread through with string to lash the bucket to a leather collar. When this device is in place the dog will not be able to reach any part of its body, but these collars are tolerated surprisingly well.

(a) Opening the dog's mouth

Fig. 30 **Giving tablets**

(b) Administering the tablet

Giving Tablets
It is better not to crush tablets or to hide them in food. Once you have the knack of giving them, the procedure will be quite simple.
1. Open the dog's mouth with the left hand by tilting the head upwards with the thumb and index finger pushed in from outside the lips behind the dog's upper canine teeth. The jaw can then be easily opened by pressing on the lower incisors with the middle two fingers of the right hand. Keep the mouth open by pressing the dog's lips over its molar teeth.
2. Holding the tablet between the thumb and index finger of the right hand and push it as far back as possible over the back of the tongue.
3. Close the mouth, and hold it closed while stroking the throat to make the dog swallow.
Some tablets (e.g. antibiotics) are designed by veterinary pharmaceutical companies to be palatable so that the dog will take them readily from the hand. If your dog is difficult about taking tablets, ask your veterinary surgeon if a palatable form of medication is available instead.

CHAPTER 7

MISHAPS AND PROBLEMS ABOUT THE HOUSE AND OUTDOORS

About the house
Nos. 1-27

Outdoors
Nos. 28-43

This chapter provides some solutions to common problems and mishaps in the household and generally in respect of dog ownership. Each topic begins with the words "What if my dog . . .?". Hopefully the details given will help owners decide what action to take both in the short and long term to overcome and prevent the difficulty.

Homes which own dogs are never quite as immaculate as those which do not include the pleasure and companionship of pets. However, the following hints are intended to make dog ownership easier and those accidents which do occur in and around the home less serious. See also the section in Chapter 3 on the prevention and treatment of inappropriate behaviour.

"WHAT IF . . .?"(ABOUT THE HOUSE)

1 my dog is not clean overnight
2 my dog soils the floor with urine or faeces
3 my dog urinates on the carpet
4 my dog passes faeces on the carpet
5 my dog vomits on the carpet

187

6 my bitch is in season and there are male dogs in the house
7 my bitch makes bloodstains on the carpet and furniture when she is "on heat"
8 my dog sheds hair over furniture, clothing or car upholstery
9 my dog raids the kitchen rubbish bin while I am out
10 my dog has oil or tar from the beach on its coat
11 my dog gets tar on its feet
12 my dog cannot be lifted into a bath
13 my dog needs to be introduced to a new puppy
14 my dog should need to be introduced to my first baby — should I get rid of my dog
15 my puppy objects to wearing a collar and fights the lead
16 my puppy chews chair legs and doors
17 my dog needs to be introduced to a kitten
18 my new puppy needs to be introduced into a house where there is a cat already
19 my dog will not be groomed, or will not allow its ears, teeth or feet to be examined
20 my dog will not take tablets
21 my dog drools on clothing
22 my puppy bites people's hands with its very sharp teeth
23 my dog is tormented by a toddler
24 my dog knocks down a valuable ornament
25 my dog steals food
26 my dog tracks in grass cuttings which stain the carpet
27 my dog smells doggy

"WHAT IF...?"(OUTDOORS)

28 my dog passes faeces on the pavement
29 my bitch makes bleached circles on the lawn where she urinates
30 my male dog kills shrubs by urinating against them
31 my dog has trodden tar all over the car upholstery
32 my dog will not swim
33 my dog takes bread and fat put out for the birds
34 my dog gets a ball stuck in its throat
35 my dog attacks a much smaller dog
36 my dog swallows a stone
37 my dog digs in the garden
38 my dog uproots plants
39 my dog bites the heads off flowers
40 my dog has passed faeces that need to be disposed of
41 my dog is stolen
42 my dog gets lost
43 my dog gets into a fight

The character in the box above this list is Buster. We have used him to illustrate some of the mishaps and problems which can occur. Normally Buster is a well-mannered dog, but he does go off the rails occasionally.

About the House
Early planning will help:
1. Decide collectively as a family which parts of the house are "no go areas" for the dog; for instance he can be trained never to set foot on carpeted areas, sit on the settee, or never to go upstairs. Make sure that no member of the family encourages the dog to break these rules.

2. Never allow a young puppy the free run of the house. Restrict it to easily cleaned areas unless you can keep it under close observation.
3. Do not expect a puppy or a young dog to be 100 per cent obedient if you are not present to warn him about committing offences. Be realistic about the amount of good behaviour you can expect from an unsupervised dog.
4. Above all, avoid putting the dog into a situation where he can spoil articles you value or commit other behavioural errors. Prevention is always better than cure.

What if my dog is not clean overnight?

1. What if my dog is not clean overnight?

It is normal for adult dogs to have the very occasional accident but this should not occur regularly. Puppies cannot be expected to be clean for long periods until they are six months old. In an older dog consider:
1. Is the night too long? Eight to ten hours shut in may be as long as the dog can take.
2. Are there early morning disturbances by milkmen etc.? Once the dog is awake he may need to be let out.
3. Does the dog actually pass urine and faeces when he is let out last thing at night? You may need to accompany him in order to encourage him to concentrate on these actions until they become habits.
4. Will an alteration in diet and/or feeding times make any improvement?
5. Does the dog suffer from some condition affecting the digestive or urinary systems? A veterinary consultation will be necessary to decide.
6. Does the floor of the dog's sleeping place retain the smell of urine and faeces to that he is confused as to what is the right place? Cleaning with a strong solution of bleach, which should be left on the floor for ten minutes and then rinsed with plain water, should eliminate residue smells.

Consider: Providing the dog with a closed wire crate in which to sleep if all else fails, *provided* he is not left enclosed more than eight hours at night and four to five hours during the day.

2. What if my dog soils the floor with urine or faeces?

Immediate Reaction: whose fault was it?

> *Yours* for not giving the dog the opportunity to go out at the appropriate time?

189

His for not asking to go out or refusing to perform when taken out?

Neither. If the dog is old or ill, or has had diarrhoea, these episodes must be excused.

Immediate Action:
1. Pick up solid material with kitchen paper and put into newspaper for disposal.
2. Mop up pool of urine into bucket with special sponge/cloth kept for the purpose.
3. Wash floor with detergent cleaner which *does not contain ammonia.*
4. Rinse and wash over with water containing disinfectant.

NOTE. Stages three and four must be separate operations, disinfectant is useless on a soiled floor.

While performing actions one to four express your disapproval facially and verbally if the accident has been the dog's fault. Smacking or other chastising is inappropriate, while the old fashioned "rubbing his nose in it" does nothing but reveal an ignorance of the dog's natural functions.

Prevention: Re-think the dog's routine and provide more opportunities for it to get out to the garden — e.g. dog flap in door. If the dog is to be left so long that elimination is inevitable, cover an area of the floor thickly with newspaper. If illness is suspected, consult the veterinary surgeon.

What if my dog urinates on the carpet?

3. What if my dog urinates on the carpet?

Immediate Action:
1. Blot up urine with kitchen paper or, if copious amounts, by laying sheets of newspaper on the pool, weighting them down and changing them frequently as they become saturated.
2. Clean the area with carpet cleaner which does not contain ammonia.
3. Dry with iron, hair drier, or hot water bottle.

Prevention: Review dog's routine as above but establish whose fault it was.

Provide exit to garden via dog flap if appropriate. If illness is suspected, consult veterinary surgeon.

4. What if my dog passes faeces on the carpet?

Whose fault was it — see "What if" No. 2.

Immediate Action: 1. Note consistency and content in case of illness.
2. Pick up with kitchen paper, put into newspaper and dispose.
3. Wash and dry quickly as above to avoid staining.
4. Endeavour to remove all smell, as puppies in particular may return to same spot.

Comment: Carpet tiles are ideal where dogs are kept, as individual tiles may be taken up for cleaning and airing and may be interchanged if soiling is heavy.

5. What if my dog vomits on the carpet?

Immediate Action: 1. Observe colour and contents of vomit, and any foreign bodies therein, since veterinary attention may be required.
2. Prevent dog from re-eating vomit.
3. Pick up solid matter with kitchen paper and put into newspaper for disposal.
4. Wash area of carpet with warm water and biological washing powder, having first tested the carpet for colour fastness to the washing powder chosen. Dry with hair drier or iron.

Subsequent Action: Consult Chapter 4 Part I "What if my dog is vomiting". Contact veterinary surgeon if vomiting continues.

Prevention: A dog which is vomiting frequently should be surrounded with newspaper on top of plastic sheeting. Clean the face and chest of a long-haired dog. A bib made out of towelling will prevent further soiling.

6. What if my bitch is in season and there are male dogs in the house?

Practically all male dogs recognise the odour of a bitch in season, as indeed nature intended them to do.

It is almost a cruelty to keep a male dog in the same house as an "in-season" bitch and they will almost certainly evade your attempts to keep them apart, as during the middle-third of her season, the bitch is just as eager to meet the dog as he is to find her.

The dog may refuse to eat, and become thin and poor-coated through frustration. Tempers become frayed and fights may ensue with other males.

Immediate Action: Proprietary pills and lotions are generally ineffective in masking bitch odour. Either bitch or dog must be boarded elsewhere.

Subsequent Action: Consult a veterinary surgeon about the prevention of heat on a temporary or permanent basis. Spaying or chemical methods are available. Castration of the male

191

may be effective but he may still show some mating behaviour.

See the section in Chapter 2 on oestrus control and "What if my bitch is mismated?" (No. 31) and "What if my bitch is found to be pregnant unexpectedly?" (No. 32).

What if my bitch is in season and there are male dogs in the house?

7. What if my bitch makes bloodstains on the carpet and furniture when she is "on heat"?

The amount of bloodstained discharge when in season varies from bitch to bitch. Some bitches will lick themselves much more frequently when in season and so cause little problem, other bitches are not so meticulous.

Immediate Action: 1. Use salted *cold* water to soak the stain out of fabrics.
2. Wash in biological washing powder.
3. Clean floor and carpets in similar manner.

Prevention: 1. Confine bitch to easily washed areas while she is in season.
2. Cover furniture with old sheets or similar cotton material.
3. Consider fitting the bitch up with sanitary pads and knickers, which can be bought at pet shops or improvised at home.
4. If the bitch is not to be bred from, consider eliminating all the nuisance of seasons. Consult your veterinary surgeon about the prevention of heat by spaying or chemical means. See the section in Chapter 2 on bitches.

8. What if my dog sheds hair over furniture, clothing or car upholstery?

Dog hair varies tremendously in the way it adheres to other fabrics. Really long hair can be easier to remove than the short hair shed by Bull Terriers, Dobermanns and similar coated dogs.

You may find any of the following aids useful:

- Stroking furniture and clothing with a rubber glove on the hand.
- Sellotape wrapped around the fingers, sticky side outmost, and stroked over fabric pile.
- Brushing with a damp nailbrush; wiping with a damp cloth.

All these methods roll the hairs together and make them easier to remove. A special attachment for the vacuum cleaner, obtainable at pet shops, is available which can be helpful.

Prevention: Groom the dog frequently — daily when hair is being shed in quantities.

If hair is being shed excessively or throughout the whole year have the dog checked for possible underlying skin disease or hormonal upset.

Discuss the dog's diet with your veterinary surgeon to ensure especially that it is getting sufficient B vitamins and unsaturated fatty acids.

What if my dog raids the kitchen rubbish bin while I am out?

9. What if my dog raids the kitchen rubbish bin while I am out?

Immediate Action: Try to identify what has been eaten in case the dog later becomes ill.

Subsequent Action: Empty or remove the rubbish bin before you go out. Train the dog using the methods described in the behaviour section of Chapter 3 that it must *never* touch the bin.

Prevention: Reinforce the behaviour while working in the kitchen by having the rubbish bin prominently placed and standing open. Admonish the dog by saying "NO!"

and/or banging a saucepan on the sink *immediately* the bin is approached.

10. What if my dog has oil or tar from the beach on its coat?

Immediate Action: Be extremely careful of using any inflammable liquid, such as petrol or carbon tetrachloride, on the dog's coat. It may be preferable to cut off as much of the affected hair as possible, and then to wash the dog in mild detergent and/or canine shampoo, finishing with a plain water rinse. It can be helpful to apply sun tan cream, first working it well into the affected area and then washing it off with warm water containing a "soft" detergent, such as washing-up liquid.

11. What if my dog gets tar on its feet?

Immediate Action: Clip out the hair and lumps of tar between the pads. Soak the foot in a jug or tall tin containing vegetable oil, put butter liberally on the paws or work in some sun tan cream if that is available. When tar is loosened, wash feet in warm water containing a "soft" detergent, such as washing-up liquid, to remove grease and rinse well in plain water so that detergent does not remain on the skin.

If the tar deposit is very heavy, consult a veterinary surgeon at once, as special measures of cleaning may be necessary.

What if my dog cannot be lifted into a bath?

12. What if my dog cannot be lifted into a bath?

Large dogs can be bathed quite successfully on the kitchen floor, or on the lawn in good weather. The following method works:

1. Take off leather collar and make the dog a collar of strong cotton or nylon material to use as an anchor.
2. Assemble two sponges, towels, and as many buckets of warm water as you can muster. Dilute shampoo in a jug of warm water (always use a shampoo made for dog hair, not a human shampoo).
3. Put a ring of vaseline around the dog's eyes to keep out soapy water.
4. Soak the dog's coat with warm water using the first sponge.
5. Apply shampoo with the second sponge, lather, rinse with the first sponge and clean water, lather again.
6. Finally rinse with clean water until all shampoo is out of coat. In summer, finish off with spray from garden hose.
7. Towel dry and finish with hair drier.

13. What if my dog needs to be introduced to a new puppy?

Many older dogs take on a new lease of life when a new puppy is brought into the home, provided certain precautions are taken early on:
1. Get the puppy as young as possible. At six weeks puppies are confident and unafraid, but by eight weeks the puppy may be entering a "fear period" (see page 66) and may be much more difficult to acclimatise.
2. Allow the older dog to become accustomed to the puppy while you are present, and then allow brief periods of free socialisation, always *supervised*.
3. It may be helpful to make an enclosure for the puppy in which it can be left safely for the first few weeks in your home when you are not present. Panels sold to enclose compost heaps are ideal for the purpose.
4. Protect the older dog's rights. Do not allow the puppy to make free with its toys, its bed or its food. It can be helpful to remove the most favoured canine possessions at this time to prevent problems.
5. Make sure the older dog has a full share of attention, and always give a small titbit every time the puppy is fed — older dogs are fed less frequently than puppies.
6. Do not leave the two alone when you are absent until they are at ease with one another — a good indication is if the pair choose to share a bed.
7. Puppies can bite an older dog's feet and ears quite painfully. Most adults growl and snap to warn a puppy that such behaviour is not permitted, but some puppies do not heed the warning and some adults are too vigorous in their reaction, so some human intervention is sometimes needed.
8. Consult your veterinary surgeon about taking the older dog to canine gatherings, or to places where many dogs are exercised, until after the puppy is vaccinated.

14. What if my dog should need to be introduced to my first baby — should I get rid of my dog?

Jealousy of new babies is very uncommon, despite the fears of new parents.

A well-kept healthy dog is unlikely to be a disease risk to the baby. It is a sad thing to discard a dog which has been a good friend to you and will in the future be a good friend to the child, and it is a pity that this action is often urged on new parents by relatives and friends who are prejudiced against dogs.

Jealousy should not occur if you plan the introduction of the dog to the baby with care, assuming that you have already taught your dog good companion animal behaviour. The following tips may help:

1. Let the dog sit beside you when the baby is attended to and talk to the dog as usual.
2. The baby's cry may be a completely new sound to the dog, and may convey a distress message to him. Teach the dog that it may look but not touch or jump up to cot or pram.
3. If the dog is large and vigorous, make arrangements for it to have sufficient exercise, as walking with a pram may not be enough.
4. It can be dangerous to tie a dog to a pram and leave it unsupervised.
5. Discourage the dog from licking the baby.
6. Do not let young babies pull the dog's ears and tail.
7. Provide a place into which the dog can retreat away from the baby.
8. Never the leave the dog alone with the baby, especially when the baby is at the crawling stage. Remember that dogs, especially large dogs, can be very vigorous in play.
9. Do not tempt providence by letting the baby play and crawl around the dog's feeding bowl. The dog should be fed separately and any food that is left must be picked up without delay.
10. Make a gesture of giving the dog extra attention once the baby has been put to bed — give it a few privileges at this time.
11. Take the baby or the dog with you if you have to leave a room even for a few moments. It is better to be safe than sorry.

What if my dog should need to be introduced to my first baby — should I get rid of my dog?

What if my puppy objects to wearing a collar and fights the lead

15. What if my puppy objects to wearing a collar and fights the lead?

Some puppies seem to object strongly to anything around their neck, but body harnesses are not a good idea.

Try the following strategy. Put the collar and lead on immediately before feeding the dog. Put the food on the far side of the room where the dog can see it. Hold the lead while the dog goes over to the food and let it trail while the dog is eating. Repeat at several meal times so that the dog is diverted from fighting the collar and associates collar and lead with something pleasant.

16. What if my puppy chews chair legs and doors?

Puppies have an in-built need to chew, which reaches its peak at six to ten months old, although many are compulsive chewers from six weeks old. The trick is to prevent this problem arising by giving only a limited number of "toys" that the dog can chew. It is not a good idea to give an old slipper or a brush, since the dog will not be able to distinguish between that or new shoes and useful brushes. Chew-objects should be unrelated to household items. This activity calls for the behavioural control methods outlined in Chapter 3 and responds to instant punishment by the thrown object. Set up the situation and as soon as the dog starts to chew the item punish it by a well-directed thrown object. Alternatively it may help to provide the puppy with large marrow bones, and direct his attention to his own chews every time you see him attack furniture. If all this fails consider confinement in a wire crate for short periods when you cannot watch the puppy, and put temporary protection around fixed pieces of furniture, e.g. metal angle strip around corners of cupboards, a sheet of perspex or aluminium on the lower half of doors.

Finally, anti-chew sprays can be bought at pet shops — the most expensive ones are very effective, the cheaper varieties are not. (Bitter Apple is the brand that works.) However it is much better in the long term to train the dog that chewing leads to punishment and that not chewing is more rewarding. Finally it is wise not to make dogs mouth-conscious by encouraging them to play tug of war games.

A puppy may chew in order to ease pain in the mouth caused by teething. Consider rubbing on a soothing gel made to ease teething in babies. The veterinary surgeon may be able to help in such cases.

17. What if my dog needs to be introduced to a kitten?

Dogs can become very fond of the household cat, even those that are chronic chasers of unfamiliar cats. A little strategy used at the time of introduction of the kitten makes the foundation for an easy relationship.

1. Bring the kitten into the house in a wire carrying basket so that the dog can become accustomed to the scent and look of the kitten.
2. Give the kitten an escape route so that it can sit on a high cupboard out of the dog's reach.
3. Put the kitten's sanitary tray and food where the dog cannot interfere; dogs are attracted to cat faeces.
4. Do not leave the two together until you are sure a mutual respect has developed.
5. Most kittens can take very good care of themselves against one dog, but "pack" action by several dogs is a greater risk.
6. Finally praise the dog and give it delectable food rewards when it behaves properly towards the cat, but admonish it promptly if it chases the cat or objects to its presence.

18. What if my new puppy needs to be introduced into a house where there is a cat already?

Individual adult animals take additions to the household in a variety of ways, and it is not possible to predict how the cat will react.

Many cats will be reserved and sulky at first but most will come to accept the situation and will soon be sharing their bed with the newcomer.

Some cats resort to urine-marking indoors to express their displeasure at any change in the household. Judicious preparation for the new arrival will help.

1. Well ahead of the puppy's arrival, put the cat's sanitary tray and feeding area in a place the puppy cannot reach.
2. Provide a comfortable sitting area for the cat on a high level.
3. Make sure the cat is clear of fleas and ear mites as these are transmissible to dogs.
4. If you have a cat door, you may wish to keep it closed while the puppy is young and to train the cat to use a window instead.

19. What if my dog will not be groomed, or will not allow its ears, teeth or feet to be examined?

Puppies should be made to submit to grooming and having various parts of their anatomy examined from the first day in the new home, even if they have very little coat at that time.

Either groom the dog on the floor or put something on the table top that will not slip about and which the dog can grip. An old piece of rubber-backed carpet is ideal. Some people advocate putting the dog on a slippery table surface to make it feel insecure and so *likely* to remain quiet. If this approach is adopted be very careful that the dog does not slip off the table and injure itself. One problem with this method is that the dog will tend to crouch low making grooming difficult.

What if my dog will not be groomed, or will not allow its ears, teeth or feet to be examined?

If grooming is done regularly it will be unnecessary to have long and painful disentangling sessions. The correct grooming tools and the use of "disentangling" rinses makes the process easier. Consult the dog's breeder or ask for advice at a pet shop or grooming parlour.

Remember to praise the dog for good behaviour and punish it effectively if it growls or makes a fuss. If the dog shows a tendency to misbehave or even snap in such situations, go through the dominance exercises described in Chapter 1, Part II.

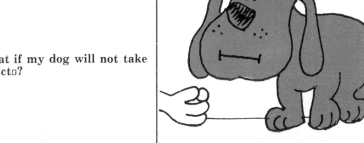

What if my dog will not take tablets?

20. What if my dog will not take tablets?

It is important to practise tablet-giving from the time you have the puppy. Put small vitamin/mineral supplement tablets deliberately down the throat, although they are actually palatable enough for the puppy to eat them.

Actual medicinal tablets are much more satisfactory given in the throat whole, than crushed on food or disguised in other ways.

Do it this way:

1. Cup your finger around the puppy's muzzle, open the top jaw by pressing the lips in the gap just in front of the carnassial teeth in the upper jaw

and slip your thumb, protected by the dog's lips, behind the large canine tooth on the side nearest to you.

2. With the opposite hand, open the mouth wide by pressing down on the incisors with your little or fourth finger, pop the pill on to the centre of the tongue as far back in the mouth as you can. If the tablet is put in the right place the dog will have no option but to swallow it.

3. Hold the mouth closed and stroke the throat until the dog swallows the pill, then praise the dog and release it.

21. What if my dog drools on clothing?

Some dogs with loose flews (jowls) cannot help saliva running out of their jaws. Tantalising a dog with food increases the tendency to drool.

Action: Allow the saliva to dry on clothing, then brush with a stiff brush or rub two surfaces of the cloth together.

Subsequent Action: Protect unsuitably dressed visitors with a clean cloth to put across their laps or make the dog stay in its basket or bed.

22. What if my puppy bites people's hands with its very sharp teeth?

Many people like to offer a puppy their finger to bite, but when the habit is established, elderly people with prominent veins and fragile skin may not enjoy the sensation.

Action: The command "No!" accompanied by an immediate sharp tap on the muzzle should deter the puppy. Give the dog its own chew-object in exchange.

        Ask other members of the family not to encourage hand-biting.

What if my dog is tormented by a toddler?

23. What if my dog is tormented by a toddler?

It is very difficult to impress tiny children about what is unkind, cruel or dangerous, when they are at the stage of exploring and developing their own skills. Many dogs will tolerate bad treatment from children which they would not endure from anyone else.

The dog should always have some escape route so that it can remove itself if the persecution becomes too trying.

Discreet supervision is *always* necessary.

If the dog is long-haired, check the coat regularly to make sure that rubber bands have not been put around neck or legs, or other objects have not been attached to the coat.

Keep small plastic toys away from the dog — if swallowed they may cause an obstruction in the digestive system.

What if my dog knocks down a valuable ornament?

24. What if my dog knocks down a valuable ornament?

All dog-owning households should be covered for Third Party liability as a social necessity. A dog that chases sheep or trips up an old lady may incur its owner many thousands of pounds of damage.

Similarly, damage done in someone else's house or car may be covered by this policy. Some insurance companies also offer an extension to household policies which offers cover for accidental breakages within the home.

Prevention: With puppies and small children, breakages are best avoided by removing precious objects from low or fragile tables. Do not allow the dog to become excited in a well-furnished room, for example, put the dog into the kitchen while you get ready to go for a walk or prepare its food.

Play should only be allowed in "safe" areas of the house.

25. What if my dog steals food?

It is a normal instinct of dogs to take anything edible which it can reach — hounds are especially good at snatching food, even the steak from under the grill!

201

It may be possible to train a dog to the extent that it will not approach a laden dinner table, even when all humans are out of the room, but this is a very high standard of control. It is easier to teach a dog to go to its bed and stay there until the order is given to move again. Dogs should always be sent to their own place in the kitchen while cooking is going on.

Some people advocate the folding wire crate, already described as a training aid, to be invaluable in such situations, but if training is undertaken diligently and the dog regards its owner as a true pack leader, such devices should not be required.

26. What if my dog tracks in grass cuttings which stain the carpet?

As soon as they are noticed pick up as many of the clippings as possible using a stiff nylon brush and pan or a vacuum cleaner. Treat any stains without delay as follows. Using a weak solution of methylated spirits in cold water, make a ring larger than the stained area and gradually work in towards the stain. Then wash in the same way with a good carpet cleaner, rinse and dry thoroughly with an old towel.

27. What if my dog smells doggy?

Check the smell of your house regularly, by taking a deep sniff when you come in from the fresh air. Unfortunately it is all too easy to get accustomed to animal smells which other people find very unpleasant. There should be little risk of the single or two pet house becoming smelly, but where dogs are kept in quantity and there are always puppies around, the risk can be a real one.

You will find that with even one pet, housework and laundry is increased. With more dogs, these tasks will occupy even more time, and may be one of the limiting factors in acquiring more dogs.

Useful tips:

The more dogs you have in your home, the greater the case for having washable furnishings and floor-coverings. You may want to consider vinyl chair covers and carpet tiles, which can be lifted and cleaned, rather than solid carpeting. Do not let dogs sit on upholstery which cannot be cleaned.

Kitchen floors should be coved at the edges, if possible, to facilitate cleaning.

Clean up urine and faeces thoroughly and immediately, and disinfect with a product containing chlorine. Do not use a "pine" disinfectant as the scent compounds badly with urine and intensifies the smell.

Do not leave dogs shut in the house for long periods so that they cannot avoid soiling — consider having a dog door into a safe enclosure.

Do not keep a male dog, or allow a male dog to visit, when entire bitches are coming into oestrus. It is almost inevitable that the male will scent mark objects in the house with a particularly odorous stream of urine.

Consider chemical control of heat or spaying if bitches are not wanted for breeding, for they too have a distinctive scent when in oestrus.

Air rooms frequently, and wash dog bedding often. Woollen blankets and feather cushions hold dog scent while polyester fur fabric does not.

Groom long coated dogs right down to the skin frequently and give daily attention to the anal area where faeces may hang on the coat. The older dog does not have such a good "cut-off" by the rectal muscle and may soil the hair around the anus.

Trim overlong hair on the male dog's sheath very carefully, as this may be a cause of drops of urine being carried on to bedding. Where there are old or sick dogs, examine the bedding twice a day in case urine is being passed in the bed.

Some types of skin and coat emit more odour than others, particularly the dogs which were once working dogs kept outside. This is an important point to research when choosing your dog.

All dogs smell when they are wet. The remedy is to dry them as soon as possible. You can make or buy a towelling bag fastened with Velcro, which covers the dog completely from the neck down, enclosing the body, legs and feet, and the dog will dry very quickly inside it. This is a very useful aid to have in the car in case your dog gets wet on a walk and especially if you have a long-coated breed.

When there is an unusual amount of body odour from a dog which does not normally offend in this way, examine the dog very carefully for infected ears, or a putrefying wound or skin lesion, all of which can give rise to a distinct and unpleasant smell. Look carefully through the fur of a thick-coated dog to see if there is anything embedded in the fur or skin.

If an elderly or sick dog has as untraceable body odour, consult the veterinary surgeon, taking with you a fresh urine sample in a sterilised bottle, as the condition may be indicative of a kidney or liver problem.

Keep a particular watch on the dog for coprophagy or scavenging, as well as the habit of rolling in fox, badger, or other animal excreta, or on rotting carcasses, on country walks. Much of this behaviour is normal to the dog but should be prevented in the domestic pet.

Finally, although dogs normally do not need bathing very often, do not be afraid to bath your dog if you think it is smelly. Use a good dog shampoo and consider the advisability of using an insecticidal rinse which can be obtained from your veterinary surgeon.

Outdoors

28. What if my dog passes faeces on the pavement?

Anti-fouling laws are here to stay and must be enforced as a social necessity. Owners must recognise the need to clear dog faeces away in parks and on pavements, and local authorities must co-operate by providing plenty of disposal bins.

Immediate Action: Always carry a plastic bag or one of the scooping gadgets available from pet shops when exercising your dog in a public place.

Do not be too proud to pick up after your own dog!

Prevention: Give your dog the opportunity to pass faeces in an acceptable place before taking it for walks on the pavement or on beaches.

What if my dog passes faeces on the pavement?

29. What if my bitch makes bleached circles on the lawn where she urinates?

Immediate Action: The grass can be prevented from going yellow by pouring on two or three gallons of water immediately the urine is passed.

Prevention: With patience the bitch can be trained to use a concrete, gravel or soil area.
Prevention is not possible if bitch is allowed to use the lawn.

What if my male dog kills shrubs by urinating against them?

30. What if my male dog kills shrubs by urinating against them?

Most male dogs, including those that are castrated, establish marking posts around their territory on which they urinate regularly. Low growing conifers, especially junipers, seem to be favourite sites but any plant will do!

Immediate Action: Douse the plant with quantities of water which may save it from urine burn.

Prevention: Leave the dead shrub in position rather than replacing with another or put a wooden post in its place. Close observation of the dog and the command "NO!" when it approaches the area may induce the dog to alter his site. This is an ideal situation for punishment by a thrown object, having first set the scene and waited in hiding for the dog to offend. See Chapter 3.

31. What if my dog has trodden tar all over the car upholstery?

Immediate Action: Check the dog's feet first as there may be more tar there. See "What if my dog has tar on its feet?" (No. 11).

Subsequent Action: Clean upholstery with proprietory cleaner according to instructions on the bottle. Beaucaire gives excellent results. Sun tan cream can be useful in "dissolving" the tar before it is removed with the cleaner.

N.B. Sometimes the veterinary surgeon will prescribe a medicated shampoo which has to be left on the coat for a certain length of time, or which is not rinsed out at all. The dog will have to be supervised, and probably held, all the time the shampoo is wet in the coat, otherwise it will try to lick itself dry, and will almost certainly vomit. It may also try to roll in the nearest flower bed.

What if my dog will not swim?

32. What if my dog will not swim?

All dogs can swim if they have to, but many find it difficult to climb out of pools with vertical sides, so great care must be taken with garden swimming pools, especially when they are partially covered. Tragedies have occurred. Many dogs are afraid of waves thundering on a beach, and are reluctant to jump into a river from a steep bank.

Choose a lake with a gentle slope into the water and play with the dog in the shallows until it gains confidence. Teaching your dog to swim could prevent an accident later.

33. What if my dog takes bread and fat put out for the birds?

This is a common canine trait, even among dogs which are not greedy over their own food. This behaviour is not of major concern, but allowances must be made for the amount of food eaten and the dog's diet reduced accordingly, to prevent it from becoming overweight.

Prevention: Provide a bird feeding table out of the dog's reach.

Comment: Remember that if your dog is reluctant to eat its food, you could do worse than throw it out on the grass!

What if my dog gets a ball stuck in its throat?

34. What if my dog gets a ball stuck in its throat?

This is a two person emergency.

One person should hold the dog's mouth as wide open as possible, being careful not to obstruct the nose. With the other hand, pull the dog's tongue forward as far out of the mouth as possible. The other person should try to grasp the ball with fingers, pliers or cooking tongs, pulling the ball forward, *never* pushing it further back or it will obstruct the throat even more.

As the ball becomes coated in saliva it may be even more difficult to dislodge. If unsuccessful after a few minutes, rush the dog to the nearest veterinary surgery, having first checked by telephone that the veterinary surgeon is available.

After such an episode remove all balls of that size or smaller. Buy the dog a much larger ball which will not go into its mouth.

35. What if my dog attacks a much smaller dog?

Large dogs will naturally sometimes seek to subdue a small dog which is not submissive enough, but such an action in today's society can cause considerable aggravation.

The normal action is for the large dog to put the small one on the ground and stand over it, possibly uttering a threatening growl.

Action: This situation can be broken up harmlessly if only the owners act in the right way. The small dog knows when it is overpowered and it will normally lie still. When

206

the big dog feels the lesson has been learned, it will walk away, having done no harm to the smaller one other than having called its bluff.

The owner of the small dog should refrain from screaming, calling or otherwise creating artificial tension in the scene which will alter the dogs' natural resolution of the incident.

The owner of the larger dog would do well to walk away, calling the dog encouragingly to follow in a normal manner. It is best neither to admonish or praise either dog since these actions could exacerbate the situation. Having previously taught the dog to respond to the word "Leave" can be extremely useful in such situations and, if used when an attack is threatened, will often prevent a problem (see also Chapter 3).

36. What if my dog swallows a stone?

Many puppies are addicted to eating gravel. It may do no harm but should be prevented as far as possible.

If you see your dog swallow a large stone take it to the veterinary surgeon at once, as it may be possible to induce the dog to vomit the stone, but this will have to be done quickly. Once in the intestine, the stone may cause an obstruction which can only be relieved by surgery.

It is never a good idea to throw stones for dogs. If a dog shows an inclination to eat gravel or stones on the beach it should be sharply admonished, possibly by using a suitable thrown object. Prevention is far better than cure.

37. What if my dog digs in the garden?

Digging is a natural behaviour for most dogs, but it is especially strong in Terriers and Dachshunds.

Dogs dig in order to:
- bury bones and toys — a natural instinct for secreting prizes.
- catch moles and rodents burrowing below the surface.
- create a cool hollow in which to lie during hot weather.
- create a den in which to have puppies, during natural or false pregnancy
- in imitation of human gardening behaviour.

Prevention Methods
- Keep the dog with you while you are in the garden so that bad behaviour can be corrected immediately, either by a thrown object and/or verbally (see Chapter 3).
- It can help to fill in the hole with large stones or slabs of concrete to deter the dog before filling it with earth.
- Put low fencing around flower beds until the dog has learnt garden manners.
- Bury boundary fencing at least 12" below ground, or peg down wire, to prevent Dachshunds and Terriers digging their way out.

38. What if my dog uproots plants?

It is not uncommon for a puppy to retrieve, and bring indoors to you, things that you have recently planted.

This may be because they bear your scent strongly and the dog has misguidedly thought it necessary to return the plants to you.

It would be a pity to eradicate the retrieve instinct entirely so take some time to replace the plants and to show the dog that they must not be touched, but then allow the dog to find a dropped glove, scarf etc. and encourage him to bring that to you. An intelligent dog will soon realise what is not to be touched and what can be lifted and returned to the owner.

39. What if my dog bites the heads off flowers?

Puppies often spend their first Spring and Summer sampling the vegetation in the garden, and it can be difficult to control this exploratory instinct.

Dogs can be trained, by constant reminders when you are outside with them, not to step on to flower beds but to stay on grass or path.

Preserve your choicest clumps of flowers with a circle of wire or plastic netting during the early days of puppy ownership.

Do not leave a puppy unsupervised in the garden for long periods — mischief is sure to result!

40. What if my dog has passed faeces that need to be disposed of?

Small amounts of dog faeces picked up from the garden may be put into the sewage system via the W.C. or by lifting a manhole cover.

Special dog W.C.s can be bought. They consist of a plastic dustbin-like container which is bedded into the ground and charged with a disinfectant type fluid which liquidises faeces put into it. The contents may be emptied on waste ground, dug into a pit, or emptied into the sewage system.

The faeces of adult dogs may be put on to compost heaps, but if there is any chance the faeces will contain round or tape worm eggs this disposal method is unsuitable as the compost heap will not attain enough heat to kill the eggs.

Faeces from puppies are best rolled in plenty of newspaper and burnt if possible, or else taken to an amenity tip to be buried with other household rubbish.

41. What if my dog is stolen?

There is an increasing risk that pedigree puppies and adult dogs will be stolen from cars, and even from their gardens, or when tied up outside shops.

Most of the specialist canine insurance companies offer cover for theft of the dog, together with some of the costs of advertising and offering a reward.

First check with the police, the local veterinary surgeries, and rescue kennels that the dog has not been taken in from the street. Check again every other day.

Where it is certain that a dog has been stolen, the best tactic is to have a leaflet printed showing a photograph and description of the dog. Circulate it as widely as possible and display it in shops that offer that facility. Also contact the canine press, so that breeders may be on the alert for a new dog coming into their area in possibly suspicious circumstances.

Offer a reward, but it is illegal to state that "no questions will be asked if the animal is returned", as this is conniving with the thieves.

Do not give up hope of seeing your dog again, as it may be turned loose to make its way home several days or even weeks after the theft.

But what should you do if you *find* a dog?

1. Do not be too hasty in collecting a dog which is "lost". It may know its way home and it may be best to leave it.
2. Examine any dog running loose for collar tag and/or tattooed numbers possibly in the ear or the inside of the thigh, which may give you some clue as to ownership. It is hoped that in the future tattooing will be standard and that there will be a national agency holding owners' names and addresses.

   If the dog is wearing an address tag you may advise the owner direct, or you may wish to ask a dog warden or the police to do so. If you contact the owner direct be tactful as some people, possibly because they are worried or feel guilty, can be abusive.
3. If you find a dog without a collar and name disc, contact a police station or rescue home as near as possible to the place where you found the dog. It is no kindness to take the dog to wherever you are going and to notify the police there. Communication on matters of this kind is very poor between police stations and particularly between county forces. Taking the dog out of the area may mean it is never reunited with its owners.
4. Notify the police not only of the breed of dog, if you recognise it, but also give the description, e.g. brown and white with long ears, as the police are not always good at breed recognition.
5. Provided you have notified the police of your find, you may keep the dog in your home during the seven days allowed for the owners to claim it. If you are able to do this, it is preferable to putting the dog into the police kennels or a rescue home.
6. You may have first refusal of a dog you have found if it is unclaimed by the owners after seven days, but you must keep the dog for at least a month. The original owner is not, *in law*, entitled to reclaim possession of the dog after the 7 days, from the time the finding of the dog was reported to the police.

NOTE: It is possible that some time in the future the police will be relieved of all matters relating to dogs and that these will be taken over by local authority dog wardens.

42. What if my dog gets lost?

The dog should be wearing a name tag, so that ownership can be traced. Remember to alter the tag appropriately if you are on holiday.

If the dog gets lost on a walk, turn around and follow the route by which you came, back to the starting point. The dog thus has two opportunities to pick up your scent, and can also follow his own tracks.

A dog will often return to the place where you parked the car.

Many dogs tend to remain quite close to the place at which they were lost, especially when in woodland, but if the dog has become bewildered it may conceal itself from humans, even its owners.

Immediate Action

Visit the place at which the dog was last seen early in the morning and at dusk each day, and be prepared to wait quietly for some time. Walk about slowly, as dogs see moving figures more easily than those which are standing still.

It may help to take a familiar canine companion to the scene, a bitch in season, or even a blanket used by an in-season bitch, which can work wonders for attracting a male.

What if my dog gets lost?

Report the loss separately to every police station over a wide area; to veterinary surgeons, in case the dog has been found injured; and to rescue kennels and breed rescue societies. If you suspect that the dog may have reached the London area, have someone who can identify the dog visit Battersea Dogs Home every day for the first seven days, and afterwards at a minimum of seven day intervals. Do not give up hope of recovering your dog. It is not unknown for a dog to arrive at the Home weeks, or even months, after it disappeared. The Home does not deal with telephone enquiries.

Consider having a leaflet printed with the dog's photograph.

Alert a selection of people to look for the dog but beware of having too many over-enthusiastic searchers, who may frighten the dog even further away.

Subsequent Action

Make sure your dog always wears a name tag on which your name and address are readable. Old medallions can become so blurred as to be useless.

For use on holiday, buy a cylinder name and address holder into which a slip of paper can be put bearing the current address, and remember to keep it up to date.

Medallions obtainable from the National Canine Defence League bear the words, "If found injured, call a veterinary surgeon, the fee will be paid". The vet's charges remain your responsibility, but you are assured that no-one will be reluctant to have the dog treated.

Most canine veterinary insurance policies give some cover for the costs of advertising and reward for a missing dog.

43. What if my dog gets into a fight?

Fighting to establish supremacy is a natural behaviour in dogs. When a dog has this tendency, strong domination must be established by the owner. The dog should not be taken out by people who cannot control it.

Avoidance strategy is also employed — not taking the dog into public parks etc. and taking it out at quiet times. It is important to train dogs to the word "Leave". The dog should learn that to obey the word "Leave" brings rewards. If another dog approaches, start telling it to "Leave" before a situation develops.

Once a dog is into a fight breaking up the conflict is a matter of improvisation. Fighting dogs are usually oblivious to the pain of being hit with sticks or leads, and dragging them apart is useless.

Surprise is a good friend on these occasions. Quantities of water via hose or bucket, a diversionary noise, even an unfamiliar voice shouting, may cause the dogs to break out of curiosity.

If one or both dogs are wearing collars, the collar may be twisted, with hand or stick, to momentarily cut off the air supply and allow control of the dog to be regained. But remember the risk of getting bitten in the mêlée can be quite high; it may be more prudent to walk away calling the dog to come. Dogs seldom fight to the death and usually one will surrender.

Never pull one of the participants up by the collar so that it stands on its hind legs, so exposing the underbelly to the opponent.

When the dogs have parted, get control immediately and remove them at once out of range of each other, or they will resume the fight at the first opportunity.

CHAPTER 8

VETERINARY SERVICES

Veterinary surgeons

Animals may only be treated by a qualified veterinary surgeon, except that an owner may diagnose and treat illness in his own animals, and anyone may give first aid to an animal in distress. Boarding kennel owners, trainers and people working in grooming businesses are acting illegally if they diagnose a condition and prescribe or apply medication to a dog that is not owned by them.

A student applying for a place at one of the six British veterinary colleges requires the very highest scholastic qualifications. Very few drop-out during the five year course, and even fewer fail to qualify. Just over 300 new veterinary surgeons emerge every year to join the 5,600 or so already working in the various types of veterinary practice.

On graduation, the new graduate becomes a Member of the Royal College of Veterinary Surgeons (MRCVS). These initials will follow those which denote the university attended, e.g. London University Veterinary School, also known as the Royal Veterinary College, grants the degree of Bachelor of Veterinary Medicine (BVetMed). Fellowship of the Royal College of Veterinary Surgeons (FRCVS) is granted for service to the profession or by thesis. British veterinary surgeons are addressed as Mr or Ms unless they have earned a higher degree, denoted by the initials PhD after their names, when they are entitled to the prefix of Dr. In many other countries all veterinary surgeons are called "Doctor" regardless of whether or not they have a PhD.

The Royal College of Veterinary Surgeons is the governing body of the veterinary profession and one of its important roles is acting as mediator and investigator in response to complaints from the public. The vast majority of these complaints stem from poor communication between the client and the veterinary surgeon, and it is hoped that some aspects of this situation may be eased after a study of this book.

Every veterinary practice, whether it is run single-handed by one person,

212

or whether it is owned by several partners employing a number of assistants and lay staff, is a small business which must pay its overheads, allow a reasonable profit for its principals and a return on the capital invested in equipment. Veterinary fees are worked out upon this basis; there is no nationally agreed scale of fees.

Where wide differences in charges are found, this may reflect the amount and standard of the equipment provided and the additional services offered, as well as the amount of skilled lay help available for the care of animals. Of course the area of the country will affect the fees charged. It is usually much more expensive to have dogs treated in the London area.

Veterinary nurses

The Royal College of Veterinary Surgeons supervises the training and examinations for veterinary nurses who become, after qualification, members of the British Veterinary Nursing Association. Full details of the course of tuition can be obtained from RCVS, 32 Belgrave Square, London SW1.

However, many veterinary surgeons train lay assistants to their own needs and do not require them to be formally qualified. The number of people looking for this type of work always greatly exceeds the number of posts available.

Fees

If you feel that you have been charged too much for veterinary services remember:

● You can always ask about the cost of treatment in advance. To be cautious about what you may be required to pay will not be taken as lack of concern for your dog.

● You can ask for an itemised bill to see how the total accumulated.

● Veterinary medication is often expensive to manufacture because in comparison with human needs, demand is low.

● Unlike private medical consultations and drug prescriptions, VAT is charged on all veterinary services.

● If the treatment advised is really more than you can afford, your veterinary surgeon may be able to refer you to one of the animal charities which are able to help.

Insurance

In order not to have the risk of embarrassment you may wish to take out an annual insurance policy which covers veterinary fees for illness and accident, as well as other benefits. Your veterinary surgeon will have proposal forms from several companies offering different levels of cover. All the companies exclude preventative vaccinations and elective spaying and neutering.

Most companies have an upper age limit beyond which they no longer accept dogs for enrolment, but it is important to choose a company which will insure your dog for life if it is enrolled when young. It is often the early years, and again old age, which prove to be the most expensive in terms of veterinary fees.

One company will also insure your bitch for veterinary fees which may occur during pregnancy and whelping, so it is worthwhile reviewing all the policies on offer, and also asking your veterinary surgeon which company he finds the most satisfactory to deal with.

Third Party insurance cover is a social necessity in case your dog injures another person, possibly quite innocently by tripping them, or in case it kills livestock. It is more satisfactory to have this insurance with a company specialising in animal insurance.

Consulting the veterinary surgeon

Find out from the surgery whether an appointment is necessary, or whether open surgeries are run between certain hours. With the latter system, it may be necessary to wait a short while for attention.

If you have any way of getting to the veterinary surgery, it is preferable to do so, rather than request a house call which may prove to cost more than you expect, as house calls are an extravagant use of the veterinary surgeon's time. Furthermore the veterinary surgeon can do relatively less for a sick or injured dog at your home. All the diagnostic and treatment equipment, as well as trained assistance, is available at the surgery. If you have no transport, the receptionist may well be able to tell you of a taxi service which will carry dogs.

If at all possible the person who knows the dog best should take it to the surgery. Other people may not be able to supply in detail the information the veterinary surgeon needs. Have no hesitation in writing down the history of the illness and other information about the dog, so that you do not forget what you mean to say.

Expect to pay in cash or by cheque at the conclusion of the consultation. Small animal veterinary surgeons do not expect to send out accounts for payment, and may make an extra charge if they have to do so. Very few veterinary surgeons accept credit cards.

If you have an particular phobia about injections or the sight of blood, the veterinary surgeon would much rather you explained and then waited outside while your dog is attended to. You are not the only one, by any means!

British veterinary surgeons usually dispense medication and treatments, rather than writing prescriptions for the chemist to fulfill. Ask for the name of the medication to be written on the envelope it is packaged in, and make sure you know what the dosage regime is to be, and when you are to start giving the medication.

Skin dressings and medicated shampoos sometimes have a complicated method of application. Ask for the instructions to be written down if you fear you have not understood or may forget. No one will think the worse of you.

Second opinions

There is, as yet, no veterinary "Harley Street" where you may take your dog for a consultation with a "specialist", although this may come about in time.

When it is felt that a case would benefit from the opinion of a veterinary surgeon who has taken a great interest in one aspect of canine disease, it is usual for the veterinary surgeon in general practice to refer his client to one of the university veterinary schools, or possibly the Animal Health Trust. The case will be seen by a lecturer in veterinary medicine and surgery, often accompanied by students, or a veterinary surgeon researching a particular disease.

You may request that your dog is referred to a university but you cannot make the approach on your own. Arrangements have to be made through your veterinary surgeon and the findings of the person giving the second opinion will be communicated to your own home practice. The account will also be sent to your own vet, who will pass it on to you.

Changing practices

It is a very important part of ethical veterinary behaviour that clients shall not be "poached" from one practice by another. It is also not in the best interests of a sick dog to be subjected to a variety of treatments given in ignorance of what has been done before. Therefore trying to change practices, unless for a valid and obvious reason such as moving house, may be obstructed, for the very best of motives, by the practice you are trying to change to.

If you feel unable to tell your current veterinary surgeon that you want to go somewhere else, the most tactful time to make the change is when your dog is not suffering from an illness.

The Royal College of Veterinary Surgeons decrees that every practice must offer a service to sick animals 24 hours a day, 365 days a year. In order to comply, the one or two person practice may employ part time veterinary help, or may enter into arrangements with neighbouring practices to cover "out of hours" work on a reciprocal basis. This is the reason that emergency calls are often re-routed to a telephone number and a veterinary surgeon with whom you are unfamiliar.

For non-urgent consultations, it is always possible to telephone the surgery to ask when the veterinary surgeon who has examined your dog before will be on duty.

Veterinary Hospitals

Some veterinary practices are entitled to term themselves "Veterinary Hospitals". This special status is granted by the Royal College of Veterinary Surgeons to premises where the building and the facilities reach a standard of excellence laid down by the College. Among the requirements are provision for the proper care of animals as in-patients, and there must be at least one trained veterinary nurse employed.

The veterinary hospital is not comparable with an NHS district hospital for humans. It is not the specific place to take dogs which have had an accident or are seriously ill, and it would be a mistake to think that the personnel who own or work in the hospital are necessarily of greater competence or higher qualifications than veterinary surgeons in other practices.

Veterinary hospitals function in every way as other general practices do, having their own clientele, except that they are able to offer nursing facilities to those clients who are not able to look after their sick dogs at home, or for those dogs which require expert nursing care.

Finally, being a veterinary surgeon involves more than just curing disease in animals; it means helping owners at times of worry and stress. Communicate with him, establish a relationship based on your common interest — your pet. Such mutual understanding and respect will pay dividends for everyone.

CHAPTER 9

FURTHER USEFUL INFORMATION

Dogs and the law

Activities with dogs

Educational opportunities

Address and telephone numbers

Vital signs

Household measures

Further reading

Dogs and the Law

There are a number of laws which apply to dog-ownership. They are intended to protect dogs from cruelty and misuse, to protect livestock and wild animals from dogs, and to protect people from annoyance by badly-kept dogs.

In addition, many local authorities make their own bye-laws concerning fouling of footpaths, roads and parks where dogs must be kept on leads, and public buildings into which dogs may not be taken. The notion that Cavalier King Charles Spaniels are permitted by law, dating from the time of Charles II, to flout any such laws is a complete myth.

Food shops and restaurants are encouraged by the Food Hygiene Regulations 1970 to ban dogs from their premises.

Large land-owners such as the Forestry Commission also create bye-laws prohibiting the chasing of deer, game birds etc. by dogs on their land.

Licences

Three activities require licences from the local authority, and involve inspection of the premises concerned. The licence cost is determined by the local authority.

The Breeding of Dogs Act 1973. Owners of more than two bitches from which puppies are bred for sale require a licence.

Boarding Establishments Act 1963. Anyone who boards animals for payment, whether in a private house or a kennel, requires a licence.

Pet Animals Act 1951. Anyone buying in animals for re-sale, or breeding quantities of animals for sale may be required to take out a licence to keep a **Pet Shop**, whether the premises are a conventional shop or not.

216

Selling dogs.	Dogs and puppies may not be sold in the street or any public place, or to a child under 12 years old, or in conjunction with a rag or old clothes dealing business.
Buying dogs and puppies.	In general the law decides that it is up to the buyer to be careful what he buys, and livestock is bought "as seen" without any warranty. However, if the buyer states that the puppy is wanted for a particular purpose, e.g. for showing or breeding, and in due course the dog does not fulfil that purpose, the buyer may have a claim under the Sale of Goods Act 1979. If a pedigree is given with a puppy, it must be correct. It may be regarded as an offence of obtaining money by false pretences to give an incorrect pedigree.
Dog Licence.	All dogs over six months should be licensed.

The dog owner's responsibility

Your dog must not be a nuisance to neighbours or other persons. Nuisance may be defined as persistent and prolonged barking, trespassing on other people's property, threatening or attacking people, or obstructing access to a public place or roadway.

Your dog must wear a collar bearing your address at all times when outside your property, except when working as a gundog, or herding sheep or cattle.

It is an offence to abandon a dog. Abandoning may be applied to leaving a dog in your home or kennel without regular attention and provision of food and water at appropriate intervals. One successful prosecution involved leaving some puppies from 4 p.m. on one day until 10 a.m. on the next without supervision or replenishment of water bowls.

It is an offence to allow a dog to travel in a vehicle in a way which will cause it suffering.

It is an offence to allow a dog to draw a cart or any wheeled vehicle on a public highway.

It is an offence to allow your dog to chase farm livestock and poultry, or even to appear to be about to chase or harass them. Farmers and land-owners have the right to shoot a dog found in a compromising situation near livestock. Keep your dog on a lead in the country, as sheep and cattle may panic even if the dog is doing them no harm.

It is an offence to allow dogs to chase wild deer, pheasant and game birds in Forestry Commission plantations.

It is an offence against the Cruelty to Animals Act to take part, provide the premises or even to be present at organised dog fights or baiting. Beating, torturing, or frightening a dog is an offence, both by the person carrying out the act, and the owner who permits it.

It is an offence to "cause unnecessary suffering" to a dog in any way, by committing a cruelty or by neglecting to provide for the dog's reasonable needs.

It is an offence for anyone to diagnose and treat illness in a dog which is **not his own**, unless they are a qualified veterinary surgeon or working under the direct supervision of a veterinary surgeon. All operations, with the exception of the most minor procedures, must be performed while the dog is under an anaesthetic to prevent pain being felt.

The exceptions are:

● First aid to save life or relieve pain.

● Lay persons are permitted to dock puppies' tails and remove dew claws, but only before the eyes are open, i.e. before seven days.

See also Chapter 7, "What if" No.41.

For further reference: *Your Dog and the Law*, by Godfrey Sandys-Winsch, (Shaw & Sons Ltd)

Activities with dogs

There are many activities which you can enjoy with your dog, and training your dog in the necessary skills will make you appreciate each other's companionship all the more.

Your stepping-stone to most activities will be to join a breed club or a training club, or to become interested in one of the many breed or general rescue societies. Alternatively it may be helpful to join the fund raising clubs dedicated to helping to raise money for the study of breed problems, or those trying to improve facilities at our veterinary schools.

Some suggestions are given in the following tables:

Table (a) General activities

(b) Competitive exhibiting for beauty and breed conformations

(c) Owner related activities

(d) Specialised advanced activities

Table (a) General Activities with Dogs

Activity	Suitable Dogs	Preparation	Where to get information
Competitive exhibiting for beauty and breed conformation	Only pedigree dogs registered at the Kennel Club.	See Table (b).	See canine press or write to the Kennel Club, 1-5 Clarges Street, London W1Y 8AB.
Obedience competition	All breeds, cross-breds and mongrels.	Attend a basic training club.	Ask at the veterinary surgery.
Agility competition	Not giant breeds or tiny breeds.	As above.	As above.
Informal tracking and drag hunting.	Large hounds.	Training at scent recognition.	Breed clubs and canine press.
Informal racing	Afghans, Salukis, Whippets, Terriers.	Training to tolerance of other dogs.	Breed clubs and canine press.

Table (a) (continued)

Activity	Suitable Dogs	Preparation	Where to get information
Sponsored walks	All breeds.	Basic obedience.	National Canine Defence League and other charity arranged events.
Water rescue	Newfoundlands.	Practice swims.	Breed clubs.
Sled pulling and trekking	Huskies, Eskimo Dogs.	Lead and harness work.	Breed clubs.
Working Terrier shows	Small Terriers and cross-breds.	Lead training.	Sporting press.
Lurcher shows	Hound cross-breds.	Lead training.	Sporting press.
Collecting for charity	All breeds.	Socialisation and wearing a pannier harness.	Approach a charity for authorisation.
Field trials	Working gundogs leading to award of Field Trial Champion.	Field Trial Society.	List from Kennel Club.
Working trials	Large guard breeds leading to awards of working status up to police dog level.	Working Trial Society.	List from Kennel Club.
Advertising, stage and screen acting	All breeds and mongrels.	Socialisation, immaculate obedience, extrovert personality	Animal model agencies – see Yellow Pages.
Mountain rescue	Large agile breeds.	Obedience and scent discrimination.	Mountain rescue groups in appropriate areas.
Hospital/old people's home or school visiting	All breeds.	Must be confident animals, responsive to strangers and absolutely reliable in all situations.	Pat Dog Scheme c/o Pro-dogs, Rocky Bank, 4 New Rd, Ditton, Kent ME20 7AD or on own initiative.
Picking up for a shoot	Gundogs, preferably Labradors, Flat-coats, Weimeraners.	Gundog training immaculate behaviour.	Gundog clubs. Offshoot of breed clubs or sporting press.

219

Table (b) Competitive Exhibiting for Beauty & Breed Conformation

Type of show	Who enters	Where to find information	Comment
Club matches	Ring craft club members.	At the club.	One dog randomly matched against another. An informal competition to give ring craft and judging practice.
Exemption shows	Pedigree dogs and mongrels. No need to be Kennel Club registered.	Local advertising.	The only show you can enter on the day. Many novelty classes. *Not* a good place for your first show as classes are very large.
Open shows	Dogs must be Kennel Club registered and transferred to owner's name.	Canine press.	Some shows restricted to club members but you can join when making the entry. Best place to get the help and opinion of other owners. Enter about 4 weeks ahead of show date.
Championship shows (breed or general)	As above.	Canine press.	Entries must be made 8-10 weeks ahead of show date. These shows offer Challenge Certificates in many breeds which go towards making up a Champion. Very high competitive level, high entry fees.
Crufts Dog Show	Only first prize winners in certain classes at Championship shows are eligible, or winners at Field Trials for gundog classes.	Canine press.	The only British show which has a restricted entry.

Table (c) Owner Related Activities

Activity	Type of work	Qualifications	Where to get information
Breed rescue	Collect unwanted dogs, screen new homes. Transport dogs — house displaced dogs for assessment.	Familiarity with breed.	Via breed club.
Club official	Organising club activities.	Secretarial or organisational ability. Unpaid.	Via Canine Society or breed club.
Club catering	Providing food at events arranged by clubs.	Cooking/servicing ability. Unpaid.	Via Canine Society or breed clubs.

Table (d) Specialised Advanced Activities

Activity	Qualification	Preparation
Judging	None needed except at highest level where experience tells.	Breed or exhibit for several years.
Breed note-writer for canine press	Writing ability. Nose for news, attendance at many breed events.	Breed and exhibit for several years.
Walker of puppy for guide dogs	Urban dweller in certain designated areas. Mixed family group preferred.	Contact Puppy Walk Manager, Guide Dogs for the Blind, Tollgate House, Bishops Tachbrook, nr Leamington Spa, Warwickshire.
Breed litters for Guide Dogs for the Blind	Breeding experience needed, willing to be supervised by G.D.A. officials. Bitch usually supplied by the Association.	As above.
Grooming competition	Skilled groomer in several breeds	Pet trade press.

Educational opportunities

The authors hope that this book will have stimulated many owners to find out more about all aspects of the canine race. There are now many opportunities to attend educational meetings. These are mainly at weekends, some last an afternoon, while others offer residential facilities and last days. The cost is always very reasonable considering the quality of the lecturers and the information on offer.

The British Small Animal Veterinary Association, in conjunction with Beecham Animal Health, arrange several sessions each year at venues throughout Britain. The Royal Veterinary College has a breeders' symposium, residential and non-residential, at its Field Station, Potters Bar, Hertfordshire, in early January each year. Bristol University Veterinary School holds a similar event at Langford, near Bristol in September.

All these meetings are advertised in the canine press, or information on the BSAVA/Beecham event can be obtained from Beecham Animal Health, Beecham House, Brentford, Middlesex. TW8 9BD. Details on the university symposia can be obtained from Kay White, The Pheasantry, East Dean, Chichester, West Sussex PO18 0JG. Pet Plan Ltd., the canine/feline insurance company, hold a special symposium for boarding kennel owners, and those who hope to have kennels in the future. This is run in conjunction with Duphar Veterinary Ltd. in October of each year. Information from Pet Plan Ltd., 319/327 Chiswick High Rd, London W4 4HH.

There are also combined home study and joint meeting courses in dog breeding and dog judging, kennel management and kennel staff training run by the Canine Studies Institute, RTC Associates, London Rd, Bracknell, Berkshire, RG12 6QM.

Those interested in veterinary nursing, both boys and girls do this job these days, should contact their local veterinary surgery or The British Veterinary Nursing Association through Mrs Jean Turner VN, The Mandeville Veterinary Hospital, 15 Mandeville Road, Northolt, Middlesex, UB5 5HD.

Useful addresses and telephone numbers

Veterinary Bodies and Associations

British Small Animal Veterinary Association (Registration Office),
5 St Georges Terrace, Cheltenham, Glos. GL50 3PT.
Tel: (0242) 584354

British Veterinary Association, 7 Mansfield Street, London W1M 0AT
Tel: 01-636 6541

Royal College of Veterinary Surgeons, 32 Belgrave Square,
London SW1X 8PP
Tel: 01-235 4971

Welfare Associations

Blue Cross, 1 Hugh Street, Victoria, London SW1V 1QQ
Tel: 01-834 5556

Guide Dogs for the Blind, Alexander House, Park Street, Windsor, Berks.
Tel: (075 35) 55711

Hearing Dogs for the Deaf Training Centre, 2 Chinnor Hill, Chinnor,
Oxon OX9 4BA
Tel: (0884) 53898

National Canine Defence League, 1 & 2 Pratt Mews, London NW1 0AD
Tel: 01-388 0137

People's Dispensary for Sick Animals, PDSA House, South Street,
Dorking, Surrey RH4 2LB
Tel: (0306) 888291

Pet-Health Council, 4th Floor, Walter House, 418/422 Strand,
London WC2R 0PL
Tel: 01-836 2843

Pro-Dogs, 4 New Road, Ditton, Kent ME20 7AD
Tel: (0732) 848499

Royal Society for the Prevention of Cruelty to Animals,
RSPCA Headquarters, Causeway, Horsham, West Sussex RH12 1HG
Tel: (0403) 64181

Universities Federation for Animal Welfare, 8 Hamilton Close,
South Mimms, Potters Bar, Herts. EN6 3QD
Tel: (0707) 58202.

Dog Press

Dogs Monthly, Breachurst Ltd., Unit 1, Bowen Industrial Estate, Aberbargoed, Bargoed, Mid Glam. CF8 9EY
Tel: (0443) 821839

Dog Training Weekly, 7 Greenwich South Street, London SE10 8BR
Tel: 01-858 0380

Dog World, 9 Tufton Street, Ashford, Kent TN23 1QN
Tel: (0233) 22389

Kennel Gazette, Kennel Club, 1 Clarges Street, Piccadilly, London W1Y 8AB
Tel: 01-493 6651

Our Dogs, 5 Oxford Road, Station Approach, Manchester M60 1SX
Tel: 061 236 2660

Shooting and Conservation, Marford Mill, Rossett, Clwyd LL12 0HL
Tel: (0244) 570881

Shooting Times, 10 South Street, Windsor, Berkshire. SL4 1BG
Tel: (075 35) 56061

Dog Governing Bodies

Kennel Club, 1 Clarges Street, Piccadilly, London W1Y 8AB
Tel: 01-493 6651

Pet Foods

Petfood Manufacturers' Association, 6 Catherine Street, London WC2B 5JJ
Tel: 01-836 2460

Vital Signs

Body Temperature °F	100.9 - 101.7
Body Temperature °C	38.3 - 38.7
Pulse Rate	70-100 beats per minute
Respiration Rate	15-30 breaths per minute

Approximate Household Measures

1 large teaspoonful	= ⅙ fl. oz.	=	5ml
1 tablespoonful	= ½ fl. oz.	=	15ml
1 wineglassful	= 2 fl. oz.	=	60ml
1 cupful	= 7 fl. oz.	=	200ml
1 pint bottleful	= 20 fl. oz.	=	568ml

Further reading

Dog and Cat Nutrition, edited by Andrew Edney, (Pergamon Press, 1982)
An excellent textbook for those who want to go deeper into the study of dog nutrition. It contains valuable information on puppy rearing and feeding sick animals and dogs which are working hard.

Take Them Round Please, Tom Horner, (David and Charles, 1975)
The best book on the art of showing dogs.

The Dog in Action, McDowell Lyon, (Howell Book House)
A study of anatomy and movement in all breeds.

Practical Veterinary Nursing, edited by G. J. Price, (BSAVA, 1985)
A book intended for veterinary nurses in training, parts of which will be of interest to dog owners who like to know what goes on behind the scenes at a veterinary surgery.

The British Dog, Carson I. A. Ritchie, (Robert Hale, 1981)
An easy-to-read history of dogs from the earliest times.

Your Dog and the Law, Godfrey Sandys-Winsch, (Shaw & Sons, 1984)
An invaluable guide to this complex subject.

How to Have a Well-Mannered Dog, Kay White and J. M. Evans,
(Eliot Rightway Books, 1983)
More detailed advice on managing your puppy and programming it for good
behaviour without the need for stern corrective measures.

Canine Terminology, Harold Spira, (Harper & Row, 1982)
Explanations accompanied by beautifully drawn diagrams of all the terms
dog breeders use.

Black's Veterinary Dictionary, edited by Geoffrey West,
(A & C Black, 1984)
A great standby for clarification of veterinary language.

The New Observer's Book of Dogs, Catherine G. Sutton,
(Frederick Warne, 1983)
An inexpensive little book giving instant identification and history of all
the dog breeds.

Jones' Animal Nursing, edited by D. R. Lane, (Pergamon Press, 1985)
This is the official textbook on which the training of veterinary nurses is
based. It is useful for dog owners and breeders for amplification of anatomy
and physiology.

Dog Breeding — A guide to mating and whelping, Kay White,
(Bartholomew, 1984)
An inexpensive book which offers clear explanations of the mating procedure,
preparation for whelping, the birth of puppies, rearing and selling for the
novice breeder.

Rabies — The facts you need to know, G. N. Henderson & Kay White,
(Barne & Jenkins)
Gives the history of the disease and the discovery of vaccines, as well as
describing the modern defences which Britain has against rabies, including
information about importing a dog into this country, quarantine kennels etc.

225

CHAPTER 10

DOG MAINTENANCE

Record keeping
Regular health checks

Your Dog's Personal Data

It is by no means unusual for owners not to be able to remember the incidents in their dog's life, and very often they have not had the opportunity to know what medication has been given etc.

It is of great help to the veterinary surgeon if you can contribute a full history without irrelevant detail, and it may save you money in terms of consultation time if you are able to supply the information needed. Furthermore it can be of great interest both to you and your family to keep a full record of the dog's life and history, perhaps in great detail during the first year, and then later noting down illnesses, accidents, when the dog was boarded, and the start of new behaviour patterns etc.

A record of the way a puppy was fed, weight gains, and achievements in the way of house-training and obedience will be invaluable as a reference point for other new puppies which may be acquired by family and friends.

Keep a note of vaccinations given and when boosters are due.

Always ask the nurse or receptionist at the veterinary practice to write on any container of tablets, or bottle of skin dressing, the name of the product, the strength (especially for tablets), and the dosage regime, and add this to your records, together with a brief description of any surgical procedures carried out.

It can be particularly useful to have information on any adverse reaction to medication, skin dressing or anaesthetic.

Record cards can go astray in the veterinary surgeon's office, so your back-up file can be of vital importance, and especially so if you are obliged to change veterinary practices or if, for some unforeseen reason, your dog has to be cared for by someone else.

Don't be afraid to go into the veterinary surgery with written notes to remind you about the current illness and your dog's past history. It is better to do that than forget something important. The more relevant details the veterinary surgeon has to hand the easier it will be for him to diagnose the cause of the problem and select the most appropriate treatment so that your dog will make a more rapid and complete recovery.

Finally you should not necessarily feel guilty if you have delayed taking your dog to the surgery. Almost the first question a veterinary surgeon asks in the consulting room is, "How long has this condition been present?". This is not meant to be an accusation of neglect, but it is of vital importance to the veterinary surgeon when making his diagnosis to know whether a sign of illness has been present for hours, days or weeks. Even if you know you should have consulted the veterinary surgeon sooner, it is best to be frank about the time the signs were first apparent, as it will help the dog more now that treatment is to be given.

Regular Checks for Your Dog

It makes good sense to give your dog a formal checkover for signs of illness at regular intervals. The table on page ? is provided as a guide.

Schedule of Regular Health Checks

	What to look for	Frequency				
		Daily	Weekly	Monthly	Six monthly*	Annually
Eyes	Presence of excessive discharge or pus in the conjunctiva. Check that the cornea is clear and not cloudy and that the dog can see clearly. The sight can be checked readily by throwing a titbit for the dog to catch.	X		X	X	X
Faeces	Note consistency, colour. Check frequency. Look for undigested food, foreign bodies (plastic bags, cardboard etc.).	X	X	X	X	X
Ears	Check that there is no discharge or odour coming from the ear canal. Examine ear flaps for presence of wounds or swellings.		X	X	X	X
Paws	Examine for wounds, cracks, interdigital cysts and nail bed infections.		X	X	X	X
Skin/coat	Look for areas of thickened skin and baldness particularly on elbows and hocks. Check for evidence of excessive scratching and the presence of abrasions. Test the skin's mobility. Look for worm segments around anus. Check the whole body for new warts, lumps under the skin etc. It is a good idea to chart these on a sketch of the dog's outline so that you can monitor the rate of growth.		X			
Claws	Check nail beds for signs of inflammation. Examine claws now for length and presence of splits. Don't forget the dew claws.			X	X	X
Mammary Glands	Look for presence of milk by gently squeezing the teats. Feel the glands for the presence of tumours. A good time to carry out this examination is about one to two months after the bitch has been in season or when bitches are in season.			X	X	
Genital Organs	Dogs. Check penis, prepuce and scrotum for wounds. Note size of testicles. Bitches. Look for presence of discharge from vulva. Check vulva for wounds or inflammation of surrounding skin.				X	X
Vaccination	Ask veterinary surgeon what is required.				X	X

*or when bitches are in season

228

INDEX OF DISEASES AND CONDITIONS AFFECTING DOGS

DISEASE/CONDITION	DEFINITION	FURTHER INFORMATION
ABCESS	A septic region, caused by bacterial infection, which consists of a pool of pus surrounded by a wall of fibrous tissue.	See "What if" No. 39
ABORTION	Loss of puppies (foetuses) whilst still in the womb possibly as a result of trauma, hormonal imbalance or an infection.	See "What if" No. 50
ABRASION	A superficial wound.	See Chapter 6
ACANTHROSIS NIGRICANS	A chronic black/brown inflammatory condition of the skin beginning in the armpit. Especially common in Dachshunds.	
ACHONDROPLASIA	An inherited condition leading to a failure of the long bones to grow. It has been recorded in Scottish Terriers and Poodles.	
ACNE	An accumulation of "spots" and pustules in the skin.	
ADDISON'S DISEASE	Failure of the adrenal cortex to produce hormones leading to vomiting, weakness, diarrhoea, excessive thirst and increased frequency of urination.	
AGALACTIA	Failure to produce milk possibly caused by hormonal imbalance, stress mastitis or generalised disease.	
ALLERGY	Hypersensitivity to various "allergens" which may be contained in food, environmental objects or in the air, may be manifest as skin disease or Haemorrhagic Gastroenteritis.	See "What if" Nos. 17 and 18
ALOPECIA	Hair loss, which can result from a great number of different causes.	
ANAEMIA	Reduced number of red cells in the blood. There are many causes and diagnosis can be difficult.	
ANAL ADENOMATA	Knobbly tumours situated just under the skin around the anus in older dogs.	See "What if" No. 22
ANAL FURUNCULOSIS	Sinus formation around the anus probably from an infected anal sac.	See "What if" No. 22
ANAPHYLAXIS	Hyper sensitivity to injected foreign material (usually shown as shock).	
ANOREXIA	Inappetence — failure to eat.	See "What if" No. 3
APNOEA	Cessation of breathing.	See "What if" No. 47
ARTHRITIS	Inflammation of a joint.	See "What if" No. 34
ASCARID INFESTATION	Roundworm infection.	See Chapter 4 Part III
ASCITES	Accumulation of fluid in the abdominal cavity mostly associated with heart disease or liver disease.	
ATAXIA	Unco-ordinated gait.	See "What if" No. 48

Index of diseases and conditions

DISEASE/CONDITION	DEFINITION	FURTHER INFORMATION
ATELECTASIS	Rupture of the small sacs making up the lung leading to chronic coughing.	
AUJESZKY'S DISEASE	A disease which, in dogs, is characterised by intense itching with self-mutilation, fever, dullness, salivation, facial oedema, convulsions and death. It is caused by a virus infection, usually from contact with infected pigs.	
AUTO-IMMUNE DISEASE	A condition where the body rejects its own tissues. The basic cause is a failure of the dog's immune system.	See Chapter 5
AVITAMINOSIS	Vitamin deficiency.	
BALANITIS	Inflammation of the sheath which covers the penis.	See "What if" No. 30
BALANOPOSTHITIS	Inflammation of the sheath which covers the penis, and the penis itself.	See "What if" No. 30
BLEPHARITIS	Inflammation of the eyelids usually secondary to conjunctivitis.	See "What if" No. 11
BLUE EYE	Cloudyness of the cornea associated with Infectious Canine Hepatitis (p.120).	See "What if" No. 12
BLOAT	Accumulation of gas in the stomach and/or the intestines. A true emergency.	See "What if" No. 33
BRAIN LESION	Brain damage — see also C.V.A.	See "What if" Nos. 15 and 48
BRONCHITIS	Inflammation of the bronchi. See Kennel Cough (p.124).	See "What if" No. 35
BRUCELLOSIS	Infection with the bacterium *Brucella canis* resulting in possibly neonatal puppy deaths, abortion and infertility.	
BRUISING	A "contusion" (wound) caused by a blow from a blunt object inflicting damage to the tissues under the skin.	See Chapter 4 Part IV
BURN	An injury caused by dry heat.	See Chapter 6
BURSITIS	Inflammation of a 'bursa', a fluid-filled sac which is present to protect a vulnerable part, usually a bony structure e.g. the elbow from trauma.	See Chapter 6
CALCULUS (CALCULI plural)	A stone which has formed in the urinary bladder or gall bladder.	See "What if" No. 29
CAMPYLOBACTERIOSIS	An infection with campylobacter organisms. The most common sign of this infection is profuse diarrhoea but often the infection does not cause any obvious signs.	
CANINE DISTEMPER	A serious, highly contagious virus disease of dogs (hard pad is a form of Canine Distemper).	See Chapter 4 Part II
		See "What if" No. 9
CANINE PARVOVIRUS INFECTION	A virus disease of dogs which emerged suddenly in the late 1970s.	See Chapter 4 Part II
CANKER	A lay term which used to be used for inflammation of the ear (otitis external).	See "What if" No. 14
CARBON MONOXIDE POISONING	A form of poisoning caused by breathing carbon monoxide gas.	See "What if" No. 49 and Chapter 4 Part VI
CARDIAC ARRYTHMIA	Irregular heart beats.	See "What if" No. 13
CATARACT	An opacity of the lens in the eye.	See "What if" No. 48
C.D.R.M.	See German Shepherd Syndrome.	
CHEYLETIELLA INFESTATION	An infestation of the skin with *Cheyletiella parasitavosax*, the rabbit fur mite.	See Chapter 4 Parts III and IV
CHOREA	Nervous twitching; usually a sequel to Canine Distemper infection.	See Chapter 4 Part II
COCCIDIOSIS	An infection with coccidial parasites resulting in diarrhoea.	
COLITIS	Inflammation of the colon.	
COLLIE EYE ANOMALY	A congenital disease of the eye.	See "What if" No. 13 and Chapter 4 Part II

Index of diseases and conditions

DISEASE/CONDITION	DEFINITION	FURTHER INFORMATION
EAR MITE INFESTATION	Infestation of the ear canal by the mite *Otodectes cynotis*.	See Chapter 4 Part III
ECLAMPSIA	A nervous disease in lactating bitches caused by an imbalance of calcium or glucose in the blood sometimes called Lactation Tetany.	See "What if" No. 16
ECTROPION	Outturned eyelids.	See "What if" No. 11
ECZEMA	Inflammation, usually acute and wet, of the skin.	See "What if" No. 45
EMACIATION	Over-thinness — underweight.	See "What if" No. 2
EMESIS	Vomiting.	
ENCEPHALITIS	Inflammation of the brain.	
ENDOCARDITIS	Inflammation of the lining of the heart.	
ENDOMETRITIS	Inflammation of the womb usually after whelping. But see also Pyometra.	See "What if" No. 23
ENTERITIS	Inflammation of the intestines usually associated with diarrhoea.	See "What if" No. 11
ENTROPION	Inturned eyelids.	See "What if" No. 38
EPILEPSY	Fits caused by abnormal electrical discharges in the brain.	
EPIPHORA	Tears coming from the eyes — may be associated with over-production of tears or because the ducts, which carry them away to the nose, are blocked.	See "What if" No. 11
EPISTAXIS	Nose bleed.	
EOSINOPHILIC MYOSITIS	Inflammation of the jaw muscles, the cause being unknown.	
FAINT	A temporary loss of consciousness.	See "What if" No. 43
FALSE PREGNANCY	Signs of pregnancy and lactation in bitches which have not been mated or which have failed to conceive. Also sometimes called phantom pregnancy or pseudo-pregnancy.	See Chapter 2 (The Bitch)
FILAROIDES OSLERI	A roundworm which produces lesions in the lining of the trachea and bronchi giving rise to a chronic dry cough.	See Chapter 4 Part III
FITS	Convulsions — see also Epilepsy.	See "What if" No. 38 and Chapter 6
FLATULENCE	Passage of wind associated with indigestion.	See "What if" No. 20
FLEA INFESTATION	Presence of dog or cat fleas on the skin. Occasionally hedgehog, human or rabbit fleas may be involved.	See Chapter 4 Parts III and IV
FRACTURE	A broken bone.	See "What if" No. 34
GASTRITIS	Inflammation of the stomach.	
GERMAN SHEPHERD DOG SYNDROME	Progressive hind limb incoordination. The cause is unknown.	See "What if" No. 48
GINGIVITIS	Inflammation of the gums, mostly associated with the accumulation of dental calculus (tartar).	See p.8
GLAUCOMA	Increased pressure in the eye leading to a blueing of the cornea.	See "What if" Nos. 12 and 13 & p.14
GLOSSITIS	Inflammation of the tongue.	

233

Index of diseases and conditions

DISEASE/CONDITION	DEFINITION	FURTHER INFORMATION
PTOSIS	Inability to raise lower eyelid.	See "What if" No. 12
PUPPY HEAD GLAND DISEASE	Inflammation of the skin and glands in the head.	See "What if" No. 39
PYLORIC STENOSIS	Contraction of pyloric valve in the stomach.	See "What if" No. 12
PYOMETRA	Accumulation of pus in the uterus occurring four to six weeks after a bitch has been in season leading principally to increased thirst. This is a serious condition. *Seek veterinary advice without delay.*	See Chapter 2 (The Bitch)
RABIES	A fatal virus disease of dogs and all warm-blooded animals.	See Chapter 4 Part II and "What If" No. 38
RECTAL STRICTURE	A narrowing of the sphincter (muscle ring) that closes the anus.	See "What if" No. 25
RHINITIS	Inflammation of the nasal cavities.	See "What if" No. 8
RINGWORM	A fungal infection of the skin.	See Chapter 4 Part IV
RUBARTH'S DISEASE	See Infectious Canine Hepatitis.	See Chapter 4 Part II
SALIVARY CYST	A cyst in the salivary gland caused by an obstruction of the salivary duct.	See "What if" No. 39
SALMONELLOSIS	An infection with salmonella bacteria causing, principally, an enteritis.	See Chapter 4 Part IV
SARCOPTIC MANGE	Skin disease caused by the mange mite *Sarcoptes scabei*.	See Chapter 4 Parts III and IV
SCOTTIE CRAMP	Hyper-activity precipitated by exercise or excitement. An inherited condition which is usually apparent by 18 months of age.	
SEBORRHOEA	A dry or greasy scaling condition of the skin. The cause is unknown.	
SERTOLI CELL TUMOUR	A tumour affecting the sertoli cells in the testicle leading to swelling of the testicle, the production of oestrogens and feminisation. Occurs in middle-aged and older dogs.	See "What if" No. 43
SHOCK	Collapse of the circulation resulting from haemorrhage, trauma, burns, anaphylaxis, accumulation of toxins in the blood, cardiac failure etc.	
SINUSITIS	Inflammation of the nasal sinuses caused mainly by infection with bacteria or a fungus.	See "What if" No. 48
SKELETAL SCURVY	A disease of fast-growing, well-fed puppies of the larger breeds. The cause is probably an imbalance of vitamin C which the dog usually manufactures within its own body. The danger age is around five months. Signs include: sudden, acute, total body pain; swollen joints; high temperature; resistance to being touched; and hind leg paralysis. *Consult veterinary surgeon urgently.* Massive doses of vitamin C can bring about a cure in as little as seven days.	
SKINFOLD DERMATITIS	Inflammation of the skin where it is deeply folded, particularly in the lower lip and around the vulva, resulting from friction between the skin folds and lack of ventilation to the area.	
SLIPPED DISC	Dislocation of the disc between the spinal vertebrae.	See "What if" No. 43
SPONDYLITIS	Inflammation of the vertebrae and spinal joints leading to rigidity of the back.	See "What if" No. 34
SPRAIN	An over-stretched or torn ligament.	
STOMATITIS	Inflammation of the mouth usually as an extension from gingivitis or periodontal disease.	See p.8

GLOSSARY
What did the veterinary surgeon mean?

Inevitably veterinary surgeons will use long or difficult words to describe various conditions and procedures. The glossary below is provided to help dog owners understand what is meant and should be used *in conjunction with* the Index of Diseases and Conditions Affecting Dogs.

Aberrant	varying from the norm.
Acute	severe and short course — applied to a disease or condition.
Adhesions	the joining together of tissues, usually applied to organs in the abdominal cavity and may occur after an abdominal operation.
Aetiology	the cause (of a disease or condition). Sometimes spelt Etiology.
Afterbirth	the membranes (placenta) expelled with the puppies during birth.
Anabolic steroid	a hormone which promotes growth. Anabolics are used only in very specific situations by veterinary surgeons.
Anaerobes	bacteria which like to grow in the absence of air. They may occur in the uterus and are often associated with inflammation of the gums.
Analgesic	a medicine which relieves pain.
Aneurysm	a dilated blood vessel.
Anoxia	lack of oxygen.
Anthelmintic	a worm remedy.
Antibiotic	a substance produced by micro-organisms which inhibits the growth of, or destroys, bacteria, e.g. penicillin. Antibiotics may be given by injection, by mouth, or applied locally.
Antihistamine	a medicine which counteracts the effect of histamine, a substance released locally in cases of insect bites or stings, and which causes inflammation in the tissues.
Antiseptic	a substance that kills or inhibits the growth of micro-organisms.
Antiserum	blood serum containing high levels of antibody — used sometimes as a treatment for virus infections, e.g. Canine Distemper.
Aural resection	an operation to open up the external ear canal to allow it to be exposed to the air — used to cure chronic ear disease.
Autogenous vaccine	a vaccine prepared from a micro-organism isolated from animals affected by an outbreak of disease.
Bacteria	unicellular micro-organisms.
Benign	not malignant, recurring, or spreading. Usually applied to tumours.

B.H.S.	Beta-haemolytic streptococci — round-shaped bacteria which may cause tonsillitis or fading puppies.
Biopsy	a minor operation to take part of an affected tissue to diagnose the cause of the lesion and reach a prognosis.
Cachexia	debility and wasting.
Callus	the swelling which develops around a fractured bone as part of the healing process.
Carcinogenic	cancer producing.
Carcinoma	a malignant tumour.
Cardiac	pertaining to the heart, e.g. cardiac failure.
Cautery	the destruction of tissue, usually to prevent bleeding, by applying a caustic substance or a hot instrument.
Chorea	involuntary muscle twitching — most commonly as a sequel to Canine Distemper.
Chronic	persisting over a long period of time, applied to a disease.
C.N.S.	central nervous system.
Coitus	sexual intercourse.
Congenital	present at birth.
Contagious	capable of being transmitted from one animal to another. Applied to a disease, e.g. Kennel Cough.
Corticosteroids	medicines which mimic the action of the steroid hormones produced by the adrenal cortex. They are used most frequently for their anti-inflammatory action.
Cryosurgery	the application of intense cold to destroy diseased tissue.
Cutaneous	appertaining to the skin.
Cyanosis	used to describe tissues which have turned purple or black due to an inadequate blood supply.
Cyst	a closed cavity filled with fluid, e.g. a sebaceous cyst.
Dew claw	an extra claw near the carpus or below the hock, usually removed when puppies are a few days old.
Diathermy	the destruction of tissue, usually to stop bleeding, by using a high frequency electric current to generate heat.
Diuretic	a medicine which increases the production of urine.
Dys-	a prefix meaning painful or difficult, e.g. Dystocia — difficult birth.
Ecbolic	a medicine which makes the uterus contract.
E. coli	a bacterium, present in the intestines, which may become pathogenic.
Electrocardiogram (E.C.G.)	a record, made by an electrocardiograph, of the heart's performance.
Electroencephalogram (E.E.G.)	a record, made by an electroencephalograph, of brain function.
Electrolytes	substances that split up into ions when dissolved in water. Electrolyte solutions are often used as transfusions in dehydrated animals.
Embolism	a plug, usually a blood clot, blocking a blood vessel.
Emaciation	excessive thinness or wasting.

Glossary

Endemic	usually applied to a disease which is present in an area at all times. Endemic is truly a medical term — the veterinary equivalent is in fact Enzootic.
Endocrine glands	glands which secrete hormones into the blood to act as chemical messengers.
Endoscope	an instrument for looking inside the body, usually through a natural opening, e.g. the vagina, but possibly through an artificial opening, e.g. a surgical wound.
Enterotomy	an operation involving cutting into the intestines.
Etiology	see Aetiology.
First intention	applied to a wound that heals promptly.
Fistula	an abnormal opening or duct leading into a natural canal, hollow organ or other part of the body.
Fomites	particles in the air or environment which may act as carriers for infectious agents.
Furunculosis	a bacterial infection of the skin whereby there are multiple openings in the skin surface through which pus drains, e.g. anal furunculosis.
Gangrene	death and putrefaction of tissue.
Gestation	period of development of the young in the womb.
Granulation tissue	tissue containing large numbers of blood vessels which occurs when wounds fail to heal promptly. It is seen particularly in large open wounds which need to heal from the bottom.
Haematology	examination of the blood.
Hormone	a chemical messenger transported by the blood and produced by an endocrine gland.
Hyper-	used as a prefix to mean excessive, e.g. Hyperthyroid, Hyperactive.
Hyperplasia	excessive growth of tissue.
Hypertrophy	increase in size of an organ or tissue.
Hypo-	used as a prefix to mean deficient or low, e.g. Hypothyroid.
Hypotension	lowered blood pressure.
Hypothermia	lowered body temperature.
Iatrogenic	caused by medication.
Idiopathic	of unknown cause.
Immunization	to make an animal resistant (immune) to disease.
Infectious	caused by disease producing micro-organisms. Infectious diseases are not necessarily contagious.
Intra-articular	given into a joint cavity. This route is not used commonly nowadays.
Intramuscular	given into the muscles. Intramuscular injections are usually given into the hind leg. This route is used generally where a quick action is required.
Intranasal	through the nose. This route of administration is used for vaccines designed to give local protection of the respiratory tract.

240

Intraperitoneal	into the abdominal cavity. This route of injection is used very infrequently.
Intubation	placing a tube in the trachea to facilitate breathing whilst under an anaesthetic.
Larva	an immature stage in the development of an insect or worm.
Lesion	a pathological change to a tissue, e.g. a wound.
Lipoma	a benign tumour of fat cells.
Malignant	severe, life-threatening, capable of spreading. Applied to tumours.
Metastases	tumours arising as a result of malignant cells spreading to other parts of the body.
Mucus	fluid produced by a mucous membrane, e.g. the lining of the vagina.
Necropsy	a post-mortem.
Necrosis	death of a tissue.
Neonatal	newborn.
Neoplasia	formation of a neoplasm or growth (tumour).
Ophthalmoscope	an instrument used for looking into the eyes.
Oral	pertaining to the mouth, given by mouth.
Orthopaedics	treatment of bones and joints.
Paraplegia	paralysis of the rear end of the body.
Paresis	partial paralysis.
Parturition	giving birth.
Pericardium	the membrane that encloses the heart.
Perinatal	in the period around birth.
Pheromone	a chemical substance secreted externally by an individual, the odour of which causes a response in another member of the same species, e.g. pheromones shed by bitches in season will stimulate others in close contact to also come on heat.
Photophobia	fear or intolerance of light.
Placenta	see Afterbirth.
Prognosis	the expected outcome of a disease, condition or operation.
Prolapse	protrusion, to the outside, of an abdominal organ, e.g. vagina or urinary bladder.
Prophylaxis	prevention of a disease.
Prosthesis	an artificial part, e.g. an artificial hip joint.
Purulent	containing pus.
Pus	a secretion from inflamed tissue, usually sticky and creamy, which contains white blood cells, serum and bacteria.
Put down	to painlessly destroy. (Also: Put to sleep.)
Pyrexia	raised body temperature, fever.
Renal	pertaining to the kidney, e.g. renal failure.

Glossary

Sepsis	bacterial infection usually causing pus to be formed.
Septicaemia	blood poisoning by bacteria and their toxins.
Serology	the examination of blood for the presence of antibodies to disease.
Sporadic	occurring occasionally.
Staphylococci	bacteria which commonly occur, particularly in association with skin disease.
Stenosis	narrowing of a canal, e.g. the intestines.
Streptococci	commonly occurring bacteria which affect dogs, particularly following a virus infection. Often a cause of Tonsillitis.
Subacute	between acute and chronic.
Subclinical	applied to a disease in which the signs are not obvious by clinical examination.
Subcutaneous	under the skin. Subcutaneous injections are used very commonly where a rapid effect is not required since this route of administration tends to be less painful.
Sulphonamides	chemical compounds which are used to kill or suppress the growth of bacteria in the body.
Superficial	on the surface. Often applied to a wound.
Suppurative	producing pus. Applied to a wound.
Syndrome	a set of signs which occur together indicating a particular condition or disease.
Synergistic	acting together to increase the effect, e.g. penicillin plus streptomycin.
Tachycardia	increased heart rate. The opposite is called Bradycardia.
Tachypnoea	increased rate of breathing.
Teratogenic	capable of producing abnormalities in puppies in the womb, applied to a medicine, e.g. Thalidomide.
Thrombus	a blood clot occurring in a blood vessel or the heart.
Tissue	an aggregation of similar cells in the body, e.g. a muscle.
Toxaemia	the spread of bacterial products (toxins) in the blood from a source of infection.
Trauma	injury, wounding, shock.
Tumour	a growth, neoplasm.
Ulcer	break in the surface of an organ, e.g. Corneal ulcer.
Umbilicus	the point on the abdominal wall where the umbilical cord emerged.
Villus	small, finger-like processes projecting from the wall of the intestine.
Virus	a sub-microscopic agent which infects animals, plants and even bacteria.
Viscus	any large internal organ (plural; Viscera).
Wood's lamp	a lamp that emits ultraviolet light. Used to diagnose some forms of ringworm.
Zoonosis	a disease that can be transmitted from animals to man.

INDEX

For specific diseases and conditions see separate index, page 229.
(KEY: IDC — Index of Diseases and Conditions)

Index